A Review of Science and Technology During the 1978 School Year

Science Year

The World Book Science Annual

1979

World Book–Childcraft International, Inc.

Chicago London Paris Rome Sydney Tokyo Toronto

The publishers of *Science Year* gratefully
acknowledge the following for permission to use
copyrighted illustrations. A full listing of illustration
acknowledgments appears on pages 430 and 431.

   13 © National Geographic Society
   17 © National Geographic Society
56-57 © California Institute of Technology and Carnegie
       Institution of Washington, from Hale Observatories
   98 © 1978 Kevin L. Martin
 126 Copyright National Geographic Society—Palomar
       Observatory Sky Survey (California Institute of Technology)
 128 Copyright Reserved
 131 Produced by Education Development Center for
       the National Committee for Fluid Mechanics Films
       with support from the National Science Foundation.
       Low Reynolds Number Flows © 1966 Education
       Development Center, Inc.
 271 © 1977 The New Yorker Magazine, Inc.
 314 © 1978 The New Yorker Magazine, Inc.
 331 Andrew N. Meltzoff and M. Keith Moore, University of
       Washington, from *Science,* Copyright 1977 by the American
       Association for the Advancement of Science.

The Cover: The remains of Lucy, found in Ethiopia form the
                oldest, most complete known human ancestor.

Preface

More than 2,000 years ago, the Greek philosopher Heraclitus wrote, "If you do not expect it, you will not find the unexpected, for it is hard to find and difficult." He could have been writing about the "hard and difficult" work of today's scientists and engineers who report on their accomplishments in the pages of *Science Year*, where the unexpected has frequently been foremost.

Astronomers, for example, who were surprised to find objects such as quasars and pulsars, continue to be surprised that they cannot agree upon what they are, where they are, and what makes them so powerful. At the other end of the scale, physicists probing the atom for the "most elementary" particles keep finding more bits and pieces that suggest even finer levels of structure.

The unexpected is found throughout this edition of *Science Year*. Robert D. Ballard, in the Special Report LIFE WHERE THE EARTH IS RENEWED, tells of studies of the ocean floor where upwelling material from the earth's interior creates warm-water vents. Remote sensing by an underwater camera, followed by visits to the sites by Ballard and others in a submersible, revealed living creatures, some never before seen, a mile and a half beneath the surface of the ocean. In LIFE IN THE TWILIGHT ZONE, J. Lee Kavanau outlines experiments on a wide variety of animals showing that their behavior under different levels of light is far more complex than anyone had believed. Donald C. Johanson, in OUR ROOTS GO DEEPER, describes the fossils that he and other anthropologists recently uncovered–finds that have resulted in the naming of a new hominid species and pushing the dawn of man back to almost 4 million years ago. And Paul MacCready explains in FLIGHT OF THE *GOSSAMER CONDOR* how his observations of hang gliders and soaring birds set him off in a direction different from others trying to build a human-powered aircraft–with successful flights and a $95,000 prize won as a result.

The Science File too has its share of reports on the unexpected. In ELEMENTARY PARTICLE PHYSICS, we read about the new upsilon particle, discovered by Fermilab physicists, that is the heaviest quark yet observed. It emphasizes how much more complex the subatomic world is than we anticipated just a few years ago. In GENETICS, we learn about genes that are split and then spliced together during gene function. They belong to a virus that uses human genes to do the splicing, a completely unexpected phenomenon in higher organisms. Astronomy continues to contribute its share of surprises, with reports of auroras on Jupiter, a brand-new (2000-year-old) star in the constellation Orion, and new sources of high-energy radiation.

British geneticist J. B. S. Haldane once commented, "The universe is not only queerer than we imagine, it is queerer than we *can* imagine." How fortunate this is for the readers of *Science Year*. It promises that there will always be a source of stories about the exciting, the spectacular, the unexpected.   [Arthur G. Tressler]

Contents

Staff

Editorial Advisory Board

Contributors

Adelman, George, M.S.
Editor and Librarian
Neurosciences Research Program
Massachusetts Institute of Technology
Neuroscience

Ahrens, Thomas J., Ph.D.
Professor of Geophysics
California Institute of Technology
Geoscience, Geophysics

Alderman, Michael H., M.D.
Assistant Professor of Medicine and
Public Health
Cornell University Medical College
Medicine, Internal
Public Health

Anthes, Richard A., Ph.D.
Associate Professor of Meteorology
Pennsylvania State University
Meteorology

Araujo, Paul E., Ph.D.
Assistant Professor
Department of Food Science and
Human Nutrition
University of Florida
Nutrition

Auerbach, Stanley I., Ph.D.
Director, Environmental
Sciences Division
Oak Ridge National Laboratory
Ecology

Ballard, Robert D., Ph.D.
Associate Scientist
Woods Hole Oceanographic Institution
Life Where the Earth Is Renewed

Bell, William J., Ph.D.
Professor of Biology
University of Kansas
Zoology

Belton, Michael J. S., Ph.D.
Astronomer
Kitt Peak National Observatory
Astronomy, Planetary

Chiller, Jacques M., Ph.D.
Associate Professor
National Jewish Hospital
& Research Center
Immunology

Corson, Samuel A., Ph.D.
Professor of Psychiatry and
Biophysics
Ohio State University
Close-Up, Psychology

Cromie, William J., B.S.
Executive Director
Council for the Advancement of
Science Writing
Science Talent Search

Crumley, Carole L., Ph.D.
Assistant Professor
Department of Anthropology
University of North Carolina
Archaeology, Old World

Davies, Julian, Ph.D.
Professor of Biochemistry
University of Wisconsin
Biochemistry

Doniach, Sebastian, Ph.D.
Professor
Department of Applied Physics
Stanford University
Physics, Solid-State

Edson, Lee, B.S.
Free-Lance Science Writer
Science Fights Fire

Ensign, Jerald C., Ph.D.
Professor of Bacteriology
University of Wisconsin
Microbiology

Giacconi, Riccardo, Ph.D.
Professor of Astronomy
Harvard University and
Associate Director
Smithsonian Center for Astrophysics
Astronomy, High Energy

Goldhaber, Paul, D.D.S.
Dean and Professor of Periodontology
Harvard School of Dental Medicine
Medicine, Dentistry

Greenberg, Daniel S., A.B.
Editor and Publisher
Science & Government Report
Edward E. David, Jr.

Griffin, James B., Ph.D.
Senior Research Scientist
Museum of Anthropology
University of Michigan
Archaeology, New World

Gump, Frank E., M.D.
Professor of Surgery
Columbia University
Medicine, Surgery

Gwynne, Peter, M.A.
Science Editor
Newsweek
Close-Up, Environment

Hamilton, Warren, Ph.D.
Research Geologist
U.S. Geological Survey
Geoscience, Geology

Hartl, Daniel L., Ph.D.
Professor of Biology
Purdue University
Genetics

Hayes, Arthur H., Jr., M.D.
Professor of Medicine and
Pharmacology
Milton S. Hershey Medical Center
Pennsylvania State University
Drugs

Jennings, Feenan D., B.S. Ch.E.
Director, Sea Grant Program
Texas A&M University
Oceanography

Johanson, Donald C., Ph.D.
Curator of Physical Anthropology and
Director of Scientific Research
Cleveland Museum of Natural History
Our Roots Go Deeper

Jones, William Goodrich, A.M.L.S.
Head Librarian
Seeley G. Mudd Library for
Science and Engineering
Northwestern University
Books of Science

Kavanau, J. Lee, Ph.D.
Professor of Biology
University of California, Los Angeles
Life in the Twilight Zone

Kay, Alan C., Ph.D.
Principal Scientist and
Head of Learning Research Group
Xerox Palo Alto Research Center
Programming Your Own Computer

Kessler, Karl G., Ph.D.
Director of the Center for Absolute
Physical Quantities
National Bureau of Standards
Physics, Atomic and Molecular

Kolata, Gina Bari, M.S.
Staff Writer
Science
Close-Up, Communications

Lewis, Richard S., B.A.
Free-Lance Science Writer
Space Goes Commercial
Space Exploration

Loferski, Joseph J., Ph.D.
Professor of Engineering
Brown University
Electricity from the Sun

MacCready, Paul, Ph.D.
President
Aerovironment Incorporated
Flight of the Gossamer Condor

Maran, Stephen P., Ph.D.
Senior Staff Scientist
NASA-Goddard Space Flight Center
The Birth of a Star
Astronomy, Stellar

March, Robert H., Ph.D.
Professor of Physics
University of Wisconsin
Physics, Elementary Particles

Maugh, Thomas H. II, Ph.D.
Senior Science Writer
Science
Thwarting Malaria's Comeback

McPherson, Charles, D.V.M.
Chief, Animal Resources Branch
National Institutes of Health
Close-Up, Zoology

Meade, Dale M., Ph.D.
Research Physicist
Princeton University
Physics, Plasma

Merbs, Charles F., Ph.D.
Chairman
Department of Anthropology
Arizona State University
Anthropology

Miller, Betty M., Ph.D.
Program Chief
Resource Appraisal Group
U.S. Geological Survey
Assessing Our Petroleum Future

Moran, Edward, B.A.
Free-Lance Science Writer
Technology

Negele, John W., Ph.D.
Associate Professor of Physics
Massachusetts Institute of Technology
Physics, Nuclear

Olsen, Edward J., Ph.D.
Chairman
Department of Geology
Field Museum of Natural History
Close-Up, Geoscience

Patrusky, Ben, B.E.E.
Free-Lance Science Writer
The Liver's Many Roles

Price, Frederick C., Ch.E.
Publications Supervisor
Ketchum, MacLeod & Grove
Chemical Technology

Rosenberg, Norman J., Ph.D.
Professor, Agricultural Meteorology
Institute of Agriculture and
Natural Resources
Greening the Brown Lands

Salisbury, Frank B., Ph. D.
Professor of Plant Physiology
Plant Science Department
Utah State University
Botany

Silk, Joseph, Ph.D.
Associate Professor of Astronomy
University of California, Berkeley
Astronomy, Cosmology

Sperling, Sally E., Ph.D.
Professor
Department of Psychology
University of California, Riverside
Psychology

Spiegel, Edward A., Ph.D.
Professor of Astronomy
Columbia University
Currents in Chaos

Temple, Stanley A., Ph.D.
Professor of Wildlife Ecology
University of Wisconsin, Madison
Close-Up, Botany

Thompson, Ida, Ph.D.
Assistant Professor
Department of Geological and
Geophysical Sciences
Princeton University
Geoscience, Paleontology

Verbit, Lawrence, Ph.D.
Professor of Chemistry
State University of New York
at Binghamton
Chemistry

Veverka, Joseph, Ph.D.
Associate Professor of Astronomy
Cornell University
Asteroids: The Missing Planet?

Visich, Marian, Jr., Ph.D.
Associate Dean of Engineering
State University of New York
Energy

Wade, Nicholas, M.A.
Staff Writer
Science
Close-Up, Science Policy

Ward, Harold R., Ph.D., J.D.
Associate Dean of the College
Brown University
Environment

Wargo, James R., B.S.
Washington Correspondent
Freed-Crown Publishing Company
Transportation

Weber, Samuel, B.S.E.E.
Executive Editor
Electronics Magazine
Electronics

Wetherill, George W., Ph.D.
Director
Department of Terrestrial Magnetism
Carnegie Institution of Washington
Geoscience, Geochemistry

Wittwer, Sylvan H., Ph.D.
Director
Michigan Agricultural Experiment Station
Michigan State University
Agriculture

Zare, Richard N., Ph.D.
Professor of Chemistry
Stanford University
A New Light on Chemistry

Zeltzer, Harry I., O.D.
Research and Clinical Optometrist
X-Chrom Corporation
Close-Up, Medicine, Internal

Contributors not listed on
these pages are members of the
Science Year editorial staff.

Special Reports

The Special Reports give in-depth treatment to the major advances in science and technology. The subjects were chosen for their current importance and lasting interest.

Life Where the Earth Is Renewed

By Robert D. Ballard

Diving to study the earth's activity on the ocean floor, scientists found communities of animals that no one had seen before

It is totally dark outside our small, thick windows. Occasionally, a tiny flicker of light passes quickly by, its source a mystery. We are falling about 30 meters (100 feet) per minute toward the rocky surface of a land where the sun never shines and the temperature hovers perpetually near freezing. Inside our small capsule, the temperature drops as we descend, and the moisture in our breath begins to condense into small droplets on the polished metal surfaces around us.

With me are geochemist John B. Corliss of Oregon State University in Corvallis and engineer Larry A. Shumaker of Woods Hole Oceanographic Institution in Massachusetts, the pilot of our craft. We have been falling for 15 minutes, and should reach our destination some 2½ kilometers (1½ miles) beneath the surface of the Pacific Ocean in about an hour. Our general location is near the Galapagos Islands, which are 970 kilometers (600 miles) west of Ecuador. Once on the bottom, we will maneuver to one of the most unusual and scientifically significant areas on earth, a spot that was visited by human beings for the first time just days ago.

In the seven years that I have been diving in remote places like this, I have made more than 100 deep descents in small submersibles, but

today's dive will be the most exciting. We are in the *Alvin,* a small but highly sophisticated research submarine from the Woods Hole Oceanographic Institution, my home base. I lean back against the craft's cool pressure hull and scan the instrument panels around me. Their strange, dim, red lights cast an eerie glow. All seems to be going well, so I relax and my thoughts drift over the details of our mission.

We are headed toward a valley whose walls are the edges of two lithospheric plates—huge segments of the earth's rigid outer crust—which are moving away from each other. Valleys like this, formed as a depression between diverging plates, are called rift valleys. We are descending into the Galapagos Rift Valley.

As lithospheric plates drift apart, lava rising from within the earth fills the resulting void and flows out onto the floor of the valley. This is unlike volcanic activity above the sea. Because of the extreme cold and high pressure of the water at these depths, the lava oozes out of the sea floor like toothpaste out of a tube and quickly hardens to form relatively low volcanoes and new crust. As a geologist, I am particularly interested in this process because it is the way in which the earth's crust renews itself.

Scientists do not know exactly what moves the earth's lithospheric plates apart. Often the opposite ends of the plates are bending down and under other plates that they abut. Perhaps this pulls the parting plates away from one another.

Another driving force may stem from the earth's attempt to give off its internal heat. Theoretically, the heat rises from the hot interior of the earth, warming the rock above just as the heat from a radiator in a room warms the air above it. The warm air above the radiator divides, part of it flowing along the ceiling in one direction and the rest flowing in the opposite direction. These separating flows exert tension on the ceiling. Similarly, the heat from within the earth warms the semiplastic rock at the base of the rigid lithospheric plates. The rock flows, as does the air at the ceiling, exerting considerable tension, and probably helps to pull the plates apart.

The parting of the plates would release some pressure within the hot rock beneath the plates, causing some of the rock to melt. The melted rock could then flow up between the plates and some of it ooze out through a vent, or volcanic opening, in the sea floor.

The author:
Robert D. Ballard
is an associate
scientist at the Woods
Hole Oceanographic
Institution in
Massachusetts.

This theory of sea-floor spreading along rift valleys is a critical part of a larger theory about the earth called "plate tectonics." Only about 10 years old, this theory makes it possible to understand and view the earth as a dynamic object that is continually changing.

Suddenly, the crackling of the intercom that links us with *Lulu,* our support ship on the surface, jolts me back to the present. Jack Donnelly, another *Alvin* pilot, has been keeping track of us from the surface: "*Alvin,* this is *Lulu.* You are north of the launch coordinates. We'll request a midcourse correction later. Over." Shumaker leans forward to answer, "Roger, *Lulu,*" and it is quiet again.

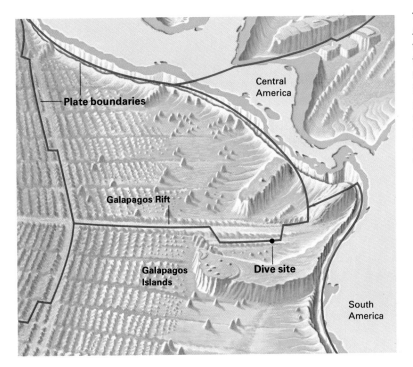

The Birthplace Below
At the Galapagos Rift, volcanic activity beneath two geologic plates renews the earth's crust. Unusual temperature rises detected along the rift from the surface brought the author and his co-workers to the dive site.

Plate boundaries

Central
America

Galapagos Rift

**Galapagos
Islands**

Dive site

South
America

The Vent Theory
In one explanation of the unusually warm temperatures detected, cold water (blue arrows) enters deep fissures created by parting plates.

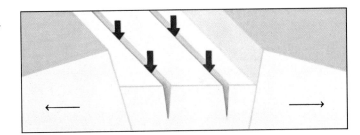

Rising molten rock flows out on the ocean floor and caps the fissures, trapping the water. Magma (orange) deep in the earth heats the water.

Continued stress cracks the capping material, opening vents through which the warm water (red) enters the sea and more fissures into which additional cold water flows.

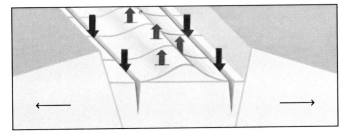

My first dives into a rift valley were in 1973 and 1974 in a joint French-American project at the Mid-Atlantic Ridge. I made those dives in the French bathyscaph *Archimède*. The bathyscaph is a large, cumbersome vehicle designed by Swiss physicist Auguste Piccard shortly after World War II. It is the oldest and simplest deep-diving craft, but it served us well.

Our initial Atlantic dives were filled with excitement. We were the first humans to enter a rift valley. Earlier, cameras lowered from surface ships to the rift had taken photographs of lava, lending support to the plate-tectonics theory. Our underwater explorations also helped to confirm the theory. We found a series of young volcanoes down the center of the valley with fresh lava flows stacked on top of one another.

The lava had assumed pillowlike shapes, most of them elongated into tubes. These tubes, called pillow lavas, form when the outer portions of flowing lava cool and harden, protecting the inner lava from the cold water. The tubes then act as conduits through which the hot lava flows away from the volcanic vents and down the steep slopes.

During the summer of 1974, we made additional dives in the bathyscaph as well as in *Alvin* and its French counterpart, *Cyana*. These modern submersibles offer several advantages over the *Archimède*. Smaller and more maneuverable, they also have more portholes for viewing. In addition, they can do more complex and sensitive tasks, such as measuring the temperature and chemical content of the water.

In our dives in *Alvin*, we not only found vast expanses of fresh lava flows, but we also discovered deep, wide fissures cutting across the flows. However, the fissures showed no signs of upwelling lava. Evidently, after the volcanoes develop, the newly cooled crust that they create is fractured by the continuing forces of sea-floor spreading.

While we were diving in the Mid-Atlantic Ridge, halfway around the world another team of scientists was using surface ships to conduct preliminary studies in the Galapagos Rift Valley. Dartlike thermometers dropped into the ocean floor by marine scientists had revealed previously that this region has an unusually high rate of heat flowing from the ocean floor to the surrounding water. The team confirmed the high heat flow and also, by towing thermometers through the water near the bottom, discovered intermittent warm spots. After analyzing their data, the scientists concluded that heat conducted from the ocean floor to the water could not account for the warm spots. Instead, they reasoned, water must somehow circulate in and out of the earth's hot upper crust to cause the warm spots. But how did the water enter the crust and leave it? The fissures we had found in the Mid-Atlantic Ridge could provide an answer. If the young lava in the Galapagos Rift Valley contained similar fractures, they might provide avenues for seawater to circulate in the crust.

Seawater, perhaps vast quantities of it, passing deep into the earth and out again would cool the crust, just as circulating water cools an automobile engine. This deep circulation is particularly interesting to

The tracking vigil, *left,* calls for intense concentration by four of the surface-ship *Knorr* team. The instruments give precise data on where the ship is and how fast it is moving relative to the bottom. They also keep track of the photography sled as it is lowered, *below,* and later towed near the sea floor.

geochemists, who have thought that the chemical salts in our oceans were carried there by rivers. Seawater moving into and out of the hot crust of the earth would change the chemical composition not only of the crust, but also of the oceans.

With this in mind, ocean scientists from several institutions carried out further research cruises to the Galapagos Rift Valley in 1975 and 1976. This time, they towed cameras and water samplers, as well as thermometers, over the ocean floor. They, too, found warm-water spots along the center of the rift valley. The cameras brought back pictures of fresh lava flows and open fissures just like those we had discovered at the rift in the Atlantic.

During one of the tows across the valley, scientists aboard a research vessel from the Scripps Institution of Oceanography in San Diego activated a water sampler at a point where water temperature suddenly rose. When they analyzed that sample, they found an unusual chemical composition, including high concentrations of helium and radon. This suggested a hydrothermal origin for the water. Could this indicate the presence of an exit vent for water that had circulated through the earth's crust?

If such vents existed, they would go a long way toward proving that seawater did circulate in this way. In March 1976, scientists decided to send the *Alvin* on an expedition to search the Galapagos Rift Valley for these vents. Our dive is a part of this expedition.

This time it is Shumaker who breaks the silence: "*Lulu,* our depth is 500 meters and our altitude is 2,000 meters." "Roger, *Alvin,*" Donnelly replies from above. "Come to a course of 175 degrees."

The silence resumes and my thoughts wander to the events immediately preceding this dive. We set sail for the Galapagos Rift Valley on the research ship *Knorr* on Feb. 8, 1977, arriving several days ahead of

The Big Discovery
Water-temperature data, *bottom,* is compared with photos taken in sequence, *below and below right,* as the *Knorr* and the photosled tracked the rift. The sea floor is barren at typical low temperatures. But when temperatures rose, indicating a possible vent, clams appeared in great numbers, *opposite page.*

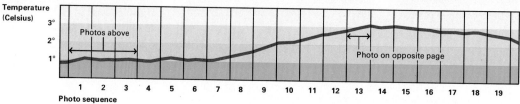

the *Lulu* and the *Alvin* to do preliminary work in the dive area. Our satellite-tracking system, which uses signals from satellites to navigate, told us when we had arrived in the rift area. But we needed to know exactly where we were with reference to the bottom. Slowing to a few knots, *Knorr* began probing the sea floor below with its sonar, or echo-sounding, system. As we zigzagged back and forth across the area, we compared the profiles of the bottom obtained by this sonar to a detailed sonar map of the rift area made for us by the U.S. Navy. One by one, we found the various features drawn on the Navy map—the north and south walls that flank the valley, then the central axis, and, eventually, individual volcanoes. Next, we had to provide a way to determine our exact position continuously as we moved about.

Assured of our location, we dropped four transponders, underwater sound generators whose beeps would broadcast their exact locations on the ocean floor. These locations would be programmed into the large computer aboard the *Knorr*. Then, through the computer, the beeps could be used to indicate our exact position on a map of the ocean floor displayed on a screen. Watching this display, Captain Emerson Hiller steered the *Knorr* to the point at which we wanted to begin our search for warm water.

We then lowered a heavy steel sledlike device over the side on the ship's 0.6-millimeter (½-inch) towing wire. This device has equipment designed primarily for sea-floor photography, but it also includes

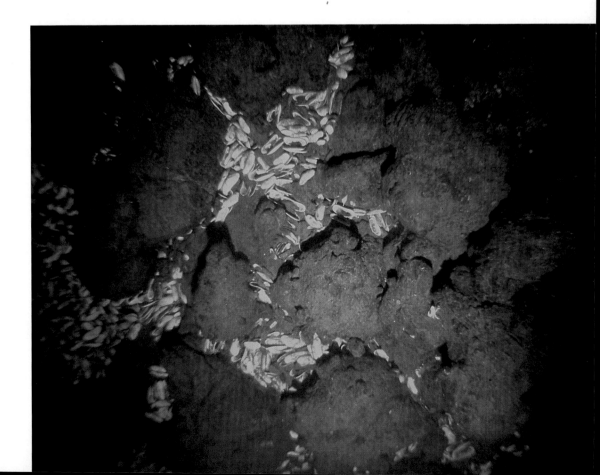

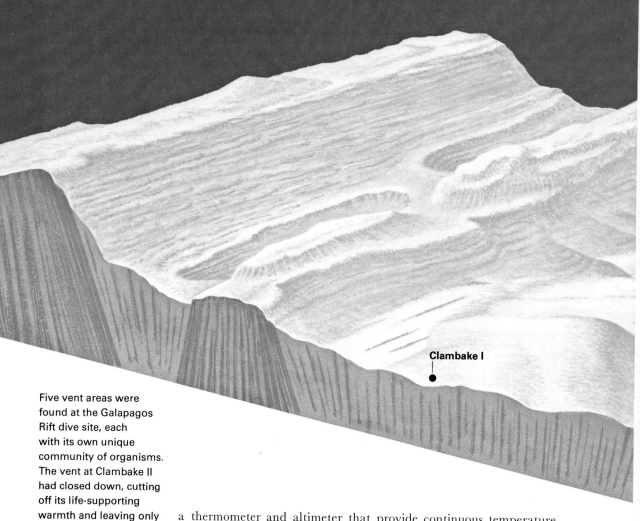

Clambake I

Five vent areas were found at the Galapagos Rift dive site, each with its own unique community of organisms. The vent at Clambake II had closed down, cutting off its life-supporting warmth and leaving only many empty clam shells.

a thermometer and altimeter that provide continuous temperature and height-above-bottom readings to people on the *Knorr*.

Underwater currents and several other factors swing the sled about, making it impossible to tow the device over exact, predetermined routes unless we know precisely where it is at all times. A relay transponder that broadcasts sound solves this problem. Attached to the towline, the transponder provides the information needed to project the sled's position, along with that of the *Knorr*, on the map display.

Forty-five minutes after we began lowering the sled, a timer automatically turned the camera on, and it began taking color pictures with the aid of a powerful strobe light. The light flashed every 10 seconds, illuminating about 50 square meters (60 square yards) of the dark sea floor. As we towed the sled across the rugged volcanic terrain below at about ¾ knot (about 1 mile per hour), technicians watched the altitude trace being drawn by a recorder as it monitored the sled's altimeter. They called out instructions to the winch operator to raise or lower the sled so it would not crash into the steep slopes. This was particularly exacting, because the sled must be no more than 5 meters (16 feet) above the sea floor to keep it in view of the camera.

Despite precautions, 20 minutes after beginning to traverse the bottom, the huge sled smashed into the rocky sea floor. Tension on the

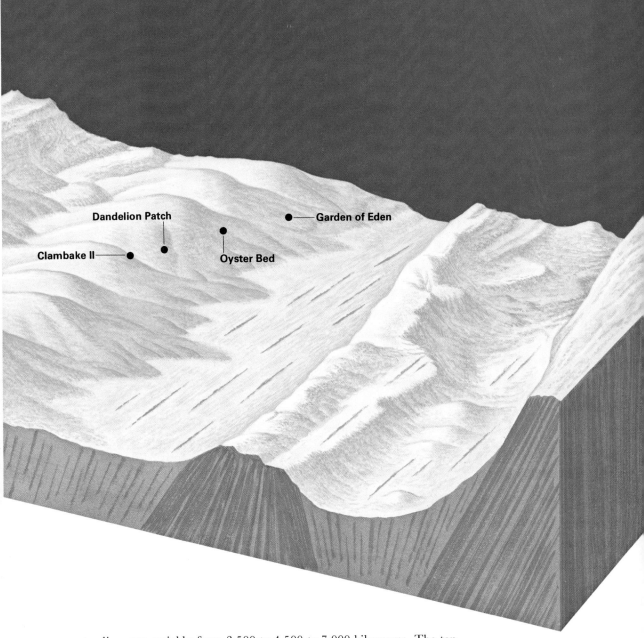

Dandelion Patch

Clambake II

Oyster Bed

Garden of Eden

towline rose quickly from 3,500 to 4,500 to 7,000 kilograms. The tension among the scientists and technicians rose proportionately. If wire tension exceeded 9,000 kilograms, the cable would break and $100,000 worth of unique equipment would be lost. But Captain Hiller quickly backed the ship, and cable was paid out to reduce towline tension. After several minutes of maneuvering, the sled pulled free and the towing continued.

Five and a half hours later, just after midnight, the water-temperature trace suddenly jumped a full degree Celsius for about three minutes. This jump represented about a 50 per cent increase at the near-freezing temperatures. And the jump would probably have been even greater had the sled been closer to the bottom. We noted the precise time and location of the sled.

Organisms new to science found at the dive site include an animal resembling a fluffy dandelion, *above,* and one draped like spaghetti on a fissure's edges and photographed in front of the collecting basket of submersible *Alvin, above right.*

After 12 hours of towing, the sled's camera had shot the last of its 3,000 pictures, and we brought it back to the surface. Once the sled was back aboard the *Knorr,* we had to wait several hours for the camera to warm up so that water would not condense on the film when it was opened. Since developing the film would take several additional hours, we all went to bed.

By late morning, a team of scientists including Massachusetts Institute of Technology chemist John M. Edmond; Jack R. Dymond, a geochemist from Oregon State University; and me were sitting in the projection room, eager to see the pictures. The first few frames were a deep blue—evidently the camera had turned on before reaching the sea floor. But the bottom soon came into view and we saw a massive pile of fresh pillow lava. At first, we saw frame after frame of pillow-lava terrain. The camera automatically prints on each frame the exact time it was taken, and as we watched the frames go by, we also kept an eye on the printed time. As the frames taken at midnight approached, our anticipation grew; the camera was nearing the point where the water temperature had jumped. Would we see a warm-water vent?

The photograph taken just seconds before the jump showed only more barren pillows. Then, suddenly, an incredible series of pictures

An octopus, *top left,* hunts for crabs at Clambake I. A sea cucumber, startled by the *Alvin,* forms a question mark as it hurries away, *above left.* Crabs and fanlike organisms, *above,* inhabit part of another area of an active vent.

appeared. The pillows were covered with hundreds of white and brown clam and mussel shells. We could hardly believe our eyes. No one had ever suspected, much less seen, such an accumulation of life in the deep sea before. After 13 frames, a time period corresponding exactly to the duration of the temperature jump, the shells disappeared. For the remaining 1,500 frames, the bottom was once again a barren lifeless expanse.

Everyone was excited. And we were anxious to dive for a firsthand look at the creatures we had discovered. Fortunately, virtually the moment we finished viewing the film, the *Lulu* and the *Alvin* arrived. While I remained aboard the *Knorr* to help tow the sled in search of other temperature rises, Edmond, Dymond, and Corliss transferred to the *Lulu* to dive in *Alvin.* That was a few days ago, and last night I was so excited by the thought of diving to see what my colleagues had seen that I got almost no sleep.

The readings on the *Alvin*'s instrument panel pull me back to the present. It is time to contact the surface. "*Lulu,* this is *Alvin,*" I report. "We have picked up the bottom on the fathometer. Our altitude is 100 meters. We'll call you back when we have landed." "Right Bob, keep a sharp eye out for the bottom."

To slow our fall, Shumaker drops two 113-kilogram (250-pound) weights from *Alvin*'s sides, and our descent all but stops. Using the vessel's high-pressure variable-ballast system, he pumps seawater out of a small titanium sphere, making us still lighter. In a few minutes, we are hovering motionless over the bottom.

"I have neutral trim," Shumaker declares. "Let's drive the rest of the way down." The noise inside the vessel increases sharply as props thrust the *Alvin* down. "I see bottom," Shumaker says suddenly. "It's a gentle slope of fresh pillow lava."

Maneuvering carefully, Shumaker stops the *Alvin* just above the bottom. In *Alvin*'s running lights, I can see that life in this area is sparse, typical of the deep sea. Without sunlight, no plant life can grow and the few animals that live here depend upon what food falls from the sunlit zone thousands of meters above.

I lean forward to the microphone, "*Lulu,* can you vector us to the vent site?" "Roger, turn to a new course of 090 degrees. It should be about 30 meters away."

Slowly, Shumaker pivots the *Alvin*. A moment later he says admiringly, "That tracking system is amazing. We have an active geothermal vent dead ahead."

My first reaction upon entering the area of the live vent is like that of a child first visiting Walt Disney World. It is hard to believe what I see—strange pink fish, a purple octopus, clusters of white crabs, and thousands of brown mussels and large white clams. Not only are many of these animals completely new to me, but they also are living without sunlight. No living community of organisms more complex than bacteria has ever been known to do this before. If I did not know that I am 2½ kilometers below the surface, in a world that is normally pitch-black, I would mistake the scene for one in a shallow tidal pool.

The water streaming from the vent shimmers milky-blue in the *Alvin*'s lights. The pillow lavas around the vent are coated with a dull-brown layer of manganese that is precipitating out of the warm vent water as it meets the near-freezing bottom water. The animals are unusually large, particularly the white clams, which average 30 centimeters (12 inches) in length. The warm water is clearly a factor in their growth, but what do they eat?

The answer to that question begins to unfold when we return to the surface. In one of the *Knorr*'s laboratories, we open the water samples we collected from the vent, and the smell of rotten eggs fills the lab. Several of us quickly open the portholes. When we analyze the water, we find it contains large quantities of hydrogen sulfide, a foul-smelling gas. Evidently, the sulfates normally in seawater are converted to hydrogen sulfide as the water passes through the warm crust.

Ironically, our expedition included no biologists—only chemists, geologists, geophysicists, and physicists. Later, however, microbiologists at Oregon State and Scripps would link the hydrogen sulfide and the living organisms. In the water samples, they would find a type of

A fish swims among tube worms 0.6 meter (2 feet) long, *above,* found in the mouth of the vent at The Garden of Eden. Zoologist Meredith Jones, *right,* dissects and examines one of these worms in his laboratory.

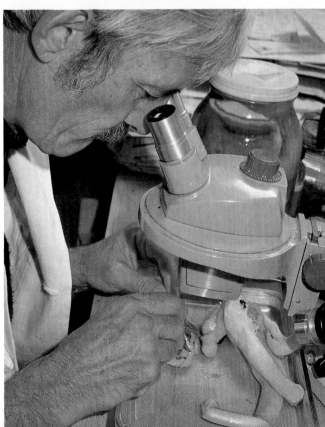

The *Alvin*'s collecting
arm captures one of the
large clams—30 to 40
centimeters (12 to 16
inches) long—found near
the vents, *right.* The
clam is examined, *below
right,* in a laboratory
at the Harvard Museum
of Comparative Zoology.

bacteria that simply loves hydrogen sulfide. And in the digestive systems of some of the clams from the rift, they would find millions of these bacteria. Evidently, the bacteria use the hydrogen sulfide and other substances in the water to grow and multiply rapidly in total darkness, providing large concentrations of food in the warm vent water for the other animals to eat. So, the area near a sea-floor vent is a world unto itself, warming and feeding its living community independent of the sun.

During the two months we spent in the Galapagos Rift Valley, we found five vents, four of them active and one inactive. Each has its own unique biological community living around it. Our jubilation at such a significant discovery accounts for the whimsical names that we chose for each vent area.

In the first area that we found, the dominant animals are unusually large white clams, only a small percentage of them alive; most are open, empty shells. The empty shells, plus the presence of several empty beer cans that had been thrown off a passing ship, led us to call the area Clambake I.

We called the inactive area, the second area we discovered, Clambake II. We found no living clams or warm water there. Instead, the lava flows are covered with thousands of empty, slowly dissolving, white clamshells. Evidently the vent in this area shut off, leaving the community around it to die of cold and starvation.

The third area is the Dandelion Patch, named for an unusual and previously unknown animal that is spherical in shape and resembles the fluffy head of a dandelion gone to seed. The Dandelion Patch is the least developed of the four active vents. Its primitive nature is probably due to the fact that the water coming out of the vent there is the coldest and does not contain hydrogen sulfide.

Mussels grow at the Oyster Bed, the fourth area. They are smaller than those at Clambake I and were initially mistaken for oysters.

The last vent we discovered has the most varied population and many of us rate it the most impressive. So we called it the Garden of Eden. The biggest animal living there is a red worm about 60 centimeters (24 inches) long that lives in an erect, white tube. The largest known worm of its type, these animals live in the vent water just where it exits from the sea floor. The pillow lavas nearby are covered with limpets, small shelled creatures whose closest relatives had previously been found only in shallow water.

The diversity of life forms from one vent area to another, despite the seeming similarity of the areas, is a puzzle. Some biologists have suggested the "founders theory" as a solution to the puzzle. In this theory, the first organism to arrive in a habitable place can often dominate the area. That might be particularly true of places like the vent areas. Each area is small, about the size of a football field, so the first animal there may quickly reproduce and monopolize this unique real estate.

Specimens of nearly all the unusual animals we saw and collected were given to specialists at Harvard University, the Smithsonian Institution, the University of California, and other laboratories where they are being investigated and described in detail. Meanwhile, we are making plans to return to the vents in 1979 with a shipload of biologists who have a long list of experiments to perform and questions to answer. In addition to recording what creatures and how many live in each vent area, the biologists hope to bring many new specimens to the surface to study them in special aquariums on the research ship. They have also designed small chambers which the *Alvin* crew can place over animals on the ocean floor. These chambers contain equipment to monitor each animal's metabolic processes without disturbing it. I hope to extend the search farther down the valley where I may find additional vents with still different forms of life.

One thing is certain: The sea floor is no longer the province of geoscientists alone. It is now a source of growing interest for chemists and zoologists as well.

Space Goes Commercial

By Richard S. Lewis

The space shuttle, a vehicle for transporting people and freight to and from earth orbit, promises to revolutionize manufacturing and scientific research

"Liftoff!" announces the voice from Launch Control. The Space Shuttle Orbiter, *The City of Topeka*, shudders and begins to rise vertically off its pad. You feel as though a cosmic hand were pushing you back against your seat, and for a moment you fear it will stop your breathing. But you breathe.

In deep, calm voices, the shuttle commander and the pilot, who are seated in front of you, read off cabin pressure, increases in speed, and electrical-systems data. Then the furious roar of the twin solid-rocket boosters and the shuttle's three main rocket engines becomes muted as you overtake the speed of sound, hurtling toward the silence of interplanetary space. Now your only sensation of rockets blasting is a deep vibration in the bones of your arms and legs, your ribcage, the base of your spine, and your skull.

Although you have practiced simulated launches and landings time and again during your training at the Lyndon B. Johnson Space Cen-

ter near Houston, the sensation of the boost can never be reproduced exactly on the ground. The pressure of three times normal gravity exerts a firm but not too uncomfortable weight during the eight-minute trip to low earth orbit.

As a payload specialist, a new category of scientist or engineer in charge of experiments or handling payloads, you have nothing to do during the ascent but relax and enjoy the flight. You peer through the thick right-hand windshield of fused, silica glass but see only a darkening sky fringed with high cirrus clouds. How dull. You wanted to see the earth receding from you.

Shuttle Flight Control comes on the air and announces that it now has you on an invisible, unbreakable, electronic string that will keep you linked to Houston throughout your seven-day mission.

Two minutes into the flight, you feel the shuttle shudder as the two solid-rocket boosters shut down and detach. The boosters can be used up to 20 times. They will fall on blossoming parachutes into the Atlantic Ocean, where a ship waits to rescue them from the waves.

Your space vessel continues under the thrust of its three liquid-fuel engines. After six more minutes of flight, the main engines cut off and vibration ceases.

The craft shudders again as the big main propellant tank detaches. At launch, it was filled with 680,000 kilograms (1.5 million pounds) of liquid hydrogen and liquid oxygen to fuel the orbiter's main rocket engines. Now empty, it is thrown away—the only part of the shuttle system that is not reusable. It should break up and burn as it falls back into the earth's atmosphere; any fragments that do not burn should splash down in a remote part of the Indian Ocean.

The City of Topeka, which began the mission as a rocket-boosted airplane, is now a spacecraft coasting into orbit. The force of gravity vanishes. You are weightless, floating in free fall around the earth.

Orbiter Control in Houston informs you that your space plane is traveling at 28,000 kilometers (17,500 miles) per hour at an altitude of 128 kilometers (80 miles). Even though you are strapped in your seat, you feel as though you are drifting.

You listen as the commander and pilot talk confidently with Houston. There is a soft surging motion as two small rockets in the orbiter's tail ignite to boost the craft to an altitude of 185 kilometers (115 miles). The space shuttle can orbit at altitudes of up to 965 kilometers (600 miles). The space plane rolls slightly, and you can see the earth far below, brown and gray with a fringe of dark blue at the horizon. For the first time, you see the earth as a revolving planet.

Now it is time to go to work—as a plant physiologist in space. In addition to performing laboratory experiments on plants, it is your job to operate cameras that see in the visible and infrared regions of the electromagnetic spectrum. The cameras photograph commercial timber resources throughout the world for a group of United States, Canadian, and European paper manufacturers who require very specific

The author:
Richard S. Lewis
is a free-lance
science writer.

The Shuttle and its Future

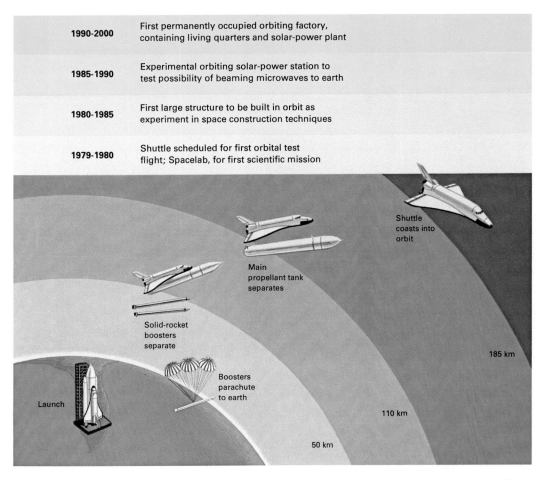

1990-2000	First permanently occupied orbiting factory, containing living quarters and solar-power plant
1985-1990	Experimental orbiting solar-power station to test possibility of beaming microwaves to earth
1980-1985	First large structure to be built in orbit as experiment in space construction techniques
1979-1980	Shuttle scheduled for first orbital test flight; Spacelab, for first scientific mission

Shuttle coasts into orbit

Main propellant tank separates

Solid-rocket boosters separate

Boosters parachute to earth

Launch

185 km

110 km

50 km

The space shuttle will be propelled into orbit in 1979 by two reusable solid rockets and a huge propellant tank. It will carry up the European *Spacelab* in 1980. Subsequent plans call for major engineering feats leading to living and working in space.

kinds of data gathered over a short period of time and who could not afford to launch their own satellite for this limited purpose. You take your position at a console and operate the controls that open the outer doors of the cargo bay to expose your cameras and other recording instruments.

The work you will be doing during the next week is an example of the change in emphasis from space exploration to space exploitation. Because of the shuttle, space flight has become an international commercial enterprise. Corporations pay to have satellites hauled from the ground to low orbit and buy cargo space for experiments on new manufacturing techniques that will someday bring about another industrial revolution. In addition, the shuttle serves as the first stage for launching lunar and interplanetary missions.

You fit into this scheme as a rookie member of the corps of astronauts and payload specialists in the Space Shuttle Transportation System (SSTS). If you measure up, you will have a career. This is Part

II of the space age and a brand-new ball game. Even the name of the game has changed. The National Aeronautics and Space Administration's (NASA) Office of Space Flight in 1977 became the Office of Space Transportation Systems. You are on its payroll, and, except for your personnel file and the photograph on your identification card, there is no official reference to the fact that you are a woman.

A scene from the 21st century? Not at all. Such flights should be common by the mid-1980s. As of mid-1977, the spacecraft itself was off the drawing board and in the air.

The Age of the Shuttle opened on the morning of Aug. 12, 1977, in California's Mojave Desert. At 6,736 meters (22,100 feet) above the desert, Commander Fred W. Haise detonated a set of explosive bolts. Instantly, the delta-wing space plane soared free of the Boeing 747 that had carried it aloft.

Haise and pilot Charles G. Fullerton flew the 68-metric-ton *Enterprise* 53.8 kilometers (33.35 miles) around a U-shaped course to a flawless landing. The wheels touched down on the dry lake-bed runway at Edwards Air Force Base with a shrill squeal at 180 nautical miles per hour. Thousands of spectators cheered as the space plane rolled 3 kilometers (2 miles) before halting, trailing a curtain of fine dust. Millions of Americans watched the 5½-minute spectacle on television. The first hurdle was passed, and the orbiter continued to perform well in later test flights in the lower atmosphere at altitudes as high as 8,107 meters (26,000 feet). NASA officials look forward confidently to its first orbital flight in 1979.

Instead of the cone shape of earlier space capsules, this new generation of manned space vehicles is a hybrid spacecraft-airplane with wings spanning 23.7 meters (78 feet) and a rudder for flying in the atmosphere, and rockets for maneuvering in space. This design reflects a cost-conscious approach to space flight. Its main feature is reusability. The orbiter can be used up to 100 times. It will be launched vertically from remodeled Apollo pads at the John F. Kennedy Space

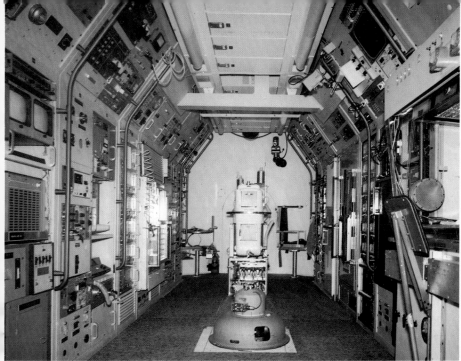

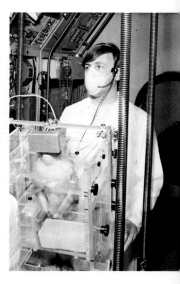

Spacelab, above, contains equipment for a wide range of scientific experiments. A scientist rehearses an experiment on animal eye muscles, *right,* that he will conduct in orbit. *Spacelab* and an exposed array of telescopes and other instruments, *below,* will fit in the shuttle's cargo bay.

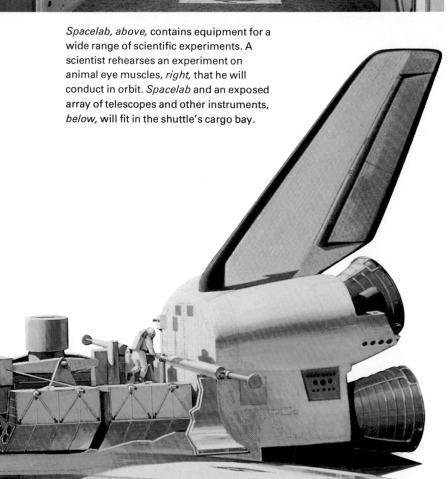

Center at Cape Canaveral, Fla. Standing on its tail in the launch position, the 37-meter (122-foot)-long orbiter is dwarfed by its blimp-shaped propellant tank, which stands 47 meters (154 feet) high, and the solid fuel boosters, each 45 meters (149 feet) long. In space, after the solid rockets and the propellant tank are dropped, the crew must rely on two maneuvering rocket engines mounted on either side of the aft fuselage and 44 smaller thrusters to control the space plane.

The orbiter's roomy cabin in the front part of the craft has two levels—one containing controls for piloting the craft, the other containing living quarters. The cabin measures 72 cubic meters (2,550 cubic feet) and can transport seven persons and squeeze in three more in an emergency, such as a space rescue. The 4.5- by 18-meter (15- by 60-foot) cargo bay can carry 30,000 kilograms (65,000 pounds) up to orbit and bring back 14,000 kilograms (32,000) pounds.

When the craft returns to earth, a landing system will use a micro-wave beam to guide it down to a runway 4,500 meters (15,000 feet) long by 91 meters (300 feet) wide. This runway is part of the $240-million remodeling program that has converted the Kennedy Space Center from the era of Apollo moonflights to the era of the shuttle.

With a fleet of four shuttles, NASA plans 60 flights a year by the mid-1980s, 40 from the Kennedy Space Center and 20 from duplicate launch and landing facilities at Vandenberg Air Force Base in California. Most of the West Coast launches will be for military purposes.

If the shuttle performs up to expectations, it will reduce the current cost of moving people and materials to low earth orbit about 10 times, the equivalent of a drop from $1,000 to $100 a pound. So NASA views the shuttle as the basis of a multivehicle space-transportation system that could translate from fantasy to fact such projects as mining the moon, operating factories in orbit, building satellite solar-electric power stations, and developing space colonies where thousands of people might live. There will also be a chance for individuals—including high school students—to participate in shuttle missions. A NASA program, nicknamed the Getaway Special, will allow individuals, companies, and universities to rent space for experiments aboard the shuttle at prices ranging from $3,000 to $10,000. Some companies plan to donate their rented space for student experiments.

Although the shuttle is new and untried in space, two additions to it are already well along in development. They are Spacelab, a manned laboratory that will ride into orbit and back to earth in the shuttle's cargo bay, and an upper-stage rocket that can launch vehicles to the moon or into deep space.

Spacelab is being built in West Germany for the European Space Agency (ESA), which represents 10 of the 11 Western European nations that make up ESA. This NASA-ESA partnership, the first such long-term international spacefaring venture, will enable participating European nations to enter the arena of manned flight. Up to four European scientists and technicians will ride the shuttle with U.S.

pilots and commanders on Spacelab missions. *Spacelab I* is scheduled to be launched in 1980.

The Spacelab is smaller and more compact than NASA's huge Skylab experimental space station, with which it is sometimes confused. It has two types of laboratory facilities—a pressurized workshop for scientists and open platforms for mounting telescopes, spectrometers, cameras, and other devices.

The workshop consists of two cylinders, each 2.7 meters (9 feet) long and 4.2 meters (13 feet 9 inches) in diameter. One segment, which contains life-support and data-processing equipment as well as laboratory facilities, can be used alone. Or it can be joined with the second cylinder, which is fitted out entirely as a laboratory.

Like payload specialists, the Spacelab scientists riding the shuttle will need only limited training at the Johnson Space Center, not the rigorous physical conditioning and long training required of astronauts. In NASA's view, any healthy person should be able to ride the shuttle. The only condition that would bar a person from space flight is a high susceptibility to motion sickness.

The scientists will ride with the crew in the shuttle cabin during the vehicle's launch and re-entry. They will eat and sleep in the lower level of the cabin, moving back to the Spacelab workshop through a cylindrical connecting tunnel.

The second addition to the shuttle system, the upper-stage rocket, will be carried aloft in the orbiter's cargo bay. It will then be attached to the satellite that it will boost to high orbit or the spacecraft that it will launch to the moon or other planets.

Another contribution is being made by the Canadians, who are developing a remotely controlled mechanical arm that will lift satellites out of the orbiter cargo bay and retrieve satellites for servicing or return to earth. When a satellite is destined for very high orbit, the arm will position the satellite with its rocket for launch. The arm is more than 15 meters (50 feet) long and has six joints. It will be operated with delicate precision from the rear flight deck by a crew member aided by a computer. It can also operate automatically.

In November 1977, the George C. Marshall Space Flight Center in Huntsville, Ala., announced plans to develop a small rocket-powered craft called the Teleoperator Retrieval System (TRS) that will retrieve satellites from orbits higher than the space shuttle can fly. The TRS will be carried in the orbiter's cargo bay to the vicinity of the satellite. A mechanical arm will remove the TRS, and release it into space. A crew member will fire its rockets by radio command and use television cameras to guide it to the satellite. Then the TRS will tow the satellite back to the orbiter.

The shuttle will open up uses of space that will have dramatic effects on earth in such varied areas as energy, health care, and manufacturing. The high-vacuum, zero-gravity conditions of space provide a manufacturing environment with advantages unobtainable on earth.

A solar-powered space station, *overleaf,* and other large structures will be built with materials and workers carried into earth orbit by the shuttle.

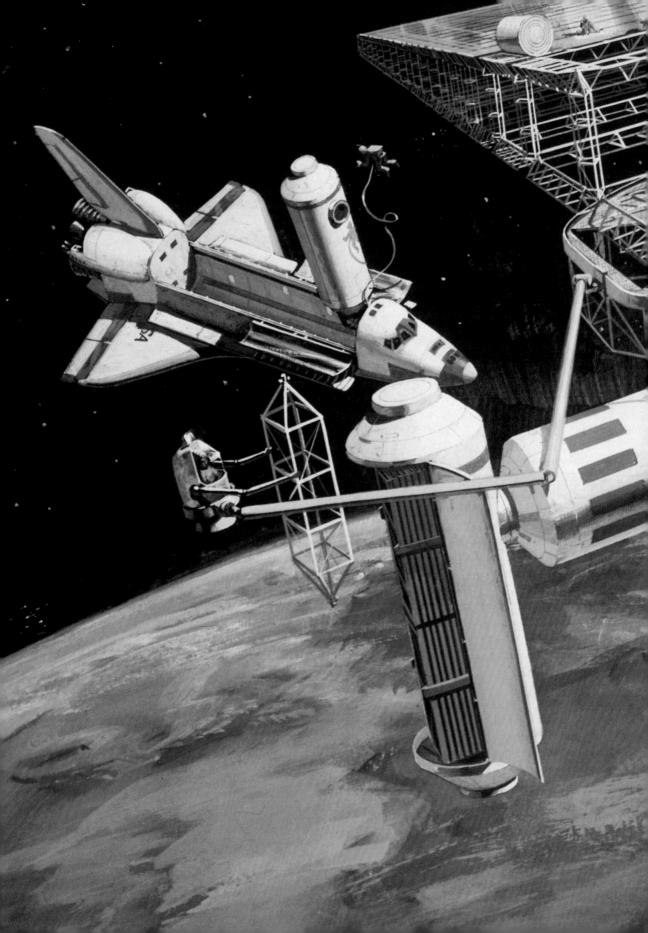

Without the pull of gravity that tends to flatten surfaces, perfect spheres – ball bearings, for example – can be created.

Experiments on Apollo and Skylab between 1970 and 1974 showed that zero-gravity conditions also allow the mixing of unusual combinations of materials – such as steel and glass – to produce superstrong and heat-resistant metal alloys and semiconductors. The force that gravity exerts on atoms and molecules does not allow such chemically different substances to combine on earth. Flawless silicon and germanium crystals can be mass-produced in space, and this could lead to improved transistorized electronics, microwave devices, integrated circuits, lasers, light-emitting diodes, and computer memories able to store vast amounts of information.

Set free after its piggyback ascent on a jumbo jet, *above,* the shuttle glides from a flight test to a perfect landing in the California desert, *right.*

The immense propellant tank, *left,* that will fuel the shuttle's main engines rolls out of its assembly building near New Orleans. A reusable solid-fuel rocket, *below,* that will be strapped to the propellant tank undergoes testing in Utah.

The pharmaceutical industry will also benefit from space-manufacturing techniques. Biological materials, from enzymes to blood cells, can be isolated more efficiently in space. For example, astronauts on the 1975 Apollo-Soyuz Test Project flight ran a test for separating the enzyme urokinase from kidney cells. Urokinase is highly effective in dissolving blood clots, but very difficult to produce on earth and, therefore, very expensive. The cost of such difficult-to-prepare drugs might be greatly reduced by making them in space.

Some experts foresee using the moon's deposits of aluminum, titanium, and silicates to provide the raw materials necessary for building large solar-power satellites, space stations, and orbiting factories. According to *Outline for Space,* a NASA study published in 1976, it would be cheaper to get raw materials for constructing space structures from the moon and process them there or in space than to haul prefabricated parts up from the earth.

Other scientists have studied the possibility of mining iron and nickel from asteroids that pass near the earth. One study estimated that metals worth more than $5 trillion could be obtained if a nickel-iron asteroid of 1 cubic kilometer (0.24 cubic mile) could be maneuvered into earth orbit with rocket engines attached to the asteroid.

These are the kinds of projects that will involve the astronauts, engineers, and scientists of the SSTS as the next century begins. The work of payload specialists like yourself will then seem quite routine.

Your week has passed swiftly, filled with the tasks of observing, adjusting equipment, doing housekeeping chores, and practicing daily exercises. It is time to go home. Four computers—a main computer and three backup computers—and an automatic control system will guide you back to earth. The pilot turns *The City of Topeka* around so that the shuttle's two maneuvering rockets can take the craft out of orbit, then the computer fires the rockets.

An orbital mission accomplished, the shuttle glides toward its special runway at the Kennedy Space Center in Florida on the last leg of its space journey.

Even though you have practiced this phase in the flight simulator at Houston, you are not quite prepared for the onset of weight as the shuttle plunges into the atmosphere at a 30- to 40-degree angle and air resistance builds up a force of 1.5 gravities. Although you cannot see the wings' leading edges, you seem to detect a red glow through the window. The orbiter plunges earthward at nearly 8 kilometers (5 miles) per second, shielded from the fiery heat of atmospheric friction by square tiles of coated silica fiber. The tiles are backed by a high-temperature-resistant material on the nose and leading edges of the wings. The tiles are reusable and, if damaged, can be replaced.

Cabin temperature rises noticeably, but the environmental-control system can handle it. It will not get hotter than 30.2°C (90°F.). Aside from the red glow, there is nothing to see out of the window. You are still far above the clouds.

During the long descent, the spacecraft once more becomes an aircraft, the heaviest glider ever built, with the computer handling its rudder and other controls. According to the flight plan, the shuttle re-enters the earth's atmosphere 140 kilometers (87 miles) above the Pacific Ocean southeast of Hawaii, traveling in an easterly direction.

It is in a long glide that will carry it nearly one-fifth of the way around the earth, about 8,000 kilometers (4,960 miles).

During that ride, the shuttle's velocity must be reduced from about 14,400 knots to 180 knots in order to land safely on the Kennedy spaceport's runway. Even though it has no power, at this tremendous speed in the atmosphere the shuttle can maneuver 1,600 kilometers (992 miles) north or south of its east-west flight track. So it could land at most major airports in North America or Europe if an emergency made that necessary.

Silence descends on the cabin except for the hiss of the air-conditioning system as the radio suddenly goes silent because a sheath of ionized (electrified) air generated by friction surrounds the spacecraft and blocks transmission and reception. The radio blackout ends as the spacecraft slows down. Simultaneously, the coastline of Mexico appears. Then, Mexico City, the Yucatán Peninsula, and the Gulf of Mexico roll by. Next, the west Florida coast appears. By the time you reach Disney World and Orlando, you are down to an altitude of 21,336 kilometers (70,000 feet) and your home port is only 50 kilometers (31 miles) away. The steep angle of descent continues on the shuttle's final approach. To observers on the ground, it looks as though the craft is coming straight down on them. The cabin is now filled with conversation between the shuttle pilot and the Air Traffic Control Center in Miami.

The broad sheet of the Banana River flashes as the shuttle makes a long turn toward the spaceport to the southeast. At this point, the spaceport's microwave scanning beam locks onto the orbiter's automatic landing system, checks the orbiter's landing path, and tells the onboard computers whether to make any adjustments. Commander and pilot could sit back in their seats with arms folded, because the landing is entirely automatic. But of course, they are hunched over the controls, watching the instruments and ready to take over at any sign of computer failure.

The computer abruptly levels the craft's glide, and the orbiter sinks toward the runway like a conventional airplane. After touchdown and a roll of 2,605 meters (8,547 feet), an automatic braking system brings *The City of Topeka* to a screeching stop.

Service equipment moves out to meet the spaceplane, but you must wait in your seat inside the space shuttle for at least 15 minutes until the outside of the vehicle cools off. Finally, the hatch opens and, unaccustomed to the force of gravity, you stagger out amid venting waste gases. You are home.

Nostalgia for your week in orbit began even as you were landing. From your window, you caught a glimpse of the pad from which you were launched. It was bare. But on the next pad, another shuttle was being loaded and serviced for flight. Somewhere on the grounds of the Kennedy Space Center, another group of astronauts and scientists are getting ready for the next mission on the space shuttle.

Our Roots Go Deeper

By Donald C. Johanson

Fossil bones and ancient footprints give us a glimpse of the earliest known human ancestors and add nearly two million years to the human family tree

Today the landscape is desert, a harsh world for the Afar nomads who scratch an existence out of the barren countryside. The hot sun parches the land, robbing it of all moisture. But occasionally the sky darkens, the air becomes heavy, and a cool torrential rain fills the dry gullies. For the Afar people, the rain is a godsend. For scientists like me, who are interested in human evolution, the rain is equally important. It erodes the 3-million-year-old lake beds of the area and uncovers invaluable clues to our prehistoric past. Human fossils unearthed there are helping to reconstruct the earliest stages of human existence.

I was first drawn to the Afar region in eastern Ethiopia in 1972. My close colleague, French geologist Maurice Taieb, had found several places where fossilized remains of many kinds of mammals could be found on the surface. Later discoveries from one such place, the Hadar site, would add a startling new chapter to the story of human evolution. These exciting finds, older and more complete than any previous discoveries, have stimulated a major rewriting of the early origins and history of the family *Hominidae*, to which man belongs. Hominid fossils 3 million to 4 million years old have provided glimpses of a creature that may represent the common ancestors from which all later types of humankind evolved.

In 1924, Australian anatomist Raymond A. Dart found the first fossil "apeman" to be discovered in Africa at Taung in South Africa. That specimen consists of a skull and the fossil impression of the brain of a 6-year-old child who died perhaps 2 million years ago. Dart christened the fossil *Australopithecus africanus*, meaning the "southern African ape." It had a small brain, apparently walked upright, and had teeth more like those of a human than an ape. Dart believed it to be the "missing link," the connection between humans and apes that scientists had been searching for since British naturalist Charles R. Darwin first described the theory of evolution in 1859. But Dart's contemporaries received this claim with great skepticism.

Robert Broom, a Scottish biologist turned paleontologist, recognized the importance of Dart's discovery, and was convinced that other sites must exist in South Africa. His search took him to the Sterkfontein Cave near Johannesburg in the Transvaal region in 1936, where he found skulls of adult apemen. Then other searchers found human fossils at Kromdraai in 1938 and at Swartkrans 10 years later. The specimens indicated that these creatures were somewhat larger and more muscular than those found earlier. Broom believed that they were a separate species and called them *Australopithecus robustus,* the "southern robust apeman." The two forms of *Australopithecus* became known collectively as australopithecines. The more lightly built type is commonly called the gracile form and the more massively built type, the robust form.

With increasing work going on and the discovery of more sites in South Africa, many exciting specimens came to light. Shortly after Broom's death in 1951, his assistant, zoologist John T. Robinson, now at the University of Wisconsin, Madison, began to interpret the meaning of the two forms of early hominids. Could the large ones be males and the smaller ones females? This seemed unlikely because they had never been found together at the same sites. Finally, after long and careful study, Robinson suggested that the two forms reflect different dietary adaptations. The robust form, distinguished by a massive face, large molars, small front teeth, indications of large muscles, and many other features, was probably a vegetarian. It needed its molars and strong jaw muscles to grind plant material. The gracile form was more of an omnivore—that is, it ate some meat as well as plants. Clearly, both were hominid—they walked upright and had a life style different from that of the apes. Robinson made the suggestion, still widely accepted, that the vegetarian robust form eventually became extinct. The gracile form, he felt, gave rise to modern man by a series of evolutionary steps.

Most scientists agree that the South African sites that yielded the gracile form are older than those in which the robust form was found. However, they cannot date these sites accurately. Dynamite used to free the fossils from the hard rocks of the region·destroyed the geologic context that would help to fix the dates. But those fossils and

The author:
Donald C. Johanson is director of scientific research and curator of physical anthropology at the Cleveland Museum of Natural History.

Where the Bones Were Buried

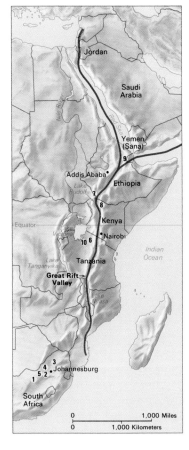

Fossil Sites

1. Taung
2. Sterkfontein
3. Makapansgat
4. Kromdraai
5. Swartkrans
6. Olduvai
7. Omo
8. Lake Rudolf
9. Hadar
10. Laetolil

Australopithecine fossils have been found in a cluster of sites in South Africa. They have also been found, along with fossils of the genus *Homo*, in sites along East Africa's Great Rift Valley, as far north as Hadar.

Robinson's interpretations of them formed the initial groundwork for tracing early human evolution in Africa.

The search for fossil man then shifted to eastern Africa. The major geologic feature of East Africa is the Great Rift Valley, actually a series of valleys and lakes that runs north to south. The Red Sea is a geologic continuation of the valley. For millions of years, the area was highly volcanic. Scientists have dated the volcanic deposits laid down during that time through the potassium-argon method, which measures the slow decay of potassium 40 to argon 40. Fossils embedded in or between the volcanic layers can thus be dated by this method with great accuracy.

For nearly 30 years, Louis S. B. Leakey and his wife, Mary, searched for hominid fossils. Then, in 1959, Mary Leakey found the nearly complete skull of a robust australopithecine at Olduvai Gorge in Tanzania. Hyper-robust, with enormous molars, it was dubbed *Zinjanthropus boisei*, but commonly called "nut-cracker man" because of its massive jaws. It was dated by the potassium-argon method to 1.8 million years old.

Raymond Dart, *above,* holds the Taung skull that he found in South Africa in 1924 to begin the great African fossil hunt. Robert Broom and his assistant, John Robinson, *above right,* study australopithecine finds they made at Sterkfontein in 1947.

The anthropologists also found stone tools in the excavation and bones of extinct animals that had been broken and smashed, apparently for their nutritious marrow. Could it be possible that this creature made stone tools and perhaps even hunted? Judging from the skull, the brain was small, perhaps too small for such sophisticated skills and activities.

The answer came late in 1961. The Leakeys found a lower jaw, some skull bones, and some limb bones that provided the necessary clues. Calculation of the brain volume and detailed examination of the teeth of this and related finds suggested that another, more advanced, hominid species lived in the same area at Olduvai. The brain was much larger, the skull more modern in shape, and the teeth smaller than those of the hyper-robust *Zinjanthropus.* In 1964, anthropologists placed the newly discovered hominid in the genus *Homo*—which includes modern man, *Homo sapiens.* Its full name is *Homo habilis,* meaning "skillful man." Louis Leakey believed that *Homo habilis* made the stone tools and broke the bones found at Olduvai. These finds were the first evidence that two types of hominids lived in the same general area at the same time.

The Great Rift Valley has continued to be a virtual paradise for anthropologists. Indeed, some have begun to think of the valley as the true Garden of Eden where humanity began its development. New hominid sites were found at Lake Natron in Tanzania in 1964, Kanapoi in 1965, and Lothagam in 1967. Major expeditions began searching the Omo Valley in 1967 and the area east of Lake Rudolf (called

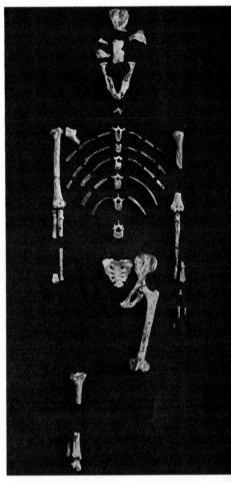

Recent discoveries have pushed human prehistory back in time. Skull 1470, *top left,* is about 2 million years old; "Lucy," *above,* is more than a million years older; and "First Family," now being studied in the laboratory, *left,* is as old as Lucy.

Lake Turkana in Kenya) in 1968. These sites, located in or adjacent to the rift valley, have all been precisely dated. The fossil-bearing sediments there span a time range from almost 6 million to less than 1-million years ago. The scientists found many different kinds of mammalian fossils along with the hominids, enabling them to reconstruct the climates and terrains in which these ancient creatures lived. Stone tools that were unearthed there indicate the early cultural capabilities of our human ancestors.

The Omo Research Expedition, led by anthropologist F. Clark Howell of the University of California, Berkeley, yielded numerous fossils, including some hominids ranging from about 3 million to 1-million years old. Hominid teeth about 3 million years old appear to be like *A. africanus*, others about 2 million years old are like those of *A. boisei*. Some later remains are identified as *Homo habilis* and even *Homo erectus* – "upright man," between *Homo habilis* and *Homo sapiens*. Meticulous field work by anthropologists, paleontologists, geologists, and other specialists in the Omo has established the site as one of the most important in the Great Rift Valley.

One of the best-known fossil-man sites in Africa is being studied by Richard E. Leakey and his team along the eastern shores of Lake Rudolf. Richard, a son of Mary and Louis Leakey, explored ancient lake beds there in 1968 and soon collected beautifully preserved and complete hominid specimens. Many of the fossils found were similar to *Zinjanthropus*, now called *Australopithecus boisei*, found at Olduvai. The discovery of female robust individuals was particularly important. It provided information on sexual differences in early hominids and finally proved that the gracile and robust forms were indeed different. Discoveries continued to accumulate and in 1972, Richard Leakey announced the finding of the 1470 skull – named for its collection number. The large-braincd skull, considered to be *Homo habilis*, is dated to about 2 million years ago. This hominid probably fashioned the stone tools excavated from deposits dated to about 1.8 million years.

In 1976, Leakey announced that he had discovered a skull that was unquestionably *Homo erectus* at east Lake Rudolf. The skull is important for two reasons: It is dated to 1.5 million years ago, making it the oldest accurately dated fossil of this form yet found, and it was found in the same level as *A. boisei*, indicating that these two forms lived side by side on or near the shores of Lake Rudolf.

Up to this point, the picture seemed to be fairly clear. *A. africanus*, the gracile hominid, is found in older deposits than the other forms. Most anthropologists believe it is the ancestor of *Homo habilis*. All that

A four-footed ape's thighbone, *below,* left, rises almost vertically from the knee joint. The thighbones of both *A. afarensis,* middle, and *Homo sapiens,* right, angle outward so that they can join the hip at the proper angle for upright walking. *A. afarensis* was smaller than modern man, but its hand size was quite similar, *below right.*

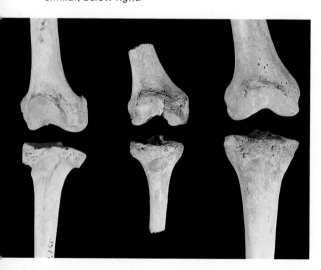

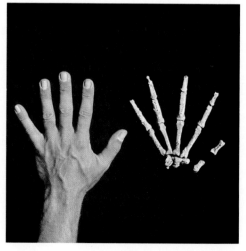

was required for *A. africanus* to become *Homo habilis* was an increase in brain size, some changes in the teeth, and the development of stone toolmaking. *A. africanus* is also considered to be an ancestor of *A. robustus* and *A. boisei*. The robust hominid form was a vegetarian that did not appear until about 2 million years ago. It became extinct while *Homo habilis* continued to evolve into *Homo erectus*. All this fit the available evidence nicely until the 1970s.

Late on an October day in 1973, I walked into a dry gully and spotted the first fossil hominid specimens at the Hadar site. When I first put the two bones together and realized that they formed a knee joint, I could not believe that they were human. They were smaller than any previously known, but their shape and the way they fit together revealed that they were hominid bones. After several years of intensive and detailed laboratory analysis, we concluded that this is the knee of a human ancestor who could walk upright the way we do. The angle formed by the two bones is within a few degrees of that found in modern human knees and quite unlike the knees of apes. But most astonishing was the age of these bones. Careful geologic studies indicated that they are close to 3.5 million years old. I had found the oldest evidence of human bipedal walking.

Geologist James Aronson measures the decay of potassium 40 to argon 40 in volcanic rocks with a mass spectrometer to fix dependable dates for Hadar site fossils.

Many anthropologists believe this peculiar means of locomotion is a critical development in mankind's evolution. It freed the hands and arms for use in toolmaking, carrying food, and carrying babies. It also permitted our ancestors to stand upright so they could see over the tall grass of the open savannas or plains to search for food and keep watch for predators.

Taieb and I took a research expedition to the site in 1974, determined to find more hominid fossils. With a team of about 15 scientists and students, we began to comb the sediments for fossils. While geologists mapped the area and collected rock samples, other specialists collected fossil bones from elephants, gazelles, giraffes, hippos, monkeys, rhinos, and even the tiniest remains of lizards, bats, and rodents.

This thorough multidisciplinary study allowed us to reconstruct the ancient environments of the Hadar site. The main geologic influence on the site seems to have been volcanic action, which changed the drainage patterns and other characteristics of the area. The site was marshy from about 3.3 million to 3.1 million years ago. Then a lake formed, probably after an eruption blocked some rivers or streams. About 2.8 million years ago, the drainage changed again and the site seems to have been a river delta until about 2.6 million years ago.

Paleoanthropologists found fossil jaws and teeth whose strong resemblances to those of *Homo habilis* prompted us to place the finds provisionally in the genus *Homo*. In November, I spotted an arm-bone fragment on the ground while graduate student Tom Gray and I were collecting fossils. It was very small, but obviously hominid. As we leaned over to examine the find, we saw that the hillside was littered with bone fragments. To our amazement, the site contained 40 per

Expedition members relax after a day of collecting in the field at the Hadar site, *above.* Kebede, the Ethiopian cook, prepares breakfast at dawn, *above right.*

cent of a human skeleton. The structure of the pelvic bones showed the skeleton was that of a female. We named her "Lucy." The inspiration for the name came from the Beatles' song "Lucy in the Sky with Diamonds," which was on a tape we played that night as we were celebrating the find.

Lucy was about 20 years old when she died of unknown causes. She stood only about 107 to 122 centimeters (3½ to 4 feet) tall, and her brain was probably small. She suffered from arthritis of the spine. Compared with modern humans, her arms were somewhat long relative to her legs. She apparently had lived near the edge of a lake. The fossilized turtle and crocodile eggs and even crab claws found nearby may have been part of her diet.

We now know that Lucy is among the oldest human ancestors yet found. Her skeleton is also one of the most complete. Early indications suggested that she was related to *Australopithecus africanus*.

When we began work again in Hadar in 1975, we made an even more startling discovery—a "paleograveyard." Some kind of natural catastrophe, perhaps a flash flood, killed at least 13 persons and buried them in a natural grave. The 13 individuals included both males and females. At least four were children, one represented by the nearly complete skull of a 4- or 5-year-old. The rest were adults and young adults. It seems probable that these individuals lived together and are

thus the earliest evidence of human cooperative behavior. So we named the group the "First Family."

While we were making these discoveries, Mary Leakey's group was making new finds at Laetolil, a site in Tanzania. In 1974, they found teeth and jaws from 12 individuals. These fossils were dated to between 3.5 million and 3.75 million years, and preliminary assessment suggested placing the fossils in the genus *Homo* along with our finds at Hadar.

Then Mary Leakey and her team made an astonishing discovery at Laetolil in 1976. In volcanic ash laid down nearly 4 million years ago, they found hominid footprints. Five impressions of a short, broad foot have been uncovered. With more complete study, they may provide us with important information pertaining to early hominid posture, gait, stature, and perhaps even weight. The Leakey team also found footprints made by such animals as antelopes, elephants, giraffes, rhinos, and a sabertoothed cat.

After critically analyzing and comparing the Hadar and Laetolil fossils, my colleagues and I have

Afar workmen sift through the pebbly soil while a geologist searches for fossils, *top.* Nicole Page, an assistant to Maurice Taieb, expedition co-leader, interprets aerial photos, *above,* to make maps of the Hadar area.

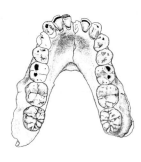

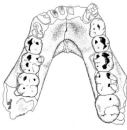

The similarity of the lower jaws found at Hadar, *top,* and at Laetolil, *above,* are strong evidence that they are from the same species, *A. afarensis.*

been forced to rethink our original impressions and consider exciting new possibilities. The similarities between the Hadar and Laetolil samples are overwhelming and there is no doubt that the hominids found at these sites were very much alike. It is obvious that they were fully bipedal, yet they had small brains and large canine teeth. After carefully studying the skull, teeth, jaws, and limb and hand bones, we are convinced that the Hadar and Laetolil material is more primitive than we previously thought. It is, in fact, the oldest, most primitive group of hominids thus far discovered.

The Hadar and Laetolil fossils clearly resemble the gracile australopithecines. However, since the older fossils are much more primitive, it is necessary to classify them in a new species which we have named *Australopithecus afarensis.* Recognition of a new species of *Australopithecus* was possible only after in-depth study of the fossil material; new hominid species are not named lightly. However, we believe that the evidence is overwhelming. Several features of the Hadar and Laetolil material set it distinctly apart from such forms as *A. africanus* and *Homo habilis.* For example, the teeth are more primitive. There are large canines and unusually shaped incisors. The first lower bicuspid in some specimens has only one well-developed cusp or pointed end, instead of two, and is thus more apelike than humanlike. The upper and lower jaws possess straight tooth rows and the jaw arches are almost rectangular in shape. As far as we can tell, the face was broad, with large cheekbones. The base of the skull is quite primitive in its muscle markings and other features. Males apparently were somewhat larger than females. The hands and feet, while very different from those of an ape, were also different from those of later, more-evolved hominids; for example, the finger bones were more curved.

The Hadar and Laetolil hominids appear to be unique. Generally speaking, they are "intermediate" in some aspects between apes and men. But the apelike features are clearly altered in the direction of humanness. Even if this were not so, *A. afarensis* would still be placed in the family of man because it could walk upright, the hallmark of the family *Hominidae.*

What implications does this new species have for the commonly accepted theory of human evolution? We think that *A. afarensis* was the ancestor of both *A. africanus* and *Homo habilis.* The evidence is in the teeth, the tools and, most importantly, in the brain. Changes in the teeth of the undifferentiated, ancestral *A. afarensis* form led in one direction to *A. robustus* and *A. boisei* through *A. africanus* and in another direction to *Homo habilis.* The molars and premolars, for instance, grew larger and larger with time from *A. afarensis* to *A. africanus* to *A. robustus* and *A. boisei.* The same teeth in the genus *Homo* show slighter differences in size from those of *A. afarensis.* These are the teeth that are most used in vegetarian diets – they are the grinding teeth that reduce plant matter to a digestible form. The cutting or slashing teeth – the canines, for example – were reduced in size in the australopithecine line.

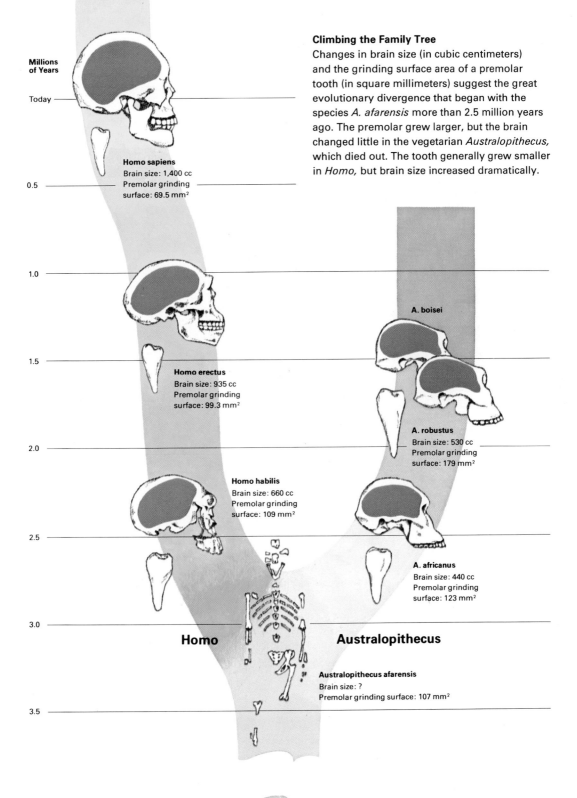

Climbing the Family Tree

Changes in brain size (in cubic centimeters) and the grinding surface area of a premolar tooth (in square millimeters) suggest the great evolutionary divergence that began with the species *A. afarensis* more than 2.5 million years ago. The premolar grew larger, but the brain changed little in the vegetarian *Australopithecus,* which died out. The tooth generally grew smaller in *Homo,* but brain size increased dramatically.

Millions of Years

Today

0.5

1.0

1.5

2.0

2.5

3.0

3.5

Homo sapiens
Brain size: 1,400 cc
Premolar grinding surface: 69.5 mm²

Homo erectus
Brain size: 935 cc
Premolar grinding surface: 99.3 mm²

Homo habilis
Brain size: 660 cc
Premolar grinding surface: 109 mm²

A. boisei

A. robustus
Brain size: 530 cc
Premolar grinding surface: 179 mm²

A. africanus
Brain size: 440 cc
Premolar grinding surface: 123 mm²

Homo

Australopithecus

Australopithecus afarensis
Brain size: ?
Premolar grinding surface: 107 mm²

53

At the National Museum of Kenya (from left), anthropologists Tim White and Richard Leakey, anatomist Bernard Wood, the author, and Mary Leakey discuss future probes into man's past.

But they are not much different from the ancestral *A. afarensis* in the *Homo* line. This indicates that the primitive *A. afarensis*, like its descendant, *Homo sapiens*, was probably an omnivore with a varied diet.

What forces made each of these evolutionary lines distinct? The *Homo* line was characterized by a progressively larger brain and the development of culture; *Homo habilis* appears to be the first definitive sign of this trend. Apparently this species survived successfully, and evolved through *Homo erectus* to *Homo sapiens* – ourselves. The stone tools they developed for hunting and butchering were of great significance. With the tools, they added meat to their diet, a richer source of energy and protein than plants. Plants probably still provided the bulk of their diet, but meat gave these individuals an important edge over other hominids.

The tools, of course, were quite primitive. A simple flake, or thin chip, struck from a stone provides a sharp-edged tool, and such stone artifacts, dated at about 1.8 million years, are found in abundance at Olduvai Gorge. Some have been found with the bones from butchered carcasses. For the moment, the oldest tools, about 2.5 million years old, are from Hadar, but no hominids have been found with them.

The second evolutionary line led to *A. africanus*, which exhibits special characteristics in its teeth and skull that forecast the condition ultimately found in *A. robustus* and *A. boisei*. This line achieved little or no cultural development, and the brain did not increase dramatically in size. The whole emphasis was on a more specialized vegetarian diet. It is certain that hominids in this evolutionary line lived alongside *Homo habilis* and even *Homo erectus*. They eventually became extinct but we do not know why.

It is doubtful that the members of the evolving genus *Homo* caused the extinction of *A. robustus*. Individuals of these two lineages may have avoided one another for a number of reasons. The vegetarians may have preferred to stay closer to rivers or the forest edge where more plant food was available. The hominids in the *Homo* line might have spent more time in open savanna areas or around water holes where game was available. In time, the vegetarians became more and more specialized while the developing *Homo* individuals began to venture into a broader range of habitats. Other plant eaters, such as the great apes and various antelopes, may have pushed the vegetarians into marginal areas until they died out. The developing and diversifying *Homo* individuals remained as the only surviving members of the family *Hominidae*.

Although we now think that the new species *A. afarensis* may well have been the ancestor of both the lineage leading to *A. robustus* and the one culminating in modern *Homo sapiens*, there are still many gaps in our knowledge of human evolution. Some scientists believe that *Ramapithecus*, a creature dating to between 8 million and 14 million years ago, is the earliest hominid, but the human fossil record is still embarrassingly incomplete. A couple of isolated teeth, a piece of an arm bone, a lower jaw with one tooth are not enough evidence for us to fill in the 4- or 5-million-year gap that lies between *Ramapithecus* and *A. afarensis*.

New discoveries will be made in deposits much older than those at Hadar and Laetolil. These will extend our knowledge of human ancestry and may revise our thinking even more. Such sites are being explored in Asia, Europe, and Africa. I believe that the Arabian Peninsula may be important in extending our knowledge. It lies on the other side of the Red Sea and is thus associated with the rift valley where so many discoveries have been made. It is not impossible that ancient sites will be found in Jordan, Saudi Arabia, Yemen, and elsewhere that will permit us to trace our ancestry to even more remote times.

A later but poorly known time range in the fossil record of human evolution is the period between 2 million and 3 million years ago. The Hadar and Laetolil fossils show that the two lineages were actively differentiating during this period. But until more fossils are discovered, the picture will remain fuzzy. We hope to learn the nature of the changes that occurred in the two hominid lineages and find where these changes took place. The quest is exciting not only for the anthropologist trudging over rough terrain under the hot sun, but also for every human being who wants to know the roots of the human species.

The Birth of a Star

By Stephen P. Maran

**Astronomers have combined theory and observation
to discover the youngest known star emerging
from the gas and dust of interstellar space**

Members of the American Astronomical Society heard some exciting news in a lecture given by Donald N. Hall of the Kitt Peak National Observatory in Tucson, Ariz. Hall announced that a remarkable source of infrared radiation in the constellation Orion is actually a recently formed star. This infrared source, the Becklin-Neugebauer (BN) object, is hotter and brighter than our sun, and possibly the youngest true star yet found. Hall's report in January 1978 climaxed 13 years of intensive study of BN. The object has been studied with infrared telescopes from mountaintop observatories, highflying jet aircraft, and balloons. Radio observations also provided important data.

The BN object was discovered in January 1965 by Eric E. Becklin, then a graduate student in astrophysics at the California Institute of Technology (Caltech). Becklin was using the 1.5-meter (60-inch) telescope at the Mount Wilson Observatory in California to map infrared radiation from the region of the Great Nebula in the constellation

The Great Nebula in the constellation Orion is in the "cradle of stars,"
the Orion Molecular Cloud 1 region where massive stars are forming.

Orion. The Great Nebula is a cloud of glowing gas centered on four hot, blue stars located about 1,500 light-years from the earth. (A light-year is the distance that light travels in a year at 299,792 kilometers per second, about 6 trillion miles.) In addition to a small patch of infrared emission, Becklin's search also revealed eight bright infrared points. Seven of them turned out to be stars that can also be seen on telescopic photographs, but the eighth one—the BN object—had no visible counterpart.

Subsequently, additional measurements of the new source were reported by Becklin and Gerry Neugebauer, an infrared astronomer at Caltech. They used an infrared photometer mounted on the Mount Wilson telescope and on the 5-meter (200-inch) Hale reflector on Palomar Mountain to obtain data at various wavelengths. The results indicated that the object's temperature is only about 400°C (800°F.), far below the temperatures of normal stars, which range from somewhat less than 3000°C to over 30,000°C. Some astronomers suggested that the BN object might be a relatively old white supergiant star in the Orion Nebula or beyond it, whose light was screened off by absorbing dust. The dust in space absorbs shorter wavelengths more than longer ones and makes a star appear redder than it really is. The effect makes a hot star appear cooler because red stars are cooler than white ones. But if the white supergiant theory were correct, it would mean that the dust in space was making BN appear billions of times dimmer than it really is, whereas studies of other stars seen through the Orion Nebula indicate that in most cases the dust dims them by no more than a factor of 16. Becklin and Neugebauer concluded that the temperature of the strange object is indeed only about 400°C. They suggested that BN is a protostar—a star in the early stages of forming from the cold matter of interstellar space. However, some astronomers continued to favor the white supergiant theory. Others suggested a third theory; BN is a newly formed star that has left the protostar stage but has not yet reached the stable condition of a main-sequence star. Such an object is called a pre-main-sequence (PMS) star.

The term "main sequence" is applied to stars that are generating the bulk of their energy at a steady rate by the fusion of hydrogen atoms deep in their interiors. When the temperatures and luminosities of stars are plotted on a graph—the Hertzprung-Russell diagram—stars in this relatively long-lived evolutionary state are found along a diagonal band. Stars at the upper left in the band are hotter, brighter, more massive, and have larger diameters than those at the lower right. All have the same evolutionary age; that is, they have reached an identical phase in their life cycles. However, the chronological ages, measured in years, of the relatively massive stars at upper left, known as O and B stars, are younger, because the more massive stars run through their life cycles more rapidly. PMS stars are in an evolutionary state just preceding arrival on the main sequence, and appear cooler than the main-sequence stars that they will become.

The author:
Stephen P. Maran is a senior staff scientist at the NASA-Goddard Space Flight Center in Greenbelt, Md.

Hertzsprung-Russell Diagram

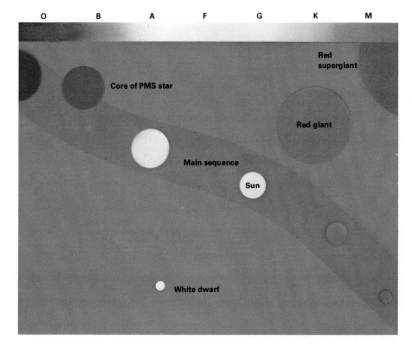

O   B   A   F   G   K   M

Red supergiant

Core of PMS star

Red giant

Main sequence

Sun

White dwarf

The Hertzsprung-Russell diagram classifies stars by luminosity and spectrum. PMS stage, main sequence stage, and red supergiant stage are the three basic states in the evolution of a massive star. The magnitude of the star determines its vertical placement.

Stars are born from a kind of primal soup known as the interstellar medium (ISM). The ISM consists mainly of three forms of hydrogen gas. The atomic form is ordinary hydrogen atoms; the ionized form is made up of hydrogen atoms broken apart into their constituent protons and electrons; and the molecular form consists of two hydrogen atoms. However, the ISM also contains some dust, microscopic rock-like particles, which are a key ingredient although they comprise only about 1 per cent of the mass of the ISM. Dust is responsible for the reddening and dimming of starlight. It is a kind of interstellar smog that has great influence on the behavior of matter and radiation in space. Because it absorbs light, especially the ultraviolet radiation from young hot stars, the dust traps energy, and does so most effectively where it is most concentrated, in dense interstellar clouds. Stars are born in these interstellar clouds, which are located in the spiral arms of our Milky Way Galaxy.

Astronomers thus far have found about 40 molecules in the interstellar medium. Among them are complex organic substances, such as alcohol and formaldehyde. Some scientists, including British cosmologist Sir Fred Hoyle, even have suggested that life on earth originated from such molecules which, trapped in the frozen matter of comets, might have rained down on our planet. It is surprising to find the molecules in the ISM, because many are unstable compounds that break up readily in the bath of ultraviolet light from the hot stars of the galaxy. However, the molecules are sheltered from this radiation

Nestled amid molecules
of interstellar gas,
an interstellar dust
grain may be like a tiny
terrestrial planet, with
a mineral core encased
in an ice envelope that
is surrounded by gas.

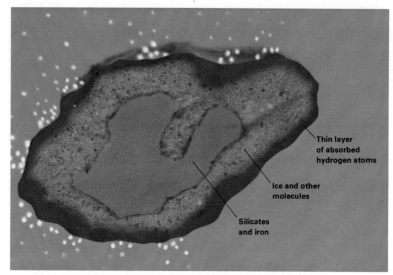

Thin layer
of absorbed
hydrogen atoms

Ice and other
molecules

Silicates
and iron

by the dust inside the thickest clouds, and they can form and survive there. In such places, nearly all the hydrogen is in molecular form. Some kinds of molecules may even form on the surfaces of dust grains, where they can remain as ice and frozen gases.

In the gaseous state, the molecules may emit or absorb radio and infrared waves at wavelengths that are characteristic of the substances as well as of their densities and temperatures. Furthermore, the observed wavelengths may be shifted by the Doppler effect, which shortens or lengthens them in proportion to the motions of the clouds toward or away from the observer, respectively. In addition, the motion of the gas within a cloud may broaden the individual spectral lines. Thus, infrared and radio telescopes, suitably equipped with spectroscopic instrumentation, can be used to determine physical and chemical conditions in even the densest interstellar clouds.

The thinner regions can be studied in ultraviolet light. Data from the *Copernicus* satellite, an automated ultraviolet observatory, have revealed a striking abnormality in the gas composition. Orbiting 740 kilometers (460 miles) above the earth's surface, this satellite found large deficiencies in iron and several other elements in the gas, compared with their abundance in the atmospheres of stars. Yet material is exchanged between the stars and the ISM as stars are born, evolve, and die, so that the composition of both should be similar. What became of the missing matter? Scientists believe that it must be trapped in the dust grains, though they are not quite certain how it got there. One theory is based on the fact that the missing elements are among the most refractory, or hardest to melt, constituents of the hot streams of atoms from the stars. Thus, as gas flows away from a star and cools, these elements freeze at relatively high temperatures, forming mineral particles in space. These particles constitute the cores of the interstellar dust grains that may be coated with ice. George B. Field, director of the Center for Astrophysics of the Harvard College Observatory in Cambridge, Mass., and a leading authority on the ISM, compares an interstellar dust grain to a planet. He made this analogy in a speech to the International Astronomical Union in 1974. "The interior of the grain, like that of the earth, is composed of iron and silicates," he said. "Its outer envelope, like the oceans of earth, is water. The whole is immersed in a gaseous atmosphere, and is bathed, like the earth, in ultraviolet light and cosmic radiation."

It may be that an interstellar cloud cannot give birth to a star unless an outside force causes the cloud to collapse. The phenomenon that triggers this process may be some kind of shock wave in the ISM. A shock wave is a disturbance that moves through a medium faster than the speed of sound in that medium. Calculations show that when a shock wave encounters an interstellar cloud, it will sweep around the cloud surface even faster than it penetrates the interior. Consequently, the shock envelops the cloud and moves into it uniformly from all points on the surface. This effect compresses the cloud until its own gravitational force, which increases as the cloud contracts, may become strong enough to continue the condensation process.

Astronomers have proposed specific triggers, or sources, of such shock waves. These include the collision of two interstellar clouds; the rotating spiral disturbance that produces and maintains the spiral arms of our Galaxy; the powerful blast from a supernova explosion; and sequential formation–the spreading of ionization and heating of interstellar gas by ultraviolet radiation from young hot stars.

When a group of stars forms, the most massive ones evolve most rapidly, ending their lives in supernova explosions. These groups of young O and B main-sequence stars, known as OB associations, seem to be composed of subgroups of different ages, each expanding into space. OB associations may form within the so-called giant molecular clouds, regions of the ISM that may contain many smaller interstellar clouds and that are made up primarily of molecular hydrogen.

Most stars probably begin as members of OB associations, although the less massive ones may not develop into visible stars before the subgroups break up. In 1953, astronomer Ernst J. Öpik of the Armagh Observatory in Northern Ireland suggested that a supernova blast somehow causes an OB association to form. That idea was revived in October 1976 when Turkish astrophysicist Hakki B. Ögelman of the Middle East Technical University in Ankara and I reviewed some recent observations of a supernova remnant called the Origem Loop. It appears that an OB association has formed in clouds compressed by the shock wave from this supernova, with its young member stars seen superimposed on the expanding shell of gas that surrounds the site of the explosion. The key point in our theory of this process, which we call a "supernova cascade," is that the stars formed by the triggering

Stars from a Spiral Shock

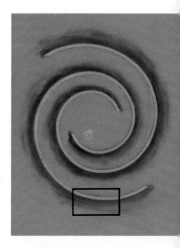

A spiral shock wave sweeps around the Milky Way Galaxy, maintaining the spiral-arm shape.

The shock wave moves through the interstellar medium (ISM), *top,* condenses it and forms new stars. Their hot ultraviolet light, *above,* ionizes the remaining gas, forming nebulae.

Supernovae Spawn Stars

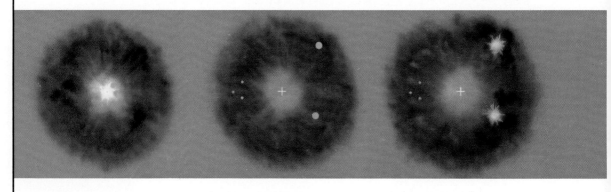

A supernova explosion produces a shock wave that moves through the ISM, where it meets and compresses the interstellar clouds.

The supernova fades, but several new stars, including two massive ones, form from the clouds compressed by the shock wave.

Rapidly consuming their hydrogen fuel, the hot massive stars become supernovae, while their less massive mates burn on at a steady rate.

Forming in Sequence

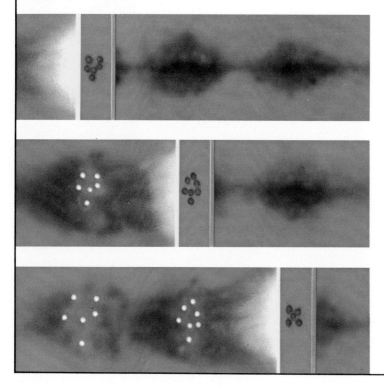

Ultraviolet radiation from an unseen hot star at the left, *top,* heats interstellar gas in a giant molecular cloud and an ionization front (yellow) forms. The expanding ionized gases of the front produce a shock wave (orange) and they move together along the galactic plane. Protostars form from interstellar material between the front and shock wave, becoming new stars. The front and shock wave move on, *center,* until they meet another clump and form more protostars. The sequence continues along galactic plane, *bottom.*

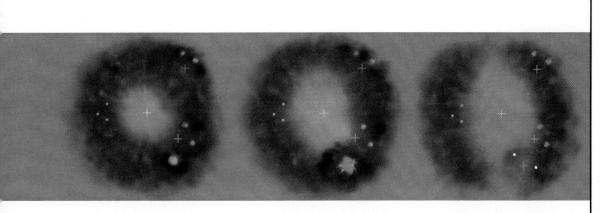

A supernova cascade is now underway as shock waves from the two new supernovae trigger the formation of two more subgroups of stars.

The most massive star in each of the newest groups becomes a supernova. Its outburst helps heat and expand interstellar gas near the newborn stars.

After third-generation supernova shock wave forms stars, it bursts from the top and bottom of the galactic disk, ending star formation.

blast from a supernova include one or two massive O stars that rapidly become supernovae themselves. These second-generation supernovae cause additional stars to form, so that each supernova may initiate a new subgroup. Astronomers at the Carnegie Institution in Washington, D.C., have found additional cases of supernova-induced star formation in other regions of space.

Astronomy, like all branches of science, advances by testing theories, and not all astronomers agree with ours. For example, Bruce G. Elmegreen and Charles J. Lada of the Harvard Center for Astrophysics have found circumstantial evidence that supports their sequential-formation theory in detailed case studies of several regions, including the area around the Orion Nebula. According to this theory, a shock wave is associated with the expanding boundary of a gaseous region ionized and heated by young O and B stars. But astronomers also have evidence that a supernova could have occurred in Orion, producing the vast Barnard's Loop that appears on wide-angle photographs of the region. So both the supernova trigger and the sequential-formation process may have been at work there. Indeed, there are astronomers who sug-

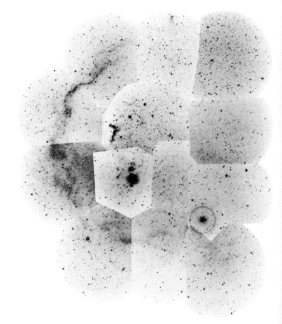

The Orion Region — A Stellar Nursery
The large crescent of Barnard's Loop at the left is probably a supernova remnant. The three bright stars above and to the left of center are Orion's Belt. The large dark patch is the Orion Nebula, which hides PMS star BN.

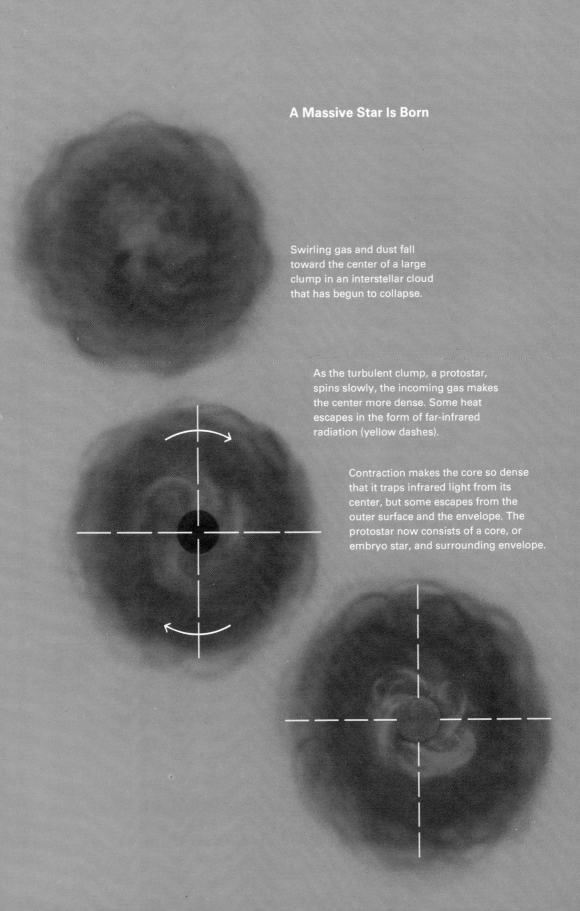

A Massive Star Is Born

Swirling gas and dust fall
toward the center of a large
clump in an interstellar cloud
that has begun to collapse.

As the turbulent clump, a protostar,
spins slowly, the incoming gas makes
the center more dense. Some heat
escapes in the form of far-infrared
radiation (yellow dashes).

Contraction makes the core so dense
that it traps infrared light from its
center, but some escapes from the
outer surface and the envelope. The
protostar now consists of a core, or
embryo star, and surrounding envelope.

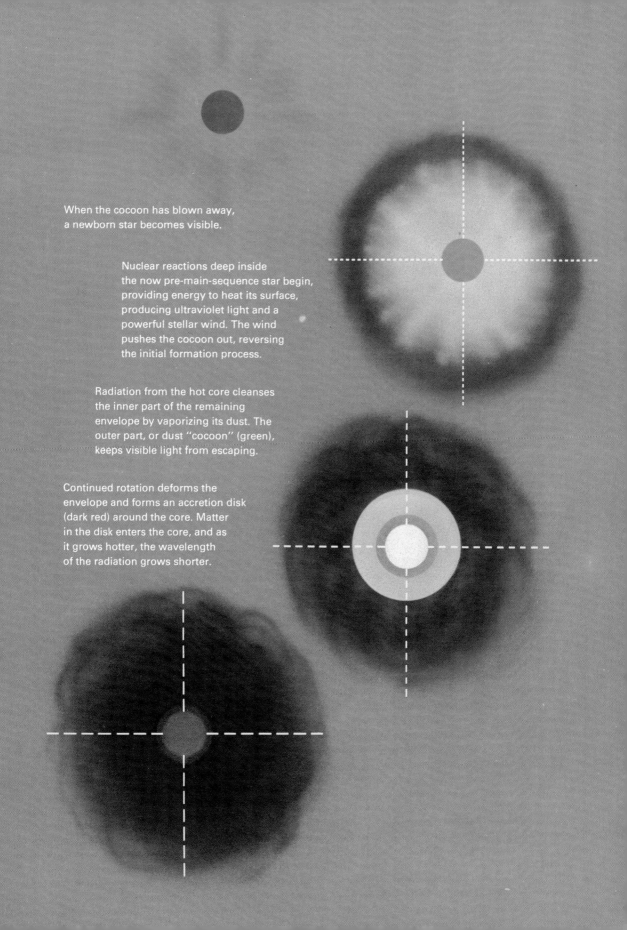

When the cocoon has blown away,
a newborn star becomes visible.

Nuclear reactions deep inside
the now pre-main-sequence star begin,
providing energy to heat its surface,
producing ultraviolet light and a
powerful stellar wind. The wind
pushes the cocoon out, reversing
the initial formation process.

Radiation from the hot core cleanses
the inner part of the remaining
envelope by vaporizing its dust. The
outer part, or dust "cocoon" (green),
keeps visible light from escaping.

Continued rotation deforms the
envelope and forms an accretion disk
(dark red) around the core. Matter
in the disk enters the core, and as
it grows hotter, the wavelength
of the radiation grows shorter.

gest that a supernova is needed to initiate star formation, which then continues by the sequential process.

Among the other trigger theories, the colliding-clouds hypothesis is supported by rather limited evidence. The spiral-wave theory seems to be the best explanation of how the interstellar clouds develop from a relatively homogeneous medium. On the other hand, some other process may form the clouds and the spiral disturbance may cause stars to form in them.

By whatever means an interstellar cloud may form, when it is triggered to collapse, it collapses in fragments—causing dense clumps in the cloud. To understand the nature of BN, let us follow the evolution of a relatively large clump, with a mass about 20 times that of our sun. When the clump has contracted to a diameter of about 3½ light-years, it becomes gravitationally unstable. That is, the gravity of the clump is powerful enough to accelerate its contents toward its center without the help of an outside force. As the matter falls toward the center, the density at the center increases, and the gas heats up. Nearly all of the heat escapes, however, in the form of radiation in the far-infrared range, at wavelengths of from 100 to 300 micrometers. The cloud, therefore, remains at close to its original very cold state, with a temperature of only about −250°C (−420°F.).

As contraction continues and the density increases, the dust becomes so thick at the center of the cloud that it absorbs the far-infrared radiation. Now, instead of escaping, the infrared light and hence the heat are trapped in the central core. At this point, the object becomes a protostar, consisting of a warm central core and the remaining infalling matter. Astronomer Richard B. Larson of Yale University, an authority on protostar formation, refers to the infalling matter as the "envelope" of the protostar and the warm core as an "embryo star." The core gets hotter and, also, more massive as the matter continues to stream in.

The embryo inside the protostar is less massive than the envelope; most of the mass is still falling inward. The protostar is probably spinning slowly, because we know that stars in general rotate. The rotation gives the outer zone of the envelope a slightly flattened or oblate shape while the part around the core, much flatter and denser, begins to resemble a discus or a deep-dish pizza. This formation, called an accretion disk, may be very important in some stellar birth sequences. In our own solar system, which developed from a much less massive clump than the BN object, the planets and asteroids formed from the accretion disk as the sun grew in the embryo core (see Asteroids: The Missing Planet?). This explains why the planets and asteroids are confined to a flat, wheel-shaped region, instead of moving around the sun in orbits at all angles.

Once the accretion disk has formed, most matter entering the core does so after falling into the disk and spiraling around in an ever-shrinking orbit. At this stage, the inflow through the disk is not due to the gravitational free fall that characterized the protostar's earlier phase. Instead, a process of viscous drag causes the inward spiral of matter in the protostar's accretion disk.

As the accretion disk feeds more mass into itself, the embryo star contracts, growing ever denser and more massive. The compression produces increasing heat. This heat energy is liberated as infrared and visible light, but the visible light cannot get past the dust of the envelope. It is absorbed in and heats the dust. At this stage, the protostar would appear to a distant observer as a fuzzy spot in the heavens, with an infrared signal characteristic of dust at a temperature of about 230°C (450°F.).

As the protostar core continues to gain mass and grow hotter, its strongest radiation shifts to shorter wavelengths of visible and ultraviolet light, all of it still screened from view by the dust of the envelope. When the dust grains in the inner envelope reach about 1250°C (2280°F.), they vaporize. The outer part of the envelope now has the form of a thick shell or dust cocoon. The boundary between the clean inner envelope and the dust cocoon forms where the radiation is not intense enough to vaporize dust grains. The outer parts of the cocoon thin out gradually into surrounding space.

When the center of the core gets hot and dense enough, nuclear reactions begin. The nuclei of atoms fuse, producing heavier nuclei and releasing nuclear energy, just as occurs in a hydrogen bomb. The reactions in a massive protostar produce energy at an enormous rate, soon exceeding the energy of the sun by several thousand times. The surface temperature of the core, bathed in the flow of energy from the center, rises to a few tens of thousands of degrees. The intense radiation from this hot surface produces a vast stellar wind that drives the remaining material of the envelope, including the cocoon, outward, eventually clearing it away. Such an object, which has evolved to the state just preceding the main sequence while still surrounded by an expanding envelope, is a massive type of PMS star. Calculations indicate that a massive star may reach the main sequence even before its envelope has blown away.

Astronomers find it very difficult to observe protostars and PMS stars because such objects are shrouded by their own thick dust. They must rely on instruments sensitive to the infrared and radio waves that can penetrate dusty regions. The theory of protostar evolution developed by Larson and others suggests that the wavelength at which the most infrared emission occurs will gradually get shorter as the objects get older and hotter. So the youngest protostars, still forming from dense clumps in the interstellar medium, should be most readily observed in the far-infrared, where available equipment, unfortunately, is most limited.

This situation will be remedied about 1981 when the Infrared Astronomy Satellite is launched as a joint project of the National Aeronautics and Space Administration (NASA) and a Netherlands agency.

Measuring the Newborn Star

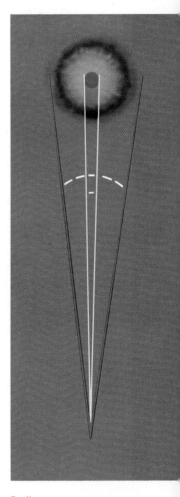

Radio-wave measurements (orange) of CO-molecule emission from the surroundings of BN revealed the size of the envelope and showed that it contained gases moving both toward and away from the earth. Infrared measurements (yellow) revealed CO-molecule absorption only in the area in front of BN. This proved that the envelope is expanding. The result agrees with the theory that BN is a PMS star.

It will carry an infrared telescope inside a helium Dewar, a huge thermos bottle containing ultracold liquefied helium. Only with such equipment can astronomers study far-infrared waves, because the warm surfaces of an ordinary telescope themselves produce enough far-infrared radiation to overwhelm the faint incoming signals from the stars. Astronomers can observe older protostars at shorter infrared wavelengths with telescopes on the ground and on high-altitude platforms, such as balloons, rockets, and planes. According to a report from Rodger I. Thompson of the University of Arizona's Steward Observatory, a protostar accretion disk may have been found by these techniques. At least that is his interpretation of observations of the infrared source MWC 349, made recently with a mountaintop telescope in Arizona and with the Kuiper Airborne Infrared Observatory, a computer-controlled telescope mounted in a NASA C141 jet plane.

Radio telescopes play an important role in mapping the molecular clouds and thus identifying regions of potential or actual star formation and determining their chemical composition. In addition, they can detect ionized gas inside the cocoon of a protostar or PMS star. By evaluating the amount of ionized hydrogen, astronomers can get a good idea of some characteristics of the hot core that produces the ultraviolet radiation that causes the ionization. Thus, the infant science of protostar observation has a variety of tools at its disposal.

Scientists have also developed methods to test the three theories of the nature of BN. The theory that BN is a white supergiant star screened by a remarkable amount of interstellar dust lost support after detailed measurements of the intensity of BN as a function of infrared wavelength became available during the 1970s. Investigators found that the measurements disagreed with the predictions of the theory.

The remaining theories identify BN as either a protostar or a PMS star. A hint of which is most likely came in April 1976 when astronomer Gary L. Grasdalen, then at Kitt Peak National Observatory, reported that infrared spectrometry had revealed an emission line of hydrogen that is characteristic of an ionized region. This would fit with the PMS model, in which an ionized zone forms inside the cocoon. However, the interpretation of these measurements was controversial, complicated by the fact that BN is behind the Orion Nebula, which is itself a large ionized region. Then, in November 1976 and February 1977, a Bell Telephone Laboratories-Hale Observatories team, led by Bell Labs radio astronomer Thomas G. Phillips, observed BN. They used a submillimeter heterodyne bolometer, a receiver that can pick up radio waves so short that they almost can be described as far-infrared. Hence, they can be focused by the mirrors of a conventional large optical telescope. The Bell-Hale team studied an emission line of the carbon monoxide molecule in a region around BN called the "plateau source" (a region that astronomers now identify as the envelope of BN). They found that this line was broadened by the Doppler effect, as a result of movement of the gas at speeds up to 25 kilometers (15.5 miles) per second or slightly more toward and away from the earth. These motions could be either the swirling turbulence of infalling material, as occurs in a protostar envelope, or the expansion of a shell of matter, as occurs when the wind of a PMS star drives the envelope outward. See CURRENTS IN CHAOS.

With two theories still in the running, the stage was set for Donald Hall's January report on the Kitt Peak infrared observations. Hall and his colleagues Stephen T. Ridgway and Fred C. Gillett of Kitt Peak, and Susan G. Kleinmann of the Massachusetts Institute of Technology in Cambridge studied BN with a new type of infrared spectrometer and the 4-meter (158-inch) Mayall telescope at Kitt Peak. They observed an absorption band of carbon monoxide in the spectrum of BN. Since the background infrared light absorbed by these molecules was the radiation of BN's own core, the observers necessarily sampled only the material directly in line between BN and the earth, and hence achieved a very narrow field of view. According to the protostar theory, this observation should reveal a range of motion of gas both toward and away from the earth about equal to that found by the Bell-Hale emission-line study, since swirling turbulence in even a small part of the envelope would comprise motions in both directions. The PMS star theory would predict that only material expanding toward the earth, at about the maximum speed found in the Bell-Hale study, would be seen. The Hall team's observations agreed almost exactly with the latter possibility–the gas is approaching the earth at 28 kilometers (17 miles) per second with respect to the central velocity of the plateau source. From this rate of motion and the present size of the plateau source, Hall infers that the envelope's expansion began about 2,000 years ago. His team also observed two infrared emission lines of hydrogen, known as Brackett alpha and gamma, that apparently arise in an ionized zone inside the cocoon. From this, they inferred that BN's core is producing enough ultraviolet light to be a pre-main-sequence B star–a star with a mass that is as much as 18 times that of the sun, within an expanding cocoon. This figure exceeds the estimate of BN's mass derived from the object's total infrared radiation–a mass only 10 times that of the sun. Earlier work had suggested that BN had a mass equal to that of 25 suns.

Further analysis and observations will almost surely resolve this discrepancy. If Hall's mass estimate is correct, there is an interesting consequence. The expansion of the envelope will gradually thin out the obscuring dust. At the same time, the bright Orion Nebula in the foreground will be expanding and dimming at least slightly. If BN does become a typical 18-solar-mass main-sequence star, it should be dimly visible to the naked eye from earth perhaps 75,000 years from now, unveiled at last by the swirling dust from which it was born. Then the original sensor of the most ancient astronomers, the human eye, can confirm a deduction that we draw now by means of the most sophisticated techniques of 20th-century astrophysics.

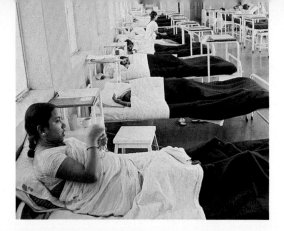

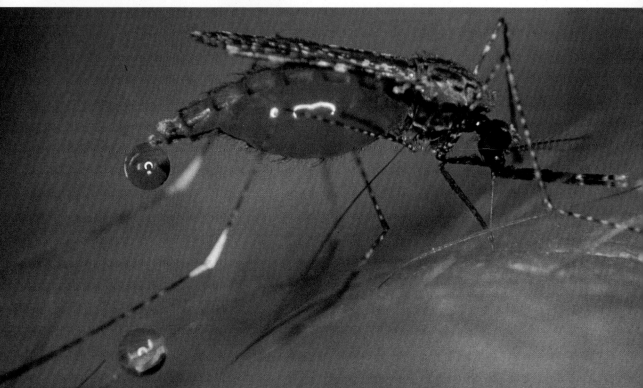

Thwarting Malaria's Comeback

By Thomas H. Maugh II

A dramatic increase in the number of cases throughout the world has put this disease back in the scientific spotlight

Malaria, for the average North American or European, conjures up images from the past of colonial soldiers in steamy jungles, mosquito netting, pith helmets, and World War II battles in the South Pacific. But more than half the people of the world have no such romanticized notions about the disease. To those living in most tropical areas of the world, a mosquito bite means more than just an irritating itch. It can be the forerunner of months of suffering—even death.

Malaria is caused by a one-celled, or protozoan, parasite that is transmitted to humans through the saliva of the female *Anopheles* mosquito. The parasite infects the victim's red blood cells, causing symptoms that include recurrent chills and fever and extreme drowsiness. Some forms of malaria can be fatal if the victim does not receive prompt medical care.

During the 1960s, scientists were optimistic that malaria could be wiped out, and in fact, great progress was made. In India, for example, the number of cases was slashed from 75 million per year in the

1950s to 40,000 in 1966. But by 1976, the number of cases had rebounded to 5.8 million. Similar increases occurred in Pakistan, Sri Lanka, and other countries in Central and Southeast Asia. Latin America also has been hard hit. In tiny Honduras alone, malaria cases increased from 7,503 in 1974 to 48,804 in 1976. And Africa registers more than 90 million cases each year. There are now more than 120-million malaria cases each year, making it one of the world's top-ranking public-health problems.

Mass campaigns against malaria relied mainly on treating victims with drugs that kill the parasite, draining and filling swampy breeding sites to cut down the number of *Anopheles* mosquito larvae, and spraying insecticides to kill adult mosquitoes. Some species of *Anopheles* mosquitoes prefer to bite their victims indoors and then land somewhere inside the building to rest. Thus, spraying the interiors of houses and other buildings with a long-lasting insecticide, such as DDT, can kill the mosquitoes before they infect someone else. These techniques along with others, such as window and door screens, eradicated malaria in such temperate climates as the Southern United States by the early 1950s and once made substantial inroads in tropical regions.

Ironically, the success of the control programs is partly to blame for the resurgence of malaria. Many countries became overconfident. Government officials cut back spraying programs, curtailed malaria research, directed funds to the military and other areas, and reduced their surveillance for the disease. Government mismanagement was also to blame. Insecticides were not ordered in time, so that deliveries often arrived after the height of the malaria season. Spraying programs were not monitored carefully, and many areas were not sprayed completely or were missed entirely. Most important, malaria-control programs were not integrated into overall government health-service systems. As a result, many of the people in charge of malaria control viewed their positions as only temporary, and they eventually switched to jobs that offered more security.

Technical problems also arose. In many areas, mosquitoes developed resistance to DDT and other insecticides; more expensive pesticides that do not remain effective as long must now be used. Furthermore, the parasite itself has become increasingly resistant to the most frequently used antimalarial drugs.

A malaria-weakened population poses a major economic hurdle for developing nations. These countries have very little money for capital investments, so they rely more on manpower than machinery. If many members of the work force are ill with malaria, this further hurts the already weak economy.

The resurgence of the disease, however, has sparked renewed interest in research on antimalarial drugs, and has also stimulated important research pointing toward the possibility of a vaccine for malaria. The protozoan that causes malaria is of the genus *Plasmodium*. More than 50 species of this protozoan attack animals. Only four species

The author:
Thomas H. Maugh II is senior staff writer for *Science* magazine.

Where Malaria Lurks

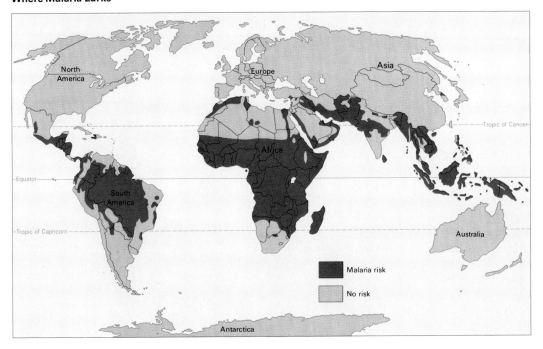

North America

Europe

Asia

Tropic of Cancer

Africa

Equator

South America

Tropic of Capricorn

Australia

■ Malaria risk

□ No risk

Antarctica

attack humans, and the two most common of these are *Plasmodium falciparum* and *Plasmodium vivax*.

Vivax malaria is a relatively mild form of the disease. Its symptoms include periodic chills and fever, an enlarged spleen, anemia, severe abdominal pain, headaches, and exhaustion following an attack. Vivax malaria may subside by itself in 20 to 30 days, but it is likely to flare up and cause a relapse many months later. It is generally not fatal, but it lowers the patient's resistance to other diseases.

Falciparum malaria is much more dangerous than vivax malaria. It produces the same symptoms plus others, including small hemorrhages in the brain and damage to lungs and kidneys. Falciparum is often fatal if not treated immediately with drugs, but victims who survive this form do not suffer a relapse.

Malaria is difficult to attack head-on because of the complex life cycle of *Plasmodium*. The parasite assumes several different forms during its life and reproduces in two distinct ways—asexually when in humans and sexually when in mosquitoes. An infected female *Anopheles* mosquito's saliva contains great numbers of the form of the parasite known as the sporozoite. When the mosquito bites, it releases the sporozoites, which enter human liver cells through the bloodstream and reproduce asexually. Each parasite's nucleus divides many times to form a clump of nuclei called a schizont. The schizonts develop into the next stage of the parasite, merozoites. These burst from the liver cell and enter the bloodstream. The merozoites then infect

Malaria is on the rise in tropical parts of the world where people live close to swampy mosquito-breeding areas.

red blood cells, where they form more schizonts. These schizonts develop into new merozoites which burst out of the red blood cells and infect other red blood cells. Most of the symptoms of malaria occur in this disease cycle when the red blood cells rupture, releasing merozoites and cellular material into the bloodstream. For this reason, malaria victims do not have a constant fever, but rather fevers that come and go.

Instead of continuing the asexual human cycle of the disease, a few of the merozoites within the red blood cells develop into male and female forms known as gametocytes. If a mosquito bites someone who already has malaria at this stage, the mosquito sucks gametocytes into its stomach along with the victim's blood. In the mosquito's stomach, the gametocytes mature to another stage called gametes. The female and male gametes unite, then pass through the mosquito's stomach lining, and on the outside of the stomach they develop into a sac containing many sporozoites. When the sporozoites mature, they migrate to the salivary glands and wait to be injected into a human and begin the parasite's life cycle again.

If the *Plasmodium* life cycle could be interrupted in either the mosquito or the human, the parasite and the disease it causes would eventually die out. The earliest of malaria treatments, discovered by South American Indians in the 15th century, was quinine, derived from the bark of the cinchona tree. Although quinine often relieves symptoms, it does not necessarily cure the disease.

The best way to end the cycle within the human is with much more effective drugs. The first of these were synthesized during World War II. The best modern treatment for malaria is a combination of the synthetic drugs chloroquine and primaquine. Chloroquine destroys the stages of *Plasmodium* that are in blood, while primaquine destroys the form that invades the liver and also kills the infectious gametocytes. These drugs are very effective against malaria strains in Africa, India, and Central America. However, a form of *P. falciparum* resistant to chloroquine appeared in the early 1960s in Cambodia, Malaya, Thailand, and Vietnam. Today, chloroquine has little effect on some strains in Southeast Asia and along the Amazon River in Brazil.

Because United States military forces were serving in Southeast Asia when the chloroquine-

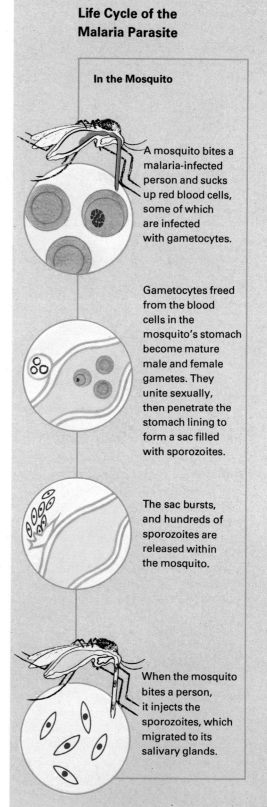

Life Cycle of the Malaria Parasite

In the Mosquito

A mosquito bites a malaria-infected person and sucks up red blood cells, some of which are infected with gametocytes.

Gametocytes freed from the blood cells in the mosquito's stomach become mature male and female gametes. They unite sexually, then penetrate the stomach lining to form a sac filled with sporozoites.

The sac bursts, and hundreds of sporozoites are released within the mosquito.

When the mosquito bites a person, it injects the sporozoites, which migrated to its salivary glands.

In the Human

Each sporozoite enters a liver cell, where its nucleus divides many times to produce a schizont.

The many nuclei of the schizont then develop into individual merozoites that burst the liver cell and enter the bloodstream.

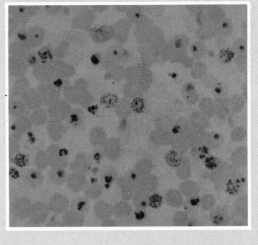

Merozoites ready to burst from blood cells appear as tiny red dots. (Magnified 880 times.)

The merozoites penetrate into red blood cells.

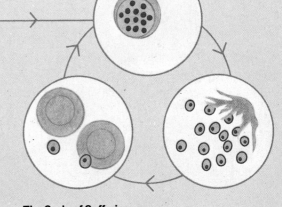

Some merozoites do not divide inside the blood cell, but grow into a larger gametocyte.

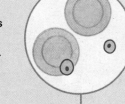

When a mosquito sucks up human blood cells infected with gametocytes, the *Plasmodium* life cycle begins again.

The Cycle of Suffering

In a person's blood cell, the merozoite forms a schizont, which develops into many new merozoites. These burst out and infect more red blood cells to continue the disease cycle. All the merozoites mature at about the same time. The periodic chills and fever of malaria occur whenever the merozoites burst from the cells.

A researcher takes
malaria-carrying
mosquitoes from a
breeding room, *top,* and
irradiates them with
gamma rays, *right,*
to weaken the malaria
parasites. Technicians
then make vaccine, *far
right,* from the weakened
parasites and inoculate
a mouse, *bottom.*

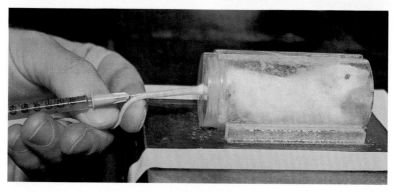

resistant strains appeared, the Walter Reed Army Institute of Research in 1964 began a major screening program to find and develop new antimalarial drugs. Since then, Walter Reed and its contractors have screened nearly 300,000 compounds that showed promise in animal tests or had chemical compositions that resembled those of existing antimalarial drugs. Seven drugs and two drug combinations proved to be effective, and several of these have already been used to cure U.S. servicemen suffering from chloroquine-resistant malaria.

One of the best of the new drugs is mefloquine, according to pharmacologist Craig J. Canfield, director of the antimalarial drug program at Walter Reed. A single dose can cure chloroquine-resistant falciparum malaria. One dose also protects a healthy person against falciparum malaria for as long as 30 days. The World Health Organization (WHO) is beginning field studies in Africa and South America to check the effectiveness of mefloquine.

The resurgence of malaria can probably be controlled in some areas, such as India, Pakistan, and Sri Lanka, simply by gearing up the mosquito-eradication programs again. But these countries may have to use newer and more expensive pesticides. However, the problem is much more difficult in a few isolated areas of Africa and Brazil where all of the pesticides now available have become ineffective. This problem is likely to spread to other areas. New pesticides are needed, but as yet there are no research programs to develop them. Drugs such as mefloquine that also protect against infection will be of some help in these places, but they are too costly for poor countries to use on large numbers of people. Furthermore, scientists believe that, based on past experience, it is likely that *Plasmodium* will develop resistance rather quickly to even the most effective drugs.

The brightest hope for these tropical regions is the possibility of developing an effective vaccine against malaria. Finding a vaccine for *Plasmodium* has been an elusive goal. For one thing, the parasite is a weak immunogen. That is, the human immune system does not react as strongly to any of its forms as it does to viruses, bacteria, and other foreign invaders. The surfaces of viruses and bacteria contain antigens, substances that the human immune system recognizes as foreign. The immune system then produces antibodies, biochemicals that attach to the antigens and direct other cells to attack the invaders. A virus can do substantial damage to the body before enough antibodies have been formed to wipe it out. But once the infection is over, antibodies remain in the bloodstream to protect against future attack. Vaccination with weakened or killed viruses arouses these antigens in exactly the same way, producing immunity without infection.

But an individual must contract malaria several times before any substantial immunity develops. Even then, the person is still susceptible to a mild form of the disease. And the immunity is only effective against one species of *Plasmodium*, sometimes only against one strain of the species. Scientists do not yet understand why this is so. Some think

Infected mosquitoes in net-covered containers bite tranquilized, vaccinated animals in laboratory experiments that test the effectiveness of antimalarial vaccines.

the various forms of the parasite can somehow disguise themselves to trick the immune system. Parasitologist David J. Wyler of the U.S. National Institute of Allergy and Infectious Diseases (NIAID) suggests that the parasite may release some substance that suppresses the victim's immune system.

Lack of an abundant source of the parasite for research has also prevented development of a vaccine. A major step toward solving this problem was made in 1976, when parasitologists William Trager and James B. Jensen of Rockefeller University developed a way to grow and maintain large numbers of asexual forms of *P. falciparum* in the laboratory—a feat that had eluded scientists since the parasite was first identified in 1880. Trager and Jensen developed a culture medium containing the right combination of nutrients, gases, and such ingredients as human blood serum and red blood cells to keep the parasites alive. These cultures can be maintained indefinitely. Previously, the parasites survived in cultures only two to four days.

Some observers compare Trager's and Jensen's accomplishment to that of John F. Enders and his colleagues at Harvard Medical School, who discovered a way to culture poliovirus, clearing the way for the development of the polio vaccine in 1955. Investigators in nearly 20 laboratories have reproduced Trager's and Jensen's culture work and are growing large quantities of *Plasmodium* for study and for use in experimental vaccines.

But the complex *Plasmodium* life cycle presents another problem. Against which stage of the life cycle would it be best to vaccinate? Researchers are using three approaches, each directed against a different stage and each with its own advantages and disadvantages.

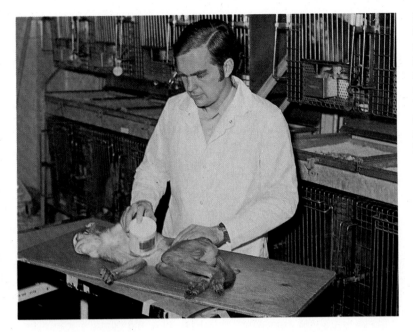

Parasitologist Robert W. Gwadz allows mosquitoes to bite a monkey whose blood contains antibodies against gametocytes. This is one step in his method for destroying malaria parasites in the mosquito.

Immunologist Ruth S. Nussenzweig and her associates at the New York University Medical Center have directed their efforts against sporozoites, the stage at which *Plasmodium* is transmitted from mosquito to animals or humans. They exposed *Plasmodium*-infected mosquitoes to X rays or gamma rays to weaken the sporozoites so that they could infect animals but could not reproduce. The irradiated mosquitoes were then allowed to bite rats and mice repeatedly, and the rodents eventually developed immunity to that stage of the malaria parasite. Nussenzweig and others obtained similar results with monkeys and with a small number of human volunteers. The same effect can be achieved by repeatedly injecting purified weakened sporozoites into the bloodstream.

Despite these successes, there are several problems. For example, the vaccination provides no protection against other stages of the *Plasmodium* life cycle, and it is crucial that the vaccination produce complete immunity. If a vaccinated person is bitten by an infected *Anopheles* mosquito and even one sporozoite escapes the antibodies produced by the vaccination, it can lodge in the liver and begin the disease cycle. In addition, the immunity produced so far lasts only three to six months, so frequent vaccinations would be necessary. Finally, only very limited quantities of sporozoites can be obtained, because they can only be collected by tediously dissecting the salivary glands of infected mosquitoes. There is presently no way to grow sporozoites in the laboratory, not even in the Trager-Jensen culture. Nussenzweig's approach suggests that humans can be immunized against malaria, but the problems indicate that vaccination with sporozoites for large numbers of people is probably not practical.

The second approach is somewhat more radical. It involves, in effect, immunizing mosquitoes against gametes, the sexual stage of *Plasmodium*. Parasitologists Robert W. Gwadz, Richard Carter, and David H. Chen of NIAID collected small amounts of red blood cells containing gametocytes from malaria-infected chickens. They then exposed the cells to X rays to weaken the gametocytes and injected them into healthy chickens. This stimulated the chickens' immune system to produce antibodies against this stage of *Plasmodium*.

Next, the scientists gave the chickens malaria by injecting them with a solution containing the parasite or by allowing them to be bitten by infected mosquitoes. The parasite went through its life cycle in the chickens and produced gametocytes in their red blood cells. While in the cells, the gametocytes were safe from the antibodies.

The scientists then had healthy mosquitoes bite the chickens. These mosquitoes sucked up the antibodies along with gametocyte-infected blood cells. As the gametocytes were freed from the red blood cells in the mosquito's stomach to become mature gametes, the antibodies immobilized them almost immediately. The male gamete could not unite with the female. Consequently, the parasite could not produce its infectious offspring, sporozoites, and the mosquito could not pass the disease along to a new victim.

Gwadz and his associates have obtained similar results in monkeys and other primates. They also have some evidence that vaccination against gametes reduces the severity of infections in monkeys, though they do not know why. But if this is true, it would mean that immunizing mosquitoes against gametes would halt the spread of the disease by reducing the numbers of parasite-carrying mosquitoes. It would also provide the individual with some protection. Unfortunately, only small quantities of gametes grow in the culture developed by Trager and Jensen. So scientists must either adapt the culture to produce more gametes or develop some other way to grow them in quantity. Progress in this area was made in November 1977, when Carter and another NIAID parasitologist, Raymond F. Beach, reported they grew substantial numbers of gametocytes in a modified version of the Trager-Jensen culture.

The third immunization method is the most promising. It involves the use of merozoites, the form of the parasite that is most plentiful in Trager-Jensen cultures and that does most of the damage in humans. In 1977, immunologist Sidney Cohen and his colleagues at Guy's Hospital Medical School in London and parasitologist Wassim A. Siddiqui of the University of Hawaii School of Medicine independently found that monkeys can be immunized against *P. falciparum* by injecting them with killed merozoites. Cohen and others had shown earlier that monkeys could be immunized in this fashion against a form of malaria that attacks only monkeys. But it was far more significant to know that merozoites could immunize monkeys against the most lethal form of human malaria.

A malaria researcher
empties a container
of mosquitoes into a
dish under a dissecting
microscope, *left,*
then removes their
salivary glands,
below, from which
he obtains sporozoites.

Mosquito netting, insect spray, and drugs are the only dependable defenses against major outbreaks of malaria.

Cohen obtained *P. falciparum* merozoites from the blood of infected children in Gambia. He grew the merozoites in culture to increase their concentration, then separated them from the red blood cells, killed them, and injected them into monkeys three times over a period of five weeks. Siddiqui killed merozoites obtained from the blood of falciparum-infected monkeys and injected them into healthy monkeys twice, three weeks apart. Then each scientist injected live malaria parasites into their monkeys. The parasites produced only mild infections or no infection. Both scientists note that their vaccines can be made just as well with merozoites from the Trager-Jensen culture.

Epidemiologist Karl H. Rieckmann and his associates at the University of New Mexico, under the sponsorship of the U.S. Agency for International Development, are comparing these vaccination methods to see which is the best candidate for intensive development. Immunization with merozoites seems to be the likely winner.

But researchers still face the problem of the weak immune-system response that any form of *Plasmodium* stimulates. They have found that a stronger, more lasting immunity can be produced not only through repeated exposure to the parasite but also by adding a chemical mixture called an adjuvant to the vaccine. When an adjuvant is injected along with a weak immunogen, the body produces many more antibodies than it would otherwise. One of the most effective adjuvants is called Freund's complete adjuvant, an emulsion containing killed bacteria and mineral oil. Scientists believe that the foreign antigens in the killed bacteria stimulate the immune system to respond more strongly. In addition, the mineral oil permits the antigens to be released slowly to prolong the body's exposure to them.

Gwadz, Cohen, and Siddiqui all found that monkeys develop immunity to malaria only when the *Plasmodium* vaccine is combined with Freund's complete adjuvant. Unfortunately, this adjuvant cannot be used in humans because it causes abscesses and other ill effects.

Immunologist George McInnes of E. R. Squibb and Sons believes that an effective adjuvant for humans will be found soon after researchers determine which stage of the parasite's life cycle is most useful for human immunization. A promising combination might be peanut oil and a bacteria called BCG. Parasitologist Paul H. Silverman and his associates at the University of New Mexico have used this adjuvant to produce immunity to a form of malaria that attacks monkeys. BCG is already used to vaccinate humans against tuberculosis, and peanut oil should be safe because it is easily broken down by the body, unlike mineral oil which is made from petroleum.

Ironically, these major advances against malaria have been made in the United States and Great Britain, where malaria is no longer a problem. But a worldwide focus on malaria research is developing. WHO in 1976 established a Special Program on Research and Training in Tropical Diseases designed to stimulate studies of malaria and five other tropical diseases—schistosomiasis, trypanosomiasis, leishmaniasis, filariasis, and leprosy—in the countries where these diseases occur. The program emphasizes developing and expanding research facilities in those countries and training their young scientists to study the diseases. The malaria portion of the program will have received about $45 million by 1981, much of it to establish facilities for testing antimalarial drugs and vaccines. A great deal of effort will also be devoted to studying the parasite's biochemistry and metabolism.

At present, no one has any illusions that malaria will be easy to eradicate. Much past research was inspired by wars and conquests—from European colonialist ventures in Africa and Asia to the Vietnam War. Research in 1978 is stimulated by the resurgence of malaria.

So far, all advances against the disease have come in spurts precipitated by crisis. Continuing research must be coupled with regular use of the antimalarial weapons that are already available if this disease is finally to be conquered.

Flight of the *Gossamer Condor*

By Paul MacCready

Soaring birds and gliding wings were keys to the design of the first successful human-powered aircraft

The *Gossamer Condor*, a human-powered airplane, flew into aviation history on Aug. 23, 1977. Pedaled and piloted by cyclist Bryan Allen, the craft successfully flew 2.16 kilometers (1.35 miles) over a figure-eight course in California in a 7½-minute flight to win the $95,000 Kremer Prize–a prize that had been offered 18 years before.

One of man's oldest dreams has been to follow the birds into the sky on wings of his own. You can see evidence of this dream in ancient paintings and statues of mythical winged heroes and flying angels, and in Leonardo da Vinci's design for wings to be flapped by a man. The dream is told in legends such as that of Icarus, whose wax wings melted when he flew too close to the sun.

It has proved difficult to translate this dream into reality. Early experimenters faced ridicule as they risked, and sometimes lost, their lives in attempts to emulate the birds. Later pioneers built on an engineering base from the new science of aero-

Pilot-engine Bryan Allen makes history with the first human-powered aircraft to successfully fly the course prescribed by Henry Kremer.

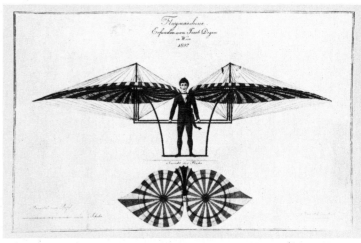

Man's attempts to fly like the birds are recorded in legends like those of Icarus, *left,* whose wings melted in the sun, and drawings like the bird-winged Flügmachine, *above.*

The author:
Paul MacCready is the president of Aerovironment Inc. He is an aeronautical engineer and an expert on gliders.

dynamics. And with the advent of the engine, aircraft designers finally achieved sustained and controlled powered flight. The era of modern aviation had begun.

Dreams of flight now were about airplanes using engines rather than man's muscle. During the next 75 years, the engines grew larger and more dependable. As a result, air transportation has evolved to where jumbo jets span the oceans and people journey at supersonic speeds. Fantastic flights have also been made with gliders, but these use nature's rising air currents rather than human power. The goal of man flying on his own puny power was virtually forgotten.

Then, in 1959, British industrialist Henry Kremer established a prize of 5,000 pounds sterling for a particular type of human-powered flight, and resurrected the nearly forgotten dream. The rules for winning the prize, which was restricted to British designers, were worked out by the Man-Powered Aircraft Group of the Royal Aeronautical Society. Without using stored energy or lighter-than-air gases, the pilot had to take off unassisted and fly a figure-eight course around two pylons 0.8 kilometer (½ mile) apart, clearing hurdles 3 meters (10 feet) above the ground at the beginning and end of the figure eight.

The height requirement meant the vehicle had to be able to fly out of the strong "ground effect" that helps to cut the drag, or retarding force, on airplanes when their wings are near the ground. The figure eight required the vehicle to be controllable. The length of the flight meant that the aircraft had to be very efficient; it had to fly a longer distance than could be achieved by the initial burst of high power that a trained athlete can put out. In all, the Kremer Prize rules defined an event that would demonstrate controlled man-powered flight over a substantial distance.

In 1961, two human-powered aircraft built by British designers got off the ground, but could not turn safely or fly far. So in 1963, Kremer doubled the prize money to 10,000 pounds and opened the competition to people in other countries. In 1973, with no winner in sight in spite of the efforts of many development groups, he raised the prize to 50,000 pounds, then worth $120,000.

In July 1976, I took my first extended vacation in years and drove across the United States from the West Coast to the East Coast with my family. During the long days of driving the interstate highways, my mind kept well away from the everyday pressures and distractions of my business and, almost without any guidance from me, began dwelling on several other topics. Suddenly, the day after we visited the Wright Brothers National Memorial at Kitty Hawk, N.C., I knew that there was a way to win the Kremer Prize.

A major element in my thinking was the fact that the competition existed—with a substantial prize. Many aerodynamicists, structural engineers, and craftsmen had devoted tremendous efforts and a great deal of time to building human-powered vehicles, but no group had come close to winning the prize. If it was to be won, some very different approach would be required.

Another element was some comparisons I made between the flying characteristics of hawks and those of hang gliders. I had recently written an article on the flight capabilities of hang gliders. I began to compare these with the characteristics of soaring birds, to see what would be needed for hang gliders to soar, as well as glide. It dawned on me that you can learn a lot about a bird in circling flight by noting its bank angle and the time it takes to complete a turn. Simple calculations then tell you the bird's flying speed and turning radius. With

The Contest Course

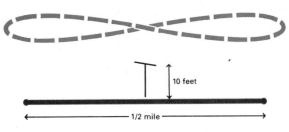

10 feet

1/2 mile

The 1.35-mile, figure-8 Kremer course with its 10-foot "hurdle," *above right,* challenged many designers. Two British entries included *Puffin II, above,* built by employees of the De Havilland Corporation, and the *Toucan, right,* a two-man craft built by Hertfordshire Pedal Aeronautics.

Combining aerodynamic behavior of the light and quick hang glider, *top,* with that of the ponderous, but efficient, California condor, *above,* led to the basic design of the *Gossamer Condor.*

some estimates of wing loading (weight per unit area of the wing), you can make good guesses about things such as efficiency and sinking speed. These observations can even be made from a moving car—which is what we did for many hours of our vacation. This kept me thinking about flight with low wing loadings and power requirements, and slow flying speeds.

The third element came from what I knew of the structure of hang gliders. With wires, aluminum tubes, and cloth for a wing sail, you can build a hang glider that weighs relatively little. An efficient hang glider takes only about $1\frac{1}{2}$ horsepower (h.p.) to keep aloft. If you could somehow triple the size of its wing without increasing its total weight to any degree, it would only take about $\frac{1}{2}$ h.p.—well within the power range of a strong bicyclist. Tripling the wing's dimensions results in nine times the wing area, and hence one-third the flying speed, one-third the sinking speed, and one-third the power.

The final vital factor was my belief that building a human-powered aircraft should be so simple and quick that, aided by a few friends, I could afford the time. So, starting with the idea of a large, light, slow-flying vehicle built with hang-glider construction methods, I was sure the Kremer Prize could be won. Thus the project began.

For the rest of the vacation I reflected only occasionally on the problem, but made a few sketches and some back-of-the-envelope calculations. After our return home to California early in August, I began working in earnest in my spare time on the details of wing configuration, stability, and structure.

I used aerodynamic theory to calculate the wing dimensions needed to permit long flights by human muscle. Pound for pound, a person cannot put out anything like the power that evolution has packed into the average bird. Thus the vehicle had to be made extremely large, yet light enough to have as much wing area per unit of power available as a soaring bird. It also had to be at least as efficient as a soaring bird–that is, it had to be able to glide at least as well.

To calculate the power required, I had to start with the fundamental concept of the balance of forces on an aircraft. In level flight, the lift, which comes from continually accelerating air downward, must equal the weight. Also, the drag, or resistance of the air, must be balanced by the thrust of the propeller. Power is a product of force and velocity, and it is the same whether you multiply the weight by the sinking speed, or the drag by the forward speed. The preliminary design of the aircraft showed that, if the weight could be kept down, a wingspan of about 30 meters (98 feet) would be desirable, with enough wing area to keep the flight speed very low–no more than 16 kilometers per hour (kph) or 10 miles per hour (mph). These values could produce a vehicle in which about 0.3 h.p. would be consumed through drag. Then, since we might be able to design a propeller that would be about 80 per cent efficient, the total power that the pilot would have to generate would be well under 0.4 h.p.

There are two kinds of drag–parasite drag and induced drag. Any object moving through air encounters parasite drag. The friction of air rubbing along all the surfaces, and the turbulence created when air flows around objects, cause parasite drag. To keep this drag down, the speed must be slow and the total surface of the aircraft must be as smooth and small as possible.

Induced drag is that associated with generating lift. In accelerating air downward, the wing is doing work and there is a drag "penalty." The penalty is smaller if the mass of air involved is larger. If you must

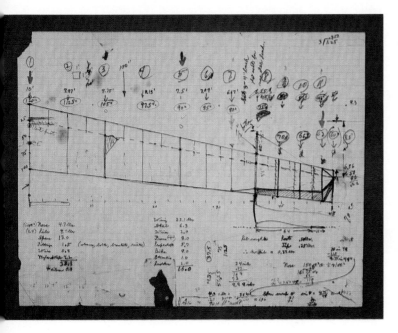

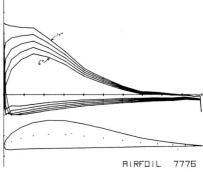

AIRFOIL 7776

Handwritten notes and sketches on graph paper, *left,* by MacCready complemented complex computer models, *above,* by Lissaman in attempts to find the ideal size and shape for the *Condor's* wing.

Tyler MacCready tests an early version of the *Condor* at Mojave Airport, *left,* while his father times the trial. Periodic crashes, *above,* when analyzed, provided important design information, rather than despair. In the course of repairs, team members like Lambie, Lissaman, Oldershaw, and the author, *below,* took the opportunity to streamline and improve the craft.

Verne Oldershaw, *left,* uses an unlikely repair tool—a steam iron— to tighten the Mylar covering on the canard. Meanwhile, the author cuts open an air vent on the cockpit, *above,* just before the prizewinning flight.

fly slowly, you want a large wingspan so you can affect a large mass of air. If the wingspan is small, you have to fly fast to keep down induced drag. Unfortunately, much of what can be done to reduce parasite drag increases induced drag, and vice versa.

Once I had settled on the concept of using hang-glider construction methods with tubes and wires, I could estimate the weight at between 23 and 36 kilograms (50 and 80 pounds). From this, I could use the preliminary aerodynamic design to tell me how big the wing should be. The philosophy that I followed thereafter was to get the wing flying controllably with an absolute minimum of additional parts. I did not know what the rest of the design would be. I only knew that it would have to fly slowly, floating rather than whizzing along.

Early in the development of our aircraft, we had to think up a name for it. In several family discussions the name *Gossamer Condor* emerged. *Condor* depicts the craft's relation to birds, particularly to the California condor, the largest soaring bird in North America. This *Condor,* however, would be far more fragile—hence the *Gossamer Condor.*

Bryan Allen pedals on an ergometer, modified to simulate the human engine conditions he would experience in the *Gossamer Condor.*

My assumptions about the wing size proved to be right, but the assumption that developing the vehicle would be quick and easy was wrong. There was no way of foreseeing just what problems would have to be overcome because no one had ever tried to fly a plane that was so large and also so light. Most problems proved easy to solve, but we had serious troubles with a few. I say "we" because many friends, including Peter Lissaman, my associate at Aerovironment, Incorporated, quickly became involved. All the members of my family participated, too. Most of this team of 16 people had technical backgrounds in aviation and knew how to fly. Unflagging team spirit shaped our collaboration and, most important, we had a clearly defined goal to work toward–the Kremer Prize.

Later in August 1976, I made the first crude 2.5-meter (about 8-foot) model out of balsa sticks and tissue, using our spare bedroom as a workshop. This model tested the structural concept of the wing and explored the need for a stabilizer. The stabilizer is a horizontal surface that keeps the vehicle at the correct angle to the wind. Changing the stabilizer angle changes the lift on it, causing the airplane to point up or down and hence to fly slower or faster. Most aircraft have the stabilizer at the rear, but it works as well at the front, and for the *Gossamer Condor,* which already had a pole out front to support wing wires, this was the most convenient spot to put it. We called it a "canard," a word used to describe a stabilizer in front of the wing.

By mid-September, we completed a 27-meter (88-foot) wingspan "model," weighing 23 kilograms (50 pounds), in the building in which floats are constructed for the Pasadena Rose Parade. This wing with tubes and wire bracing had the stabilizer out front, but there was no propeller and no pilot's position. We had to vacate the building the day after the model was finished. So, at 1 A.M., we went to the Rose Bowl parking lot and in the headlights of a few cars shimmering through a drizzle, we tested the new model. The rain doubled its weight. I ran along underneath, holding it up by the tube we called the bottom post, and two people, one at each wing tip, kept the contraption from slithering and dipping about. A clothesline, wires, and pulleys enabled me to tilt the stabilizer up or down. As the wing lifted, I hung on and became convinced that the design was what we had hoped for. That same morning we moved operations to a hangar at Mojave Airport, 129 kilometers (80 miles) north of Pasadena.

By November, the *Gossamer Condor*, now with a pilot and propeller, was being pushed into the air regularly to make flights of a few seconds, long enough to allow us to study its weaknesses—which were many. This early Mojave version had a 29-meter (96-foot) wingspan, and was 3.5 meters (11½ feet) wide. The thin ribs, spaced far apart and fastened to the front and rear spars, had shapes dictated by Lissaman's computer calculations. Only the top of the wing was covered (with transparent Mylar, a tough, light plastic), making the wing a single-surface airfoil like the sail of a sailboat. The "body" amidships consisted of an aluminum tube pointing straight down, another pointing up, a keel tube pointing back at right angles, and a tube called the bowsprit reaching out ahead at wing level. Piano wire fastened to the ends of these tubes and stretched taut to numerous places on the spars prevented the wings from collapsing.

A seat, pedals, and sprocket were attached to the bottom post and a lightweight chain connected the sprocket to the propeller. Having the propeller behind everything kept its air blast from blowing on parts of the vehicle and causing extra drag. The stabilizer was fastened in front to the tip of the bowsprit. My original concept was proving correct—we did not have to add many things to that monster wing.

Because of the *Gossamer Condor*'s simple and fragile construction and slow speed, crashes were never serious. Repairs could be made in a matter of hours, and sometimes in minutes. Even major design changes could be made quickly. However, no matter what we did, the power requirements remained too large. The most efficient flying speed turned out to be 13 kph (8 mph) and we discovered that it was vitally important to fly at constant speed. On the day after Christmas, 1976, my 17-year-old son Parker took off and flew a few feet off the ground for 40 seconds. We had to add seven or eight minutes and fly 10 times as far to win the prize, but we were well on the way.

The pilot-pedaler—the engine—was positioned to sit back, legs pumping ahead rather than down beneath the seat. We adopted this position to keep the pedaler's body away from the vertical chain, and to provide good visibility, and to leave his hands free to control the plane. Also, keeping the pilot's weight low helped with stability. We left him exposed because he would cause little drag at 13 kph.

After many trials and gentle crashes, we came to several conclusions. Our vehicle was too crudely fashioned to permit long flights. Any turbulence in the air hurt its flight capabilities. Just as important, there seemed to be no way to modify the configuration to make it stable and enable the pilot to control roll and yaw, the tendency to skid sideways. We were encountering a fundamental problem that had not arisen in the design of ordinary aircraft. In our case, the mass of air

The Forces that Affect Flight

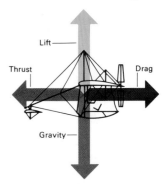

An aircraft must be designed to provide enough lift to overcome gravity and enough thrust to overcome drag, if it is to maintain level flight.

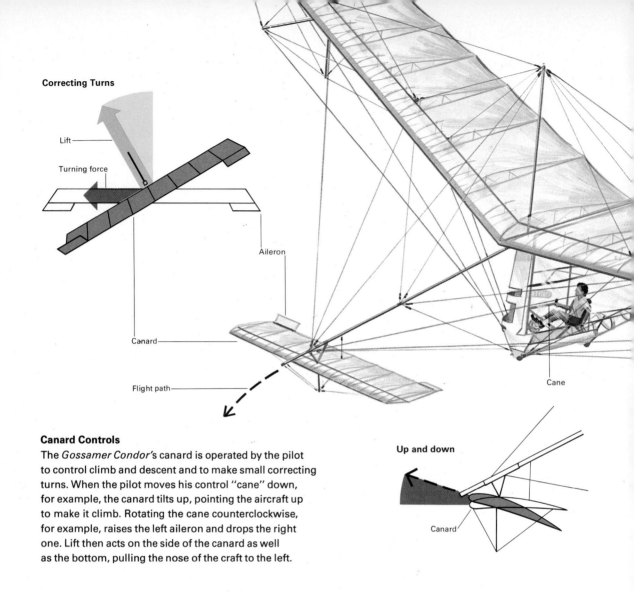

Correcting Turns

Lift

Turning force

Aileron

Canard

Flight path

Cane

Up and down

Canard

Canard Controls

The *Gossamer Condor*'s canard is operated by the pilot
to control climb and descent and to make small correcting
turns. When the pilot moves his control "cane" down,
for example, the canard tilts up, pointing the aircraft up
to make it climb. Rotating the cane counterclockwise,
for example, raises the left aileron and drops the right
one. Lift then acts on the side of the canard as well
as the bottom, pulling the nose of the craft to the left.

affected by the aircraft was much larger than the mass of the aircraft,
and both masses had to be manipulated when the craft accelerated,
rolled, or turned. This took larger control forces than were available,
and also added to the power requirements. In addition, at first we did
not realize that even gentle turbulence affected the flight characteristics at very slow speeds. Any slight turbulence along the wing altered
the angle of attack at that point. As a result, at any moment, only a
portion of the huge wings operated at peak lifting efficiency.

The wind effect was quite strong. Any wind over 3 kph (2 mph) had
enough pockets of turbulence to make the pilot work significantly
harder than he needed to in smooth air. This sounds small, but 3 kph
was 20 per cent of our cruising speed; a wind at 20 per cent of a jet
airliner's cruising speed is a hurricane. Either we had to fly faster or
find a place with very light winds. We decided to do both. To solve the
wind problem, we moved to Shafter Airport near Bakersfield where
light winds prevailed, especially at sunrise.

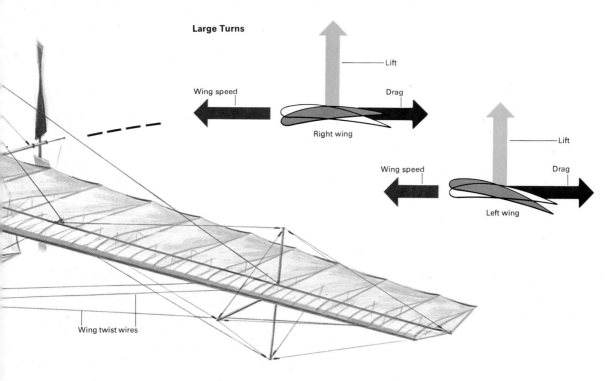

Large Turns

Lift

Wing speed

Drag

Right wing

Lift

Wing speed

Drag

Left wing

Wing twist wires

Wing Controls
Large turns of the *Gossamer Condor* are made by twisting the wings. The pilot uses a lever (not shown) beside his seat to move the wires that do the twisting. In a left turn, for example, the left wing tip moves more slowly than the right wing tip. To maintain the same lift on both wings, the left one must be tilted upward and the right one downward. The drag force remains the same, however. The slower wing gains more drag from the lifting-force interactions, but it loses some of the drag caused by air resistance.

The problem of stability and turning represented another challenge. Flying at only 10 to 18 kph (6 to 11 mph), we were pioneers seeking new knowledge. We could not use the techniques that had been developed for conventional aircraft. After a lot of brainstorming, computer analysis, and tests with a model pushed through water, we decided on a modified approach. This was to make the breadth of the wing smaller, especially at the tip. This would help increase stability and controllability, and, when we increased the speed, also lessen the effects of turbulence. The higher speed that came with a smaller wing area meant that we had to cover the pilot area with a streamlined housing to keep down parasite drag.

We soon rebuilt the *Condor* to the new configuration at Shafter. With the covered fuselage and the wing covered top and bottom, it looked much sleeker than its Mojave ancestor. On March 15, 1977, it was ready for testing. But we had to wait patiently until long after dark for the wind to diminish so the plane could be moved out of the

A Walkalong Glider

Tyler MacCready uses braced cardboard to create an updraft to keep his glider aloft.

While we were building the *Gossamer Condor*, we began to experiment with something we called a "walkalong" glider. The glider stays aloft in an updraft that you make as you walk or run along beneath it. We developed several versions and everyone had fun flying them.

A year earlier we had experimented in our living room with small paper airplanes designed like hang gliders. We discovered that when we ran under them their glide flattened out, keeping them aloft longer. Clearly, some of the air we pushed aside as we ran was flowing up over our heads and creating an updraft.

Then we made larger models with balsa wood and tissue paper that we flew outdoors. We found they could fly indefinitely and would even climb if a person ran under them holding a large shield, such as a garbage-can lid, so as to force air upward.

You can build and "pilot" one of these gliders with experiment, practice, and persistence. You will need a spacious outdoor area and a nearly windless day. As your piloting skill increases, you will be able to control the glider by moving the shield slightly. If the upcurrent is stronger under the left wing, for example, the plane rolls toward the right. If it is stronger on the tail than on the wing, the craft points down and flies faster.

The gliders we built at Shafter Airport were made from the type of plastic foam sheet used in egg cartons and containers used for carry-out meals at fast-food restaurants. You need sheets that are almost flat and about 30 centimeters (12 inches) long. Most egg cartons are not quite large enough and you can use only the tops, but they will do. Very thin 0.15-centimeter (1/16-inch) balsa is even better. It is just as light as a foam sheet and stronger. It can be found in most hobby shops.

We spent a lot of time creating and testing walkalong designs. We tried adjusting the wings to find a design that would be the easiest to fly and control. Unfortunately, the ones that fly slowest are the most skitterish when used outside in the wind.

Our most dependable design is shown here. After you make it and spend some time experimenting with it, you should be able to fly and control it. You may even be able to fly it without a shield, using just your head and hands to create the updraft. By modifying the design slightly you can experiment with special flying effects, like loops. [Parker MacCready and Tyler MacCready.]

How to Build the Glider

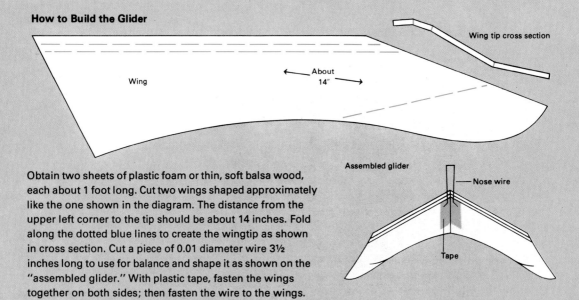

Wing tip cross section

Wing

← About 14″ →

Assembled glider

Nose wire

Tape

Obtain two sheets of plastic foam or thin, soft balsa wood, each about 1 foot long. Cut two wings shaped approximately like the one shown in the diagram. The distance from the upper left corner to the tip should be about 14 inches. Fold along the dotted blue lines to create the wingtip as shown in cross section. Cut a piece of 0.01 diameter wire 3½ inches long to use for balance and shape it as shown on the "assembled glider." With plastic tape, fasten the wings together on both sides; then fasten the wire to the wings.

hangar. Cars lined up with their headlights turned on and Tyler, my 14-year-old son whose feather weight and years of flying hang gliders had made him our senior test pilot, got in. We closed the Velcro fastening and held the wings level. I pushed and Tyler pedaled. In less than four seconds, he was aloft. It had taken noticeably less push than any other launch, and I was exulting silently as Tyler pedaled on. Not until he had been in the air 20 seconds did he come down on the tiny toy fire-engine wheels to tell us, "It's easy now!"

For me, that was the most thrilling of the hundreds of test flights we made before and after. I was certain that this particular plane, after all the bugs were eliminated, could win the Kremer Prize.

The next day, we tested the canard rocking method of initiating turns. It showed promise. The rocking control was initially done by pulling on wires; later we used control tabs, or ailerons, near the tips of the canard to let the moving air do the rocking, requiring less pilot muscle. When the lifting canard is rocked left, for example, the lift also pulls the nose of the *Condor* left. This control technique may be new to aircraft, but birds have been employing the rocking stabilizer method for about 100 million years.

B y late March, a flight lasting 5 minutes 10 seconds was achieved by cyclist Greg Miller, a California junior sprints champion whom we had recruited through a friend involved with bicycle racing. This was the longest that anyone had ever stayed up using leg power. We were jubilant. Success was near. We were wrong again. It took another five months to develop the control and efficiency we needed.

Controllability was the remaining problem to solve. The rocking canard served well to initiate turns but was inadequate as the turn continued. In a turn, the inner wing of this large-span vehicle goes so much slower than the outer wing that the lift becomes unbalanced unless the vehicle slips sideways. The cure was to introduce wing warping—a simple task because this merely required manipulating the wires connecting the fuselage to the wing tips. Surprisingly perhaps, the direction of twist is just the opposite of that used to roll and turn regular airplanes. Again, our solution was the one that birds had found and applied eons ago.

The final version of the *Gossamer Condor* has a wingspan of 29 meters (96 feet). From bottom to top, the *Condor* measures 6 meters (19 feet), and from stabilizer to propeller, 9 meters (30 feet). All tubing is aluminum. The stabilizer's leading edge is styrofoam shaped in an oven, while the leading edge of the wing is corrugated cardboard bent to shape. The propeller, built of balsa sections and tubing and covered with the Monocote material used in model-airplane wings, turns 110 times for every 90 turns on the bicycle pedals. A tiny propeller-driven air-speed indicator, vital for the pilot, is mounted where he can see it. The wing loading is about 1 kilogram per square meter (4 ounces per square foot), compared with four times that much attained by other man-powered craft that competed for the prize.

The *Condor* has taken its place among other historic aircraft in the National Air and Space Museum in Washington, D.C.

Although anyone could fly the *Condor* for a few seconds, only a good cyclist could stay up for several minutes. So we turned engine duties over to cyclist Greg Miller. Unfortunately, after long flights at Mojave and Shafter, he had to leave to compete in bicycle races in Belgium.

By making several phone calls to bicycling enthusiasts, I found Bryan Allen, a cyclist, distance runner, and hang-glider pilot who lived in nearby Bakersfield and was available to help full time on the project. He and Tyler shared the test-flying duties, and he also worked out on the ergometer, or stationary bicycle, which we modified so that he could recline on it while pedaling as he had to in the cockpit. Allen had excellent stamina and kept getting stronger as he trained until his output was on a par with champion cyclists.

A 70-kilogram (150-pound), physically fit cyclist can produce a lot of power. He can maintain an output of about 0.3 h.p. almost indefinitely. At the start of a race he also has in reserve an additional energy of 0.4 h.p.-minutes that he can draw on. Thus he can add 0.4 h.p. for one minute, or half that rate for two minutes. For example, he can add 0.1 h.p. from the reserve to the normal 0.3 h.p. for four minutes, producing 0.4 h.p. Bryan Allen was in excellent condition. The question now was whether he could exert enough added power per pound to fly the *Condor* over the Kremer course.

At dawn on Aug. 23, 1977, Allen, the *Gossamer Condor*, and the support ground crew were all ready. The official accredited by the Royal Aeronautical Society Prize Committee was called out. When the wind decreased to 3 kph (2 mph) Allen started pedaling, the little wheels rolled, and he and our huge bird floated up, up, cleared the 3-meter T bar and headed down the course, propeller turning rhythmically to produce exactly 16 kph (10 mph). Smoothly, Allen rolled the canard right and twisted the wings; the transparent, airy structure went into its first turn. Several of us rode bicycles alongside the *Condor*, shouting encouragement that rang with increasing conviction. He finally powered the *Condor* over the height marker at the end of the course with 1 meter to spare. Instinctively he shouted, "We did it!" It was the perfect summary of a team effort.

After our triumph on August 23, we spent a lot of time letting people fly our bird. My 10-year-old son Marshall was the youngest pilot. At 29 kilograms (65 pounds), he needed only about 0.17 h.p. to stay up. Sixty-year-old Maude Oldershaw, whose husband Verne was the primary structural designer-builder of the Shafter version, became the first of several women to fly the *Condor*. Being a cyclist and pilot, she flew it with ease. A total of 25 people have flown the aircraft.

Because of the *Condor*'s slow speed, it is easy to control. The potential pilot does not need to be an athlete or know anything about flying; two minutes of ground instruction followed by 10 seconds of flight with assistants pushing and directing is sufficient preparation. Then the pilot stays aloft—unless in the excitement he, or she, forgets to pedal. No one has ever been hurt in a crash. The *Condor* comes down so slowly from its low height that it is like a dream, although the bit-by-bit crumpling of the wing is a nightmare for the designer to watch.

Most of the members of the *Condor* team went to England with me for the award ceremony in London on Nov. 30, 1977. Prince Charles presented a trophy designed for the occasion, and Kremer handed us the prize check. We met people from many other countries around the world who had been working on human-powered flight.

We dismantled the *Gossamer Condor* early in January 1978 and transported it to Washington, D.C., where it was reassembled and hung in the Smithsonian Institution's National Air and Space Museum. Close by are the Wright brothers' airplane, Charles A. Lindbergh's *Spirit of St. Louis*, the X-15 that flew 400 times faster than the *Condor*, and other historic aircraft. Each of these planes had a great impact on the world of transportation. Our *Condor* is different. It, too, represents an aviation milestone, but neither it nor its descendants has any practical use. Perhaps that is one of its virtues.

On March 3, there was a dedication ceremony at the museum. Now the *Condor* belongs to the museum and the people of the United States. Each of you has a part of it, just as much as we have.

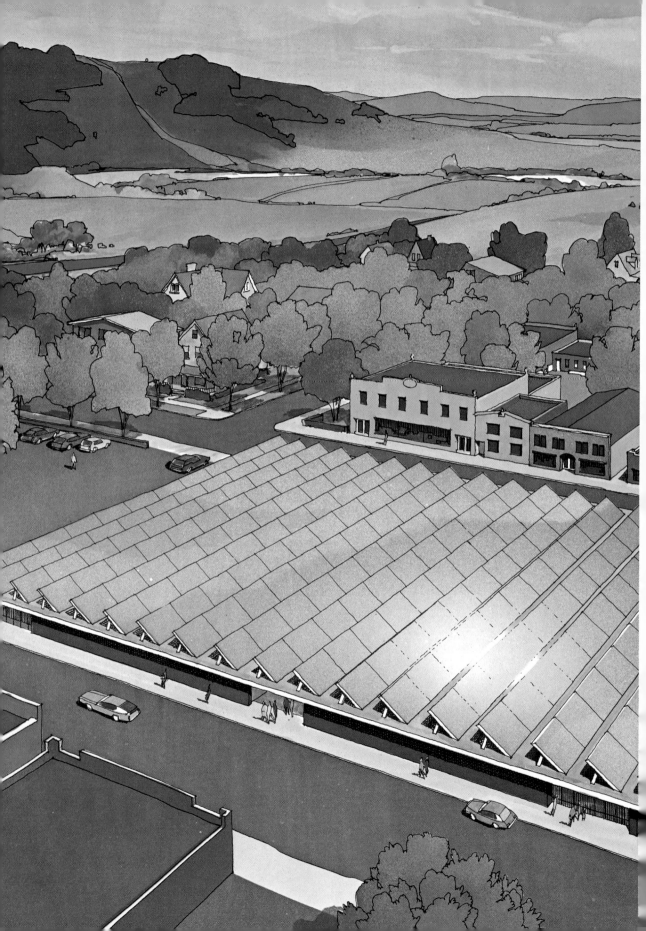

Electricity From the Sun

By Joseph J. Loferski

**If attempts to lower their costs
are successful, solar cells may
become a major source of energy**

Even a casual observer could sense the excitement in the air as the Thirteenth Photovoltaic Specialists Conference opened in Washington, D.C., in June 1978. Some 700 scientists and engineers from all parts of the world were there to discuss the possibilities of using sunlight to produce electrical power. There was a feeling that we were witnessing the early stages of a technological revolution as profound as the one triggered by the first nuclear chain reaction in 1942.

Those of us in the field of photovoltaics share a passionate interest in the conversion of sunlight into electricity through the use of photovoltaic, or solar, cells. Such cells should not be confused with solar collectors, the devices used to heat buildings and produce steam to generate electricity. Solar collectors convert sunlight into heat; solar cells convert sunlight directly into electricity.

The first experiments done with solar cells began in 1877, when physicists William G. Adams and Charles Day published a paper in England describing a selenium cell that they had developed. They also discussed the physical laws governing the movement of electrons under the impact of light.

But the solar cells that followed these early experiments were quite inefficient. They converted less than 1 per cent of the power in the sunlight they received into electricity.

It was not until 1954 that substantially more efficient solar cells were produced. Physicists Daryl M. Chapin, Calvin S. Fuller, and Gerald L. Pearson of Bell Telephone Laboratories in Murray Hill, N.J., announced in that year that they had raised the efficiency of solar cells to more than 10 per cent by making them from specially prepared silicon.

The new silicon cells appeared on the scene just in time to play a central role in the space age. Solar cells became the primary power source for satellites, the first of which was launched in the late 1950s. Today they provide the on-board electrical power for hundreds of satellites from several countries.

Long life and dependability are the primary considerations for satellite power; cost is less important. But cost becomes a major consideration when we turn to power needs on earth. Solar cells have been practical only in remote locations such as mountain peaks, deserts, and bodies of water where they provide power for meteorological observation stations, communications equipment, signal lights on oil rigs, and harbor buoys. In these places, the cost of alternative sources of electrical power is higher than the current cost of solar-cell systems.

For general power needs, silicon cells have not been able to compete economically with the fossil fuels—coal, gas, and oil. Furthermore, when practical solar cells came on the scene in the 1950s the nuclear age was just beginning. We expected to build an unlimited number of nuclear reactors that would provide all the cheap electrical energy that we would ever need.

In 1978, however, the hazards associated with nuclear reactors and the rising costs of energy due to dwindling domestic supplies of fossil fuels are changing this picture. As a result, energy policymakers are re-examining the potential for solar energy.

Solar cells are semiconductor devices similar to the diodes and transistors used in radios, television sets, and electronic computers to amplify and otherwise manipulate electrical signals passing through them. Unlike these devices, solar cells make use of sunlight for the generation of electricity.

As semiconductors, solar cells belong to a class of materials that lie between conductors such as copper, in which an electrical current flows easily, and insulators such as glass, in which it cannot flow at all. Conductors carry current by means of their many free electrons. Semiconductors have fewer current carriers, but these can be controlled to perform a variety of electronic operations.

All semiconductors can be used in solar cells that transform the sun's energy into electricity to some degree. However, certain semiconductors are particularly suitable for solar cells. They have "energy gaps"—the minimum amount of energy needed to ionize the atoms in

The author:
Joseph J. Loferski, professor of engineering at Brown University, was chairman of the 1978 Photovoltaic Specialists' Conference, held June 1 in Washington, D.C.

Inside a Solar Cell

Two semiconductor materials are needed to make a solar cell, one with excess electrons (n-type) and another with a deficiency (p-type). A p-n junction with a strong electrical field forms where the materials meet. When sunlight strikes the cell, electrons and holes (missing electrons) move through the cell forming an electrical charge. A current flows when conducting wires are attached to external contacts on the n- and p-type layers.

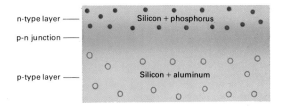

n-type layer — Silicon + phosphorus
p-n junction —

p-type layer — Silicon + aluminum

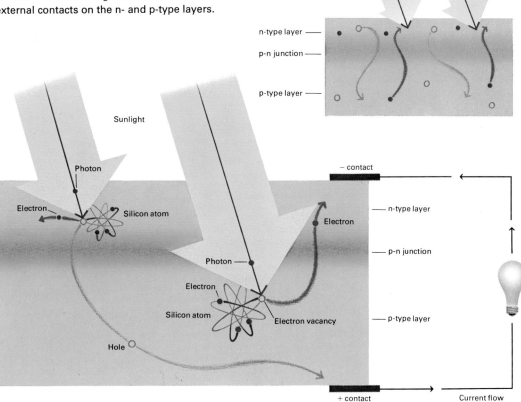

Sunlight

n-type layer —
p-n junction —
p-type layer —

Sunlight

Photon

Electron
Silicon atom

Photon —

Electron

Electron

Silicon atom

Electron vacancy

Hole

− contact

— n-type layer

— p-n junction

— p-type layer

+ contact

Current flow

the semiconductor material and set free electrons that can carry currents. This energy is between 1 and 2 electron volts. Sunlight consists of packets of energy called "photons" having a wide range of energies from about 0.3 to 3.5 electron volts. Photons with an energy greater than the energy gap of the semiconductor can produce free current carriers in the semiconductor. This is the first step in the transformation of light into electricity.

Control of the current carriers in a solar cell requires an electric field. One way to provide this field is to join two kinds of semiconductor material, p-type and n-type, in a structure that creates a p-n junction. To understand how this works, let us look at the most popular semiconductor material—silicon.

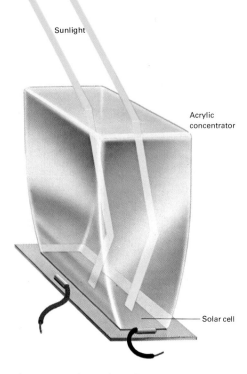

Sunlight

Acrylic concentrator

Solar cell

A concentrating solar collector made of acrylic does not require sun-tracking equipment. The acrylic is shaped so that once the sun's rays enter it from any angle they cannot escape, and can only be reflected onto the solar cell.

A silicon solar cell with a textured surface can collect more sunlight than a flat type cell. Re-reflections between nonhorizontal surfaces nearly double the light that is absorbed. (Photo magnification 2,000 times.)

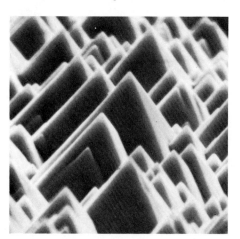

The silicon used in semiconductor devices must be made extremely pure, so that it contains less than 1 "foreign" atom for every 10 million silicon atoms. When ionizing light is absorbed in purified silicon, it breaks the chemical bonds, producing free electrons and leaving "holes" in the bonds from which the free electrons were ejected. Like the electrons, the holes "move" through the semiconductor crystal; their motion actually consists of a progression of electrons moving into spaces vacated by the movement of their neighbors. In effect, the hole moves in a direction opposite to that of the electron, acting as a positively charged carrier.

Minute amounts of certain other elements profoundly affect silicon's electrical properties. For example, if we "dope" the silicon—add 1 atom of phosphorus for every 1 million silicon atoms—electrons become the dominant current carriers. Silicon atoms chemically bond with each other by sharing four electrons. A phosphorus atom has five electrons, so when it bonds to a silicon atom there is a fifth electron free to move through the semiconductor. The material is called n-type because the dominant carriers are negatively charged.

If the purified silicon contains 1 aluminum atom instead of phosphorus for every 1 million silicon atoms, holes become the dominant current carriers. An aluminum atom has only three electrons to share when bonding to a silicon atom. The missing electron that results from this bond leaves a hole. Thus, the material becomes p-type because its dominant carriers are positively charged.

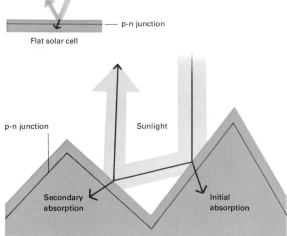

p-n junction

Flat solar cell

p-n junction

Sunlight

Secondary absorption

Initial absorption

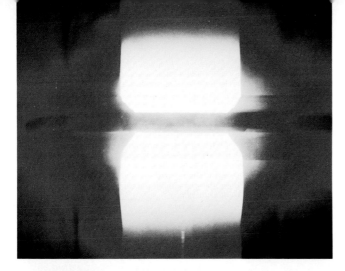

High-temperature treatment of silicon rods in a vacuum, *above left,* removes impurities. Wafers sliced from the rods, *above,* are tested individually to check the electrical contacts, *left.*

Other semiconductor materials can be made n- or p-type by treating them with properly selected impurities. Some semiconductors, however, are always n-type; others are always p-type.

Solar cells must incorporate both n- and p-types of material. In general, they are constructed like a two-layer sandwich, in which the "filling" is the p-n junction. A strong electric field is set up between the electron-rich n-type region and the hole-rich p-type region. It keeps the free electrons on the n-type side of the junction and the holes on the p-type side.

When sunlight is absorbed in the cell, it produces both holes and electrons in both the n-type and p-type materials. The electrons are minority carriers in the p-type material and the holes are minority carriers in the n-type material. The field allows the minority electrons produced by the light in the p-type material to flow into the n-type material and the minority holes from the n-type material to flow into the p-type material. This flow is an electrical current.

A p-n junction can be formed in a thin slice, or wafer, of n-type silicon, for example, by coating its surface with aluminum or an aluminum compound and heating it to about 600° to 1000° C (1112° to 1832° F.). The heat causes the aluminum to diffuse into the silicon near the surface, and this forms a p-type layer. A p-n junction forms at the boundary between the p-type diffused skin and the n-type center of the silicon.

The electric field needed to control the current carriers can also be produced by joining one p-type semiconductor to a different n-type semiconductor. The p-n junction formed between them is called a heterojunction. Or it can be produced by covering a semiconductor with a metal layer thin enough to be transparent, thus forming a metal-semiconductor junction.

To convert solar energy efficiently, not only must a solar cell contain a working p-n junction or metal-semiconductor junction, but the current carriers must also remain free long enough to travel from the place where they are generated to the junction, successfully running a gauntlet of defects in the material that can capture them. These defects, called recombination centers, are found both inside the purified silicon and on its surfaces. The number of such recombination centers can be substantially minimized by the careful control of the purification and doping processes.

Once the p-n junction is created, electrical contacts must be added to the p-type and n-type layers of the solar cell. When the cell is exposed to sunlight, the contact to the p-type material acquires a positive charge and the contact to the n-type material acquires a negative charge. Antireflective coatings are applied to the side of the cell that faces the sun to maximize the amount of sunlight that enters the cell.

Each silicon solar cell develops only about 0.5 volt when exposed to sunlight, so many cells must be combined to produce the voltages needed to operate most electrical equipment. Large numbers of such cells are arranged in arrays of various sizes. The cells are connected in series and parallel combinations to develop the desired solar-cell currents and voltages.

Silicon is one of the most abundant elements on earth. It is obtained from sand, which is silicon dioxide. The amounts of impurities such as phosphorus and aluminum that must be added to silicon to make solar cells is so small that it hardly affects production costs. Therefore, the cost of the raw materials is negligible. But extracting silicon from sand and purifying it costs a great deal, and each step in the process of converting silicon into an operating solar cell adds to this cost. In the present manufacturing procedure, one of the largest costs comes from producing single crystal ingots, or bars, from pure silicon. Silicon powder that is 99.99999 per cent pure costs about $5 per kilogram ($3 per pound), but a single crystal produced from this silicon costs about $200 per kilogram ($90 per pound).

The single crystal ingot is then sliced into wafers. The dust produced during slicing weighs almost as much as the wafers. Researchers

at Texas Instruments, Incorporated, in Dallas, hope they can reduce this waste by using laser beams to slice the ingot. Researchers at Mobil-Tyco Laboratories in Waltham, Mass., and at the Westinghouse Laboratories in Pittsburgh hope to reduce the overall costs even further by producing continuous ribbons of the thickness needed for solar cells directly from liquid silicon.

Leading semiconductor manufacturers, such as Motorola, Incorporated, of Chicago; RCA Laboratories of Princeton, N.J.; and Texas Instruments are exploring ways to automate the various manufacturing steps so that the production costs can be substantially reduced.

When silicon cells are connected in a panel to develop the necessary voltages, they cost about $10 per peak watt—that is, the number of cells needed to produce 1 watt of electricity when exposed to full sunlight on a clear day costs $10. This cost is much too high to give us electricity at prices comparable to those paid by the consumer today.

Analyses of electric power generation systems built from solar cells indicate that if such systems are to produce electricity at a cost of about 5¢ to 6¢ per kilowatt hour, roughly the price of electricity in New England today, solar cells with 10 per cent efficiency must be available at between 30¢ and 50¢ per peak watt. The U.S. Department of Energy has

Solar cells bring power to space with a Land-Sat satellite, *top left;* to the seas for gas-distribution platforms, *top right;* or to desolate arctic outposts for airport marker beacons, *above.*

announced a goal of 50¢ per peak watt by 1986. While many photo-voltaic specialists believe that this goal is possible, they do not believe that it can be reached with single crystal silicon cells. Prices from $1 to $2 per peak watt, however, may be achievable for silicon cells. There are substantial markets for cells at this price in the United States and in other countries.

What are the prospects of bringing the cost down? There are now at least 15 types of solar cells with conversion efficiencies of more than 5 per cent. Eight of these are more than 10 per cent efficient, and three have efficiencies over 15 per cent. Silicon – the only type available commercially – has an efficiency of 10 to 12 per cent.

Some of the cells made from semiconductor materials must be relatively thick in order to absorb all the photons that they can utilize. Other materials that are more strongly absorbing make better solar cells because they can be made thinner, thus requiring less of the highly purified material.

A conventional silicon wafer is about 0.5 millimeter (0.02 inch) thick, while a thin film cadmium sulfide cell is only one-tenth as thick, about 0.05 millimeter (0.002 inch). Most experts now believe that only such thin film cells can be developed for less than $1 per peak watt. However, no one has yet made thin film cells that are more than about 8 per cent efficient. Furthermore, we do not know whether thin film cells will last as long as silicon crystal cells, which have functioned dependably for decades.

The processes involved in fabricating thin film cells are inexpensive and they require substantially less material than do silicon wafers and other thicker types of solar cells. For example, thin film cadmium sulfide cells are made by evaporating the materials in an evacuated chamber or by spraying solutions of certain chemicals onto hot glass plates where they react to produce cadmium sulfide. Vacuum-produced cells are being made by Solar Energy Systems, Incorporated, of Newark, Del., in units of about 650 square centimeters (100 square inches), while sprayed cells are being made by Photon, Incorporated, of El Paso, Tex., in panels with about four times that area.

The overall cost of an installed solar-cell system can be reduced if mirrors or lenses are used to concentrate sunlight on the cell panels. Concentrators are much less expensive to make because lenses and

A silicon solar cell is sensitive to wavelengths in the visual spectrum only. But more of the sun's energy can be utilized when two cells made of other materials, one sensitive to the visual spectrum and the other to infrared waves, are connected in tandem.

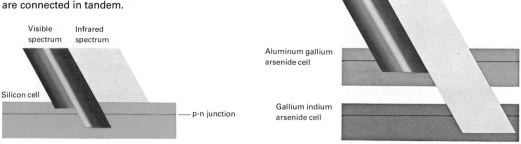

Visible spectrum Infrared spectrum

Silicon cell

p-n junction

Aluminum gallium arsenide cell

Gallium indium arsenide cell

mirrors cost much less than additional solar cells. However, concentrator systems are less useful in certain geographic areas since they can only use light rays that come directly from the sun. They cannot concentrate the diffused sunlight of cloudy days. And even on clear days, concentrators must have some sort of tracking mechanism to keep them facing the sun. A reliable mechanism of this kind adds to their cost and complexity and may make the concentrators less reliable. High-performance solar concentrators that increase the energy reaching solar cells up to 300 times have been designed and built by engineers at the International Business Machines Laboratory in Fishkill, N.Y.; the RCA Laboratories; Sandia Laboratories in Albuquerque, N. Mex.; and Honeywell, Incorporated, in Minneapolis, Minn.

The Argonne National Laboratory near Chicago has developed a parabolic collector made of acrylic that concentrates sunlight to 10 times its direct energy. The design has the unusual feature of operating without sun-tracking equipment.

Concentrators can best be used where the sun shines most of the year. For example, the daytime sky in Tucson, Ariz., is cloudless about 98 per cent of the time. A tracking concentrator delivers perhaps 13 per cent more energy annually to solar cells than they would get in a stationary flat-plate system. On the other hand, a tracking system would add little or nothing to the annual amount of solar energy reaching the cells in Cleveland or surrounding areas, where the sky is overcast much of the time.

Solar-cell efficiencies could be increased if cells made from semiconductors with different energy gaps, and therefore sensitive to different colors in the sunlight, are arranged in tandem structures. The cells would be laid on top of each other in order of descending values of energy gap, with the sunlight first striking that cell in the group that has the highest energy gap. For example, a combination of two cells—one made from silicon with an energy gap of 1.1 electron volts and the other made from a semiconductor with an energy gap of about 1.8 electron volts—has a theoretical efficiency of about 33 per cent. Researchers at a number of laboratories, including ours at Brown University in Providence, R.I., and the engineering laboratory at North Carolina State University in Raleigh, are testing many types of semiconductor materials to develop these tandem-cell systems.

Calculations show that silicon solar cells with 10 to 12 per cent efficiency could provide all the electrical power consumed in the United States if they covered an area of about 12 thousand square kilometers. Critics of solar energy suggest that such a system would remove too much land from productivity. However, this is less than 1 per cent of the total land surface in the continental United States. It is much smaller than the area covered by all the paved streets and highways, and comparable to the area covered by buildings.

Much research is also going into the nature and size of proposed solar-cell systems to produce electrical power. These units range from

Energy-producing solar
panels provide the power
for irrigation pumps in
a Nebraska field, *above.*
They will provide all
the energy needed for
the Mississippi County
Community College in
Blytheville, Ark., *right,*
to be completed
in the early 1980s.

relatively small power-generating systems that can be installed on
building rooftops to central-power stations that deliver large quantities of electricity to utility-company power grids. There is even a proposal to gather solar energy in a giant space satellite and use a microwave beam to deliver it to earth. The proposal was made in 1970 by
physicist Peter Glaser of the Arthur D. Little Company in Cambridge,
Mass. A satellite could deliver electrical power continuously because it
would be in synchronous orbit, exposed to the sun continuously. The
construction of such a system would require a national commitment
on the scale of that made in 1960 to send Americans to the moon. It
would take about 20 years to design and build the system and it would
cost several billion dollars.

The economics of small and intermediate systems has not been as clearly determined as it has been for large collector systems, in part because there are so many possible variants. The U.S. Office of Technology Assessment concluded in a report published in June 1977 that there is "no clear indication that large solar electric plants are more efficient or produce less costly energy than small, on-site facilities."

With the exception of tall multistory buildings, the average rooftop has space for enough solar cells to fill all the building's power needs. My Brown University colleagues and I have estimated that 20 per cent of the rooftop space in Rhode Island could generate enough electricity to supply all the state's needs. The problem that some see in such individual rooftop installations lies in their maintenance. The homeowner might not want to accept the responsibility for his apparatus. But utility companies could install and maintain them.

In fact, smaller systems have a number of advantages over larger ones. They can be built more rapidly and can be more effectively tailored to individual load requirements. Placing such systems on rooftops reduces the need for land and puts them close to the places where the energy will be used. Some buildings in densely populated urban areas would not be suitable because they are shaded much of the time, but proper architectural designing could greatly minimize this problem in new buildings.

One of the primary advantages of solar energy, whether in large or small systems, is that such systems are inherently modular—that is, they are formed of units or pieces. These can be increased or interchanged to meet changing needs. The cost of solar power does not depend on the size of the system as much as does power produced from coal, oil, or nuclear plants. However, storing solar-generated electricity for use when there is no sunlight poses a problem. Nickel-cadmium batteries or lead-acid storage batteries similar to automobile batteries are now used. But they are bulky and expensive. If solar power eventually becomes the major source of energy, utilities may choose to locate whatever storage system is then available at many small neighborhood centers in order to minimize transmission losses that occur when electricity is sent through wires for great distances.

Solar-cell technology is still in its infancy but it is growing at an explosive rate. The manufacturing costs should follow the lead of other semiconductor products and drop as the quantity of units increases. There is good reason for such optimism because solar-cell costs have dropped radically since 1970. They now cost 30 times less, and another drop of that size would make them competitive with existing energy sources. It is not unreasonable to expect that this will happen by 1990.

At the same time, the prices of all electrical power-generating systems now in use have no way to go but up. The question is not if solar energy will ever become competitive with alternative methods, but rather when this will occur.

Life in the Twilight Zone

By J. Lee Kavanau

Scientists found some surprises in the behavior of animals when they observed them under different levels of light

It is dusk in a small canyon on the outskirts of Los Angeles. A hawk glides in a descending circle and lands in her tree nest for the night. Directly below, a deer mouse pokes his head out of his burrow, ready to embark on his nightly activities.

Meanwhile, in my laboratory at the University of California, Los Angeles (UCLA), a cactus mouse scurries from one side to the other of his specially designed enclosure. Among other things, the mouse presses switches that vary the intensity of a dim overhead light. The changes he makes are far from random; they reveal consistent patterns of light preference.

Scientists once assumed that simply by observing only the first scene, the "natural" one, they could learn the roles that light plays in regulating an animal's activity. Such field observations showed that some animals repeated certain behavior at almost exactly the same time each day, as if they had within themselves an accurate 24-hour regulating mechanism. Scientists suspected that dusk and dawn simply provided time-setting signals for such "biological clocks."

This view had some support from laboratory studies. Captive mice, for example, could not be made to conform to light-dark cycles of more than about 27 hours or less than about 21 hours. Faced with longer or shorter ones, the mice reverted to activity cycles about 24 hours long, even though doing so required normally nocturnal, or night-active, animals to move about in bright light. The biological clock, rather than light changes, seemed to give the mice their "stop and go" signals. But I wondered if this was always true.

I became involved with these matters in an unusual way. In 1960, I was a chemical embryologist studying sea urchin development in the UCLA Biology Department, but I had been observing white-footed mice as a hobby on and off for 10 years. While trying to find a way to squeeze more time for my own activities out of a 24-hour day, I decided to perform some simple experiments with my mice to see how little sleep they could get along with and still remain in good health. I tried to keep them awake for increasingly long periods by gentle means that would do no bodily harm.

To my surprise, the mice proved to be amazingly adept at countering my tactics. Each time I added a new twist to increase the effectiveness of my method for keeping them awake, they devised ingenious new ways to get around the difficulty. For example, in one experiment, I placed the mice in a running wheel that was connected to a motor. The wheel was enclosed by glass side panes. When I turned the motor on, the wheel would turn whether the mice wanted it to or not. I thought that this would keep them awake, since they would have to be active as long as the wheel was being rotated. But the clever creatures soon learned how they could rest. By draping their bodies over the axle of the wheel and pressing their sides against the side panes, they could rest while the wheel turned. The resourcefulness of the mice in finding ways to rest despite my interference led me to challenge them on other fronts. Soon this became my major research interest.

Beginning in 1961, my studies focused on the normal behavior and learning of white-footed mice, especially how they scheduled their activities during the night. I chose the deer mouse because it is the most widespread and adaptable of the white-footed species. I wanted to find out when, how much, how frequently, and for how long the animals ate, drank, excreted, hoarded, stayed in their nest, and ran in an exercise wheel. The test mice lived in individual experimental enclosures that I designed to measure these activities. Each enclosure provided the test animals with approximately 1/2 cubic foot (.014 cubic meter) of space in which they could move about as they wished. The main part consisted of a running wheel. Off to the side, there was a nest compartment blocked by shutters that pivoted on miniature ball bearings. In addition, there was a compartment where the animals could get food and water whenever they wanted it by pressing

The author:
J. Lee Kavanau is a professor of biology at the University of California, Los Angeles. He has also been a mathematical and experimental physicist.

Deer mice, *left,* were the first animals used in the twilight studies.

Recording and computing equipment in the author's laboratory, *above,* receives data from instrumented enclosures, *above right,* used to test small animals under varying light conditions. A fossa, a primitive animal from Madagascar, *right,* runs in a wheel at the San Diego Zoo as a result of subsequent studies of carnivores.

Active during daylight, a Cooper's hawk, *above,* has caught a sunning snake. Twilight shadows shelter a young pack rat, *above right,* seeking insects. A bush baby, *right,* peers through the black of night for sleeping small birds. The versatile fox, *opposite page,* depends on hunger more than on light conditions to spur his hunting activity.

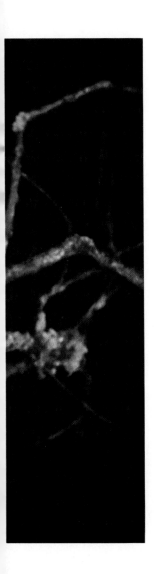

switches. Sensing and recording devices on the running wheel, the nest shutters, and the switches were linked to computers, and provided automatic 24-hour monitoring of all the animals' activities.

I tried to imitate natural lighting in these early studies. Because the sun rises and sets gradually, I used gradually changing light during twilight. Furthermore, I used dim light during the night. Earlier researchers usually just turned the lights on during the day and off at night. To my surprise, I found that the mice ran much faster in the wheel in the changing twilight than in the dim unchanging night light. This twilight behavior led me to repeat some experiments that others had done with on-off light cycles. Contrary to earlier beliefs, I found in 1961 that mice could be synchronized to much shorter periods than 24 hours. They could adapt to a 16-hour "day" if I simply employed artificial twilight and dim night light rather than turning the lights on and off abruptly as previous researchers had done. These experiments left little doubt that appropriate light changes could override signals from the biological clock.

In 1966, my students and I set out to determine if the brightness of the light and its gradually changing intensity also had an effect on the running speed of other animals. We exposed both nocturnal and diurnal, or day-active, rodents to different light levels. The first diurnal rodent subjects were eastern chipmunks. We found that their running speed generally depended solely on light level – the animals ran faster in brighter light and slower in dimmer light. But would these rodents

behave the same way in natural light? To find out, in 1967 we began to study mice and squirrels that we kept in exposed enclosures on the roof of the UCLA Life Sciences Building. We found a similar relationship between light level and running speed, but the findings were not consistent. One reason was that variable outdoor factors such as wind, cloud cover, temperature, noises, and birds flying by distracted the test animals and affected the results.

This relationship of activity to light is significant—actually a matter of life and death. In the wild, it affects the animal's behavior in obtaining food. For example, small diurnal rodents eat berries, nuts, leaves, fruit, seeds, and insects. Since all of these foods except the insects are just as available in the bright light of noon, why do the rodents favor twilight to search for them? The reason is that small animals themselves are food for larger animals. By confining their foraging to a time of day when the light is still bright enough for them to see by but not so bright that they themselves can be seen readily, the rodents try to gather as much food as they possibly can with minimal risk of running into their predators, the carnivores.

These carnivores became candidates for study, too. Once we knew how light changes influenced the prey, we began to wonder how it affected the predators. In 1968, we began to study the behavior of carnivores in enclosures that were equipped with running wheels. If you have ever watched a pet gerbil or hamster, you know that rodents like to run in exercise wheels. But would carnivores do so? Surprisingly, all those that we studied, including a coyote and a wolf, became active wheel runners. The main attraction of wheel running is doubtless the freedom to stride "straight ahead," unhindered, at almost any gait for long periods. None of the animals we tested had to run to find food—they were all fed daily zoo-diet rations—so you might say they jogged just to keep "on the move."

During our 10-year research project, we studied 48 carnivores belonging to 18 different species, ranging in size from weasels to wolves. We found that carnivores vary so much in their individual responses that it is difficult to predict test outcomes. Nevertheless, we obtained some consistent results. Our study showed that carnivores in general tend to be most active during twilight, probably because dawn and dusk are the best times to hunt. Temperature often is moderate then, and the activities of various animals overlap. Because insects are most active at twilight, rodents—the carnivores' prey—hunt then.

All individuals of a species in our study generally preferred to be active at the same time of day. Genets, relatives of the civet, and ringtails and kinkajous, animals in the same family as raccoons, were all nocturnal. Mongooses, and tayras and grisons, South American relatives of the weasel, were diurnal. Bobcats, foxes, and skunks were arrhythmic—they might be active at any time of night or day. However, members of the same species sometimes responded quite individually to altered daylengths, light levels, and feeding schedules.

Perhaps carnivores respond to light in many different ways because their eyes are designed so that they can see well over a wide range of light. For example, their eyes often are large and have large retinal images. Carnivores probably also have duplex vision, as humans do. That is, they may have larger numbers of both rod cells, for dim-light vision, and cone cells, for bright-light vision, in their retinas. Rodents, on the other hand, generally have vastly more rod cells than cone cells if they are nocturnal, or more cones than rods if they are diurnal. Therefore, although both predator and prey run fast when they are out hunting at twilight, the rodents' speed tends to be more constrained by the light level than that of the carnivores. In this respect, at least, the cards are stacked against rodents.

In all these studies, we had varied the light according to certain schedules, and our animals had to choose to be active or inactive according to the light level presented. But animals in the wild do not ordinarily face the alternative of either exposing themselves to prevailing light or stopping all activity. Instead, they usually can choose to be active in a place where the light level is altered, such as in the shelter of foliage or natural rock formations.

In an attempt to give our captive animals the same freedom to choose light levels, we set up a system whereby they could regulate the light intensity. The typical choice-making, or volitional, experiment provided 10 levels of illumination, from darkness to a level appropriately bright for the species under study. The animals learned to press switch levers with their paws. Some of the switches made the light brighter one step at a time, the others made it dimmer one step at a time. The animals usually discovered and pressed the switch levers by chance while exploring their surroundings, but they quickly associated the light changes with pressing the levers. Within a few days, most of them began to show patterns of light preference that remained the same on subsequent days.

In our first studies, we surveyed eight species of chiefly nocturnal rodents and a nocturnal mouse opossum. The rodents included California mice, Florida mice, canyon mice, two kinds of voles (meadow mice), flying squirrels, pack rats, and pocket gophers. Results of our first experiment showed that five of the species, including most of the mice, preferred various mid-dim ranges of light similar to those found in their habitats—probably because they could see best in such light. The other species surprised us by preferring darkness. Since one of the four species was a gopher, it might be tempting to conclude that it preferred darkness because it normally spends almost all its time underground. But it would not explain the behavior of the other three species—the mouse opossum and two meadow mice—because they do not spend all their time underground. It may be that the chances for survival for all four species improve when they carry out in darkness activities that do not require vision, simply because it is generally safer not to be seen.

Visual abilities of the rough-legged hawk, *above,* need bright light to be most effective. The large-eyed ringtail, *right,* can gather visual data in dimmest light. A red fox, *above right,* combines aspects of both to see by day or night.

In our volitional experiments, none of the activities the animals could engage in required vision. Food, water, and the nest were nearby, and running in the wheel in the dark presented no problems. All the animals are adapted for life in the dark, with an excellent sense of hearing and smell. They also have whiskers that help them to detect nearby objects and measure the width of holes, and they possess a good memory of surroundings. Thus it really is not surprising that they preferred darkness in the laboratory. Perhaps we should be surprised that all nine species did not prefer darkness.

In essence, this picture emerges: when small nocturnal animals that are adapted to be active in darkness can choose illumination in a situation in which vision is not needed, they may make one of three choices. They may choose the light range in which their vision is best, they may choose darkness because it would be safest under natural conditions, or they may choose both.

Even though our test animals usually had definite preferences for certain ranges of light, they often "visited" other levels briefly. Captive animals have a basic need for the stimulation of change, so these visits to other levels may be an attempt to fulfill this need.

Some of the animals in our volitional experiments usually left the light level unchanged when they decided to rest. Sometimes they curled up in the dark; sometimes they left the lights blazing. On the other hand, some showed light preferences as sharply defined during inactivity as during activity. And some were even more fussy, like a child who refuses to say good night unless a light is turned on or off.

In another volitional study, we examined the light preferences of some small- and medium-sized carnivores that prey on rodents—gray foxes, weasels, tayras, genets, and ringtails. Despite the fact that some of these animals are strictly nocturnal in the wild and superbly adapted for seeing in dim light, we found that all of them turned the light levels up quite frequently. Why? The reason may have to do with the fact that the cones are sensitive only to good illumination and produce aspects of vision that improve in brighter light, such as color vision and the ability to discern pattern and intensity. Taking our knowledge of the vision and habitats of carnivores into account, we suggest that nocturnal carnivores choose bright light simply because they see best in it. The animals may enjoy the change of seeing the colors and patterns that become apparent in bright light after periods of lower light levels. The situation may be like enjoying a perfume when it is sniffed from time to time, but not even noticing the fragrance when it is present all the time.

Having learned the light preferences of rodents and carnivores, we decided to study the behavior of primates in volitional tests, partly because primates are far more intelligent animals. In 1973, we began experiments with such small, nocturnal primates as galagos, or "bush babies," owl monkeys, and slow lorises. The animals showed marked differences in behavior. At first, they appeared to be learning much more slowly than rodents and carnivores or not learning at all. Although six primates changed the light levels hundreds to thousands of times per day, two of the six, a lesser bush baby and a slow loris, showed no preference, while the other four took much longer than expected to do so.

There was good reason for this behavior. Primates are alert, inquisitive animals. If they are kept in an enclosure with nothing to do they quickly become bored. The primates in our enclosures had something to do—they could press switches and change the light levels—so they did it almost all the time, just for its own sake. Their motivation to vary the only stimulus the environment offered overshadowed the tendency to express light preferences.

Versatile collar radio
transmitter can monitor
the activities of a
burrowing ground
squirrel, *above,* a
woods-residing fox,
top, a desert-dwelling
lizard, *above right,* or a
sea otter, *right,* in
its ocean habitat.

Those primates that eventually showed preferences chose dim night light and avoided both bright light and darkness. Nocturnal primates, of course, live in trees. They are not well adapted for activity in total darkness, and it would be very risky for them to move about in the dark. Therefore, they avoided darkness even in the laboratory, where there is no danger of falling.

After our exploratory survey of representatives from several mammal groups, I was eager to do volitional studies of a single species. I chose the cactus mouse. To reduce genetically based individual differences and to minimize possible differences in behavior depending upon experience, I decided to use only closely related animals born in captivity. The offspring of two pregnant cactus mice captured near Tecopa, Calif., in April 1973 were bred through several generations, and nine of the descendants were studied. At the time of testing they ranged from young adults of 4 months to aged veterans of 35 months.

My detailed study of the cactus mouse firmly established several aspects of its light-level preferences, some of them unsuspected. For example, we found that preferences can vary from week to week, that they may change with age, and that they may differ for closely related individuals at the same age. Furthermore, although the animals had, as expected, preferred dim light in the starlight range, they had an even greater preference for darkness.

Since 1976, I have been making a volitional study of a carnivore — the domestic cat. What I learned from cactus mice helped me in planning this project. I had studied individual mice for periods of up to several weeks, but only once or twice in each one's lifetime and after lapses of 5 to 29 months. Because the preferences of cactus mice

A curious grasshopper mouse examines the other half of the radio link to the lab.

changed with age and varied considerably, I decided to study the light preferences of cats throughout life. I have made it a point to study some of the cats repeatedly throughout their most active period, which was usually from the time they were weaned until they were about 10 months of age.

The two most impressive findings were totally unexpected. The cats showed sharply defined and consistent individual preferences, and they were extraordinarily particular about the condition of the light while they slept. As did the other carnivores we studied, most of the cats preferred bright light when they were active. But they liked bright light even more when they were resting, which may be related to the well-known feline fondness for lying in the sun. The big surprise was that, when they were active, some of the cats also liked darkness and divided their time between darkness and bright light. I believe this is one time that cat and mouse, those traditional enemies, agree. Why should this be? For one reason, both domestic cats and nocturnal rodents are well adapted for activity in the dark. In addition, despite the fact that cats are genuine predators, they themselves are preyed on by larger carnivores and large birds such as hawks. So some cats' preference for darkness probably also reflects an instinctive tendency to carry out in darkness activities that do not require vision simply because it is safer then.

These cats' preference for darkness during activity changed with age and also depended on the brightness of the brightest light available. The dimmer the brightest light, the more they preferred darkness. Some young cats tended to have a strong preference for darkness, a finding that will surprise no one who has tried to sleep in a dark room with a frisky kitten.

Since 1972, some of my students have been conducting a series of field studies with wild animals. They have discovered much new information about the ecology and behavior of mammals ranging from mice to sea otters. In the past, we often could make only educated guesses about the behavior of many secretive, nocturnal animals that are difficult to approach. Now, we are sometimes in a position, almost literally, of being able to spy continuously on their private lives.

Biotelemetry, a method of transmitting information, has made this possible. We trap an animal in one of several painless ways, and attach to it a small radio transmitter, usually on a collar. Then we release the animal at the trapping site so it can resume its activities. By monitoring the signal broadcast by the transmitter we can identify and follow the animal. With this information alone, we have obtained a tremendous amount of new field data, particularly about burrowing animals.

One of my students at UCLA, Michael Recht, has been using biotelemetry to learn about the behavior of small mammals and lizards in the Mojave Desert in California. One of his most striking findings concerns the Mojave ground squirrel. Previous researchers had assumed that when the squirrels are not seen they are not active. Recht learned that Mojave squirrels, by avoiding overheating, can be active throughout even the hottest days. From the close inspection of behavior that telemetry makes feasible, he also learned that Mojave squirrels' home range expands and contracts with the available food supply. Since the animals travel over a well-defined system of "highways" to get about in their home ranges, we can now map these routes and study in detail how the squirrels use the resources of their habitat. For example, we can learn where they find water, store food, and obtain their nest-building materials.

Another of my students, Thomas Loughlin, has used telemetry to study the activities of sea otters living off the California coast. He discovered that researchers were wrong about an activity as basic as feeding behavior. All previous observations indicated that sea otters feed only during the day, but Loughlin has proved that they do almost half their feeding at night.

The most spectacular findings have been obtained by a third UCLA researcher, Lorvel Shields, working with pack rats, California mice, and California meadow mice. Shields has perfected a transmitter-collar design by which movements and postures of the collared animals can be determined automatically. For example, changes in the spacing of pulses emitted by the transmitter indicate when the animal curls up and goes to sleep. The pulse spacing is a sensitive indicator of how snugly the transmitter is pressed against the animal's body, and this depends on the animal's position. By first observing each trapped rodent in an enclosure for a time before it is released, Shields can match the pulse-spacing modulations of the transmitted signal with the animal's posture and movements. When the animal is returned to its home range, its activities can be followed in great detail.

Using antennas in a number of locations and automatic detectors, Shields notes the location, posture, and movements of one animal continuously for several weeks. When the information received is correlated with local light level, temperature, weather, and seasonal changes in the type and availability of food, the animal's life becomes almost an open book. Shields has added greatly to our knowledge of the roles that various environmental factors play and how they influence activity patterns. Now the new knowledge he can gain about his rodents is limited primarily by his ability to deal with the vast amounts of data collected.

What began about 20 years ago as a simple question of how much sleep deer mice need led my students and me to branch out down many unexpected, exciting paths. Touching base with a variety of aspects of behavior and learning on the way, we soon found our attention focused almost exclusively on the roles light plays in the lives of animals. Several years of intensive laboratory studies of these roles inevitably raised questions that could only be answered in the field. Now our field studies compel us to branch out along still other unforeseen paths. Such is the process of scientific research.

Currents
In Chaos

By Edward A. Spiegel

Mathematicians and engineers alike search for an underlying order in turbulence, nature's most unruly process

We live in a universe composed almost entirely of fluids in motion. Blood flows through our veins; water rushes downstream to the oceans; wind chills our faces as it blows past. Often these liquids and gases flow smoothly. At other times—as when a great river pours into the sea—a complex swirling motion called turbulence results. You see turbulence in whitecaps—the frothy mixture of air and water that is whipped up on the sea on a windy day. You hear turbulence when you listen to the noise of a jet plane.

Scientists study turbulence because it affects our lives in many ways. Without turbulence, for example, cream would take about 30 minutes to become fully mixed with coffee or tea. However, with a little help from a spoon, turbulence does the mixing in seconds. This may not sound very important, but consider the same process on a large scale.

Whirling blade of an electric fan above fumes of alcohol, *above,* sets up an eddy. From his studies of water, Leonardo da Vinci drew the chaotic assembly of eddies that is turbulence, *right.*

The author:
Edward A. Spiegel is professor of astronomy at Columbia University.

Instead of a dollop of cream in coffee, think of industrial waste pouring into a river or smoke billowing into the air. Normally, turbulence disperses such pollutants quickly. Without such mixing action, wastes would stay concentrated for a longer time and would seriously endanger life in the vicinity.

Rapid mixing of material suspended or dissolved in fluids is only one of the important actions of turbulence. It also helps to move and mix properties of the fluid itself. In this way, turbulence is a crucial factor in the flow of heat throughout the earth's oceans and atmosphere, so it has a direct effect on the weather. Turbulence also carries heat through the outer part of the sun and many other stars, and it probably influenced the way swirling matter condensed to form our solar system. Cosmologists are debating the possibility that turbulence causes galaxies to form.

The importance of these far-reaching phenomena inspires many theorists to try to understand what turbulence really is, how it starts, and what it does. Other researchers want to know more about turbulence so that they can predict the weather more accurately and dispose of waste more safely.

We could deal with many other practical problems better if we knew more about turbulence. The amount of drag, or retarding force, on an automobile or truck as it speeds along the highway depends on the turbulence that forms in the air rushing past. The airflow, fairly smooth at low speeds, becomes turbulent at higher speeds, and drag increases sharply. Consequently, fuel consumption shoots up.

Aerodynamicists have studied the relationship between turbulence and drag for automobiles, trucks, airplanes, and bridges by experimenting with laboratory models in wind tunnels. Although scientists have built up a practical understanding of turbulence, they have had trouble converting this into precise theory—even though they agree on what turbulence is when they see it.

The easiest place to look for turbulence is in the stream of steam rising from a boiling teakettle. In calm air, the steam rises smoothly in a column for a time, then the stream begins to waver. Farther up, the unsteady stream suddenly breaks out into chaotic swirling motions that mix the steam with the air.

Scientists agree that the chaotic motion of the steam is turbulence, and they can describe some features of this motion, but they cannot agree on an unambiguous definition. Such problems have come up before. During the 1700s, before it was clearly understood that color could be precisely defined in terms of the wavelength of light, such philosophers as Anglican Bishop George Berkeley worried about the meaning of the word "red." What troubled them was that people could agree that a given object was "red," but no one could precisely define the term. The many scientists who are studying turbulence face a similar problem today.

We do have a very useful description of turbulence, however, that British fluid dynamicist Sir Geoffrey Taylor proposed about 50 years ago. Although Taylor described turbulence in mathematical terms, we can talk about it in ordinary language. In Taylor's picture, the eddy is the basic element of turbulence. An eddy, or whorl, is a vortex such as you see in the water when a bathtub drains. Basically, turbulence is a chaotic assembly of eddies of many, many sizes and orientations. There are eddies within eddies within eddies, all interacting intricately with one another to drive each bit of fluid along a different erratic path. To learn about the motion of a turbulent fluid in detail, we would have to follow the change in each eddy as it is influenced by all the other eddies. But we are unable to do this, even when we use the largest computers.

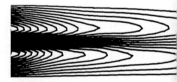

A fluid flows past a barrier in a pipe in a computer-calculated model, *top*. The flow lines wrinkle and curl into whorls, producing eddies, *above*. The flow in this case is not turbulent.

To appreciate the importance of Taylor's description, it is helpful to picture flows without turbulence as if they were layered. In such nonturbulent flows, parallel layers of fluid slide past one another. As one layer in a fluid slides past an adjacent layer, it encounters the viscous force, a retarding force that develops because the two adjacent layers exchange atoms or molecules. This exchange tends to equalize the speeds of the two layers—the faster-moving part slows down, and the slower-moving portion speeds up. Because of the viscous force, fluid next to a fixed, solid wall cannot move at all. Such flows are not really layered as is, for example, an onion, but the idea helps to picture what the fluid is doing.

Physicists use the term "shear" to describe the motion of one series of layers past another, so this kind of flow is called shear flow. In the simplest case–the column of steam, for example–the layers are unwrinkled. Such smooth flows are called laminar, which comes from *lamina*, the Latin word for layer.

When the layers in the shear flow become wrinkled, the motion grows complicated, especially when the wrinkles roll up into whorls. The fluid layers in such whorls may also slide past one another, but they are now curved in a cylindrical fashion. Shear flow, especially in a vortex, produces a twisting motion. As more and more vortexes are created, the fluid motion grows increasingly complicated and eventually becomes turbulent.

Just how complicated does motion have to become before it is turbulent? That is part of the problem of deciding what turbulence is. It is easy to distinguish between fluid flow that produces just a few large, relatively ordered eddies and the unpredictable chaos of turbulence. But is there a flow property that will help us to tell when turbulence will break out, just as temperature enables us to tell when ice melts? British physicist Osborne Reynolds of Manchester University answered this question with important experiments that he performed nearly 100 years ago.

Reynolds forced clear fluid to flow through large transparent pipes in order to learn what conditions caused turbulence to erupt. In each case, he tried to smooth the fluid's entry into the mouth of the pipe in order to minimize the confusion of swirls formed there. In order to follow the motion of the fluid, he introduced a thin stream of brightly colored dye into the center of the mouth of the pipe.

As he varied the conditions in his experiment, Reynolds found two main kinds of behavior. Sometimes the dye formed a smooth ribbon all the way through the pipe–laminar flow. But at other times, the ribbon of dye began to waver after moving only a short distance. Farther along, the waviness intensified and became quite irregular until sections of the streak of dye began to mix with the fluid. The mixing signaled that turbulence had broken out in the fluid.

Reynolds developed a simple rule for deciding when turbulence starts. With minor variations, his rule holds generally for flowing fluids whether or not they are confined to a pipe. It can be expressed in terms of a few basic measurable quantities. One of the most vital of these is viscosity, a numerical measure of the viscous force that adjacent layers of a fluid exert when they try to shear, or slide past one another. A second key factor is the difference in velocity between the fluid's fastest-moving and slowest-moving layers. Fluid in a pipe moves fastest down the center, and the layer next to the pipe wall cannot move at all because of viscosity. Thus, there is a velocity difference across the radius of the pipe. When the difference becomes great enough, turbulence erupts.

Reynolds discovered that viscosity, velocity difference, and two other factors could be combined into a single quantity, now called the Reynolds number (R). To determine R, we multiply the velocity dif-

Fluid behavior varies with the viscosity of the bath into which it is dropped. Flow of red dye is smooth in high-viscosity bath, *far left,* unstable in medium viscosity bath, *center photos,* and turbulent in bath of low viscosity, *left.*

A dye-marked fluid injected at low speed into a slower moving fluid, *left,* develops a regular succession of eddies, trapping the dyed fluid in the centers. Injected at a higher speed, the dyed fluid combines with the slower moving one in turbulence, *below left.*

Clouds of dense gas and dust billow from a volcano, *far left,* in myriad eddies of turbulent flow. An attempt to re-create the flow with a small model volcano, *left,* produces mostly large eddies and reveals the role of size in turbulence.

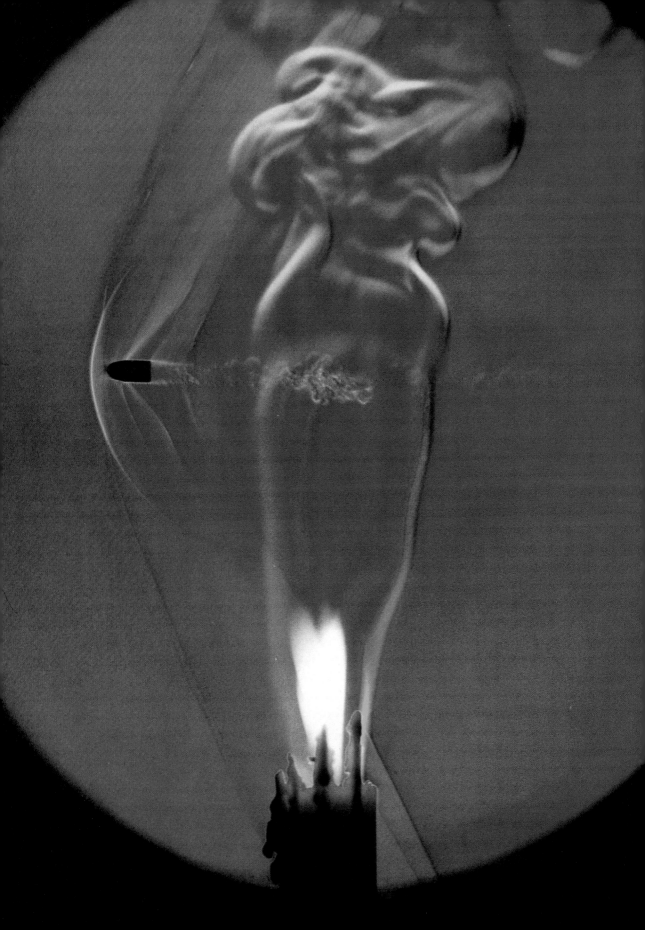

ference by the distance over which the velocity varies, then multiply by the density of the fluid, and divide that figure by the viscosity. The value of R tells us when a flowing fluid becomes turbulent. In fact, R also indicates the intensity of the turbulence once it starts, much as the temperature of a gas tells us the degree of agitation of atoms in the gas. Reynolds found that turbulence begins when R exceeds about 2,000. This comes about only if the units used to figure R are kept in the same system of measurement. Because the units in the equation all cancel out, R is a pure number, without dimensions.

R tends to be large for large pipes and small for viscous fluids. This means that the larger the pipe, the more likely it is that a fluid moving in it will become turbulent, and the more viscous the fluid, the less likely it is to become turbulent. Turbulence would always occur—even in a very viscous fluid, such as honey—if the pipe is large enough.

The remarkable feature of Reynolds' findings is that they can be applied to the diverse problems of meteorology and astronomy. Instead of using the pipe radius to calculate R, we use a characteristic size of the fluid system we are studying. R's direct dependence on size is especially significant because it means that we can expect to find turbulence in most very large systems, such as the oceans and the atmospheres of planets and stars. When R exceeds a value of about 2,000, we can expect turbulence whether the fluid is honey, water, or air, or whether the system is the wake of a ship, an ocean current, or smoke from a chimney.

The fact that R is a pure number has had an immense impact on the practical study of turbulence by engineers who design airplanes, ships, trucks, bridges, and other large objects that move through fluids or have fluids move past them. For example, if an airplane designer is concerned about turbulence occurring in the airflow next to the wings of a plane he is designing, he can build a scale model of the new design and study it in a wind tunnel to test his idea. As long as R for the wind-tunnel experiment is adjusted to match the anticipated R for the actual airplane wing, the engineer can learn what he needs to know about how the wing will perform in flight.

The fact that R is a pure number has important theoretical consequences, too. We can think of it as being the ratio of two competing forces. One, the inertial force, resists attempts to change the fluid's motion and is responsible for many things, such as creating eddies and causing them to interact. The other, the viscous force, produced by internal friction, tends to equalize the speeds of different fluid layers. When R is small, the flow is dominated by viscosity and is laminar. The transition from laminar flow to turbulent flow tends to be sharp, as if inertial force suddenly takes over. When R increases further, the inertial force becomes more and more dominant, and the motion becomes increasingly chaotic.

A supersonic bullet leaves a turbulent flow in its wake beneath a larger turbulence created in the heated air above the candle flame.

Yellow dye in water that flows past a model truck, *top,* shows the turbulence on top of the trailer that produces a drag force, raising fuel consumption. Adding deflectors to the front of the tractor, *bottom,* produces a smooth flow and cuts fuel consumption by as much as eight per cent.

You might assume that we could then ignore viscosity, but this is not so. Viscosity is still subtly involved in the behavior of the eddies. Taylor's picture of turbulence as a chaotic assembly of interacting eddies shows how. Eddies interact through the inertial force both among themselves and with the basic shear flow that started the turbulence. One important result of this interaction is that eddies of all sizes share their energy. When Reynolds' dye stream began to waver, it meant that large eddies were beginning to form, driven by the energy in the shear flow's motion through the pipe. As the larger eddies passed this energy along to smaller eddies, a population explosion of eddies began.

The viscous force constantly drains eddy energy and limits the population of eddies. Unlike the inertial force, which is reasonably democratic, the viscous force is much harder on small eddies than on large ones. Very small eddies lose their energy quickly and they try to replenish it by drawing energy from larger eddies through the inertial force. The larger eddies in turn try to recoup their losses by stealing energy from still larger eddies. But unless other forces intervene, viscosity grinds down the smallest eddies so effectively that, in turbulence, larger eddies have more energy than smaller eddies.

In terms of Reynolds' experiment, we can think of wrinkles or wiggles in shear flow as feeble eddies trying to survive viscous erosion by feeding on the energy of motion in the basic shear. If R is greater than 2,000, only those few eddies whose size is almost as great as the system itself survive. Once these eddies have a good start, they can be thought of as flows in themselves. If R is greater than about 2,000 for these large eddies, eddies will grow within them. The new eddies will be somewhat smaller than their parents, so they will have somewhat smaller Rs because of R's dependence on size. But if the new eddies have Rs above 2,000, they, in turn, will produce new eddies. And so generations of eddies spring up, with energy handed down from one to the next. Finally, when the last eddies formed are so small that their Rs drop below 2,000, the cascade of energy down through the generations ends. Viscosity overwhelms the smallest eddies and converts their energy into heat. British meteorologist Lewis F. Richardson described the cascade of energy through the eddies in this way:

> Big whorls have little whorls
> That feed on their velocity
> And little whorls have lesser whorls,
> And so on, to viscosity.

When the original R is very large, the smallest eddies in the turbulence are quite small. You can use this fact the next time you see a movie disaster scene—burning buildings, or airplanes or cars that crash and burn. You can determine whether full-sized objects or scale models were used. If the smoke billowing from the burning object has the fine texture caused by many small eddies, you know that the

Dilution of pollution through mixing is an important practical effect of turbulence.

Turbulence on a large scale appears
in the form of giant eddies in the
earth's atmosphere, *above*. Oceans
also have patterns of eddies that
appear within the general flow,
left. Computers use data from
ocean currents to model and predict
the behavior of eddies, *below.*

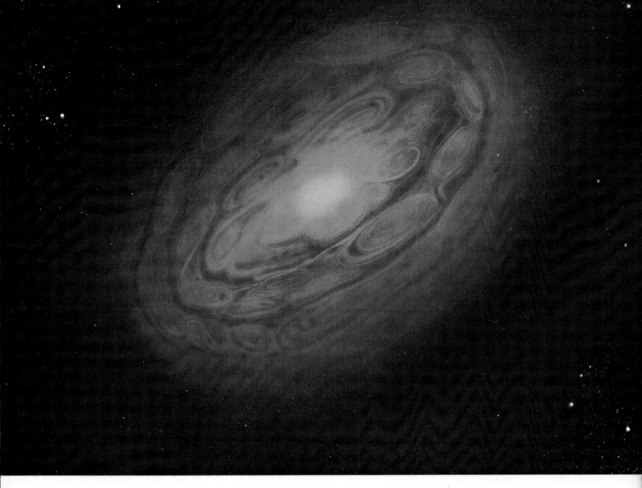

Immense eddies may
have enabled planets to
form from the turbulent
disk of gas that once
swept around the sun.

original R was large. Because R depends directly on size, a real burning plane will generate smoke with many small billows as well as large
ones. If a model is used, the original R will usually be too small to give
the details of smaller and smaller eddies.

Looking for small eddies in films may be fun, but scientists look to
intermediate-sized eddies for a deeper understanding of turbulence.
Their reasoning is simple enough. Viscosity strongly affects the smallest eddies, while the largest eddies interact mainly with the basic shear
flow. But because the intermediate-sized eddies interact mainly with
one another through the inertial force, they should hold the key to
understanding the universal properties of turbulence.

Russian mathematician Andrey N. Kolmogorov pioneered this line
of reasoning in 1941. He argued that the intermediate-sized eddies
behaved in about the same way in all intensely turbulent flows because the nature of the inertial force is the same for all of them. In fact,
the intermediate-sized eddies are usually called inertial eddies. The
sizes of the inertial eddies in different flows vary depending on the
Reynolds number of the basic flow. But if you allow for differences in
scale, you should see no average difference in the inertial eddies,

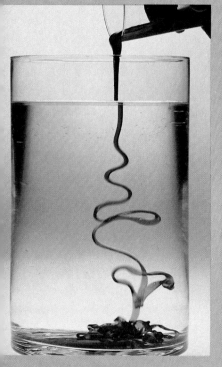

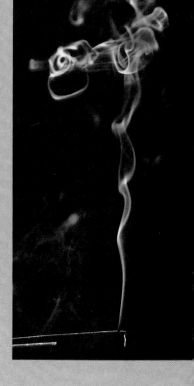

Pour syrup, which is viscous, into a glass of water and note
the smooth flow, *above*. Pouring lower-viscosity milk into the
water results in turbulence, *above right*. Smoke from an incense
stick, *far right*, rises in a smooth flow, then becomes turbulent.

whether you look at turbulence in a ship's wake, a jet of water, or in
one of Reynolds' pipes.

Kolmogorov used simple mathematics and some sweeping hypotheses to create a simple law describing how energy is distributed
among inertial eddies. He assumed that inertial eddies are homogeneous—that is, they look about the same in all parts of the turbulent flow.
He also assumed that the eddies in a given region look the same, no
matter from what angle they are viewed.

Kolmogorov's law provided an exact mathematical relationship
(the Kolmogorov spectrum) between inertial eddy energy and size. It
also provided a simple theoretical prediction that could be checked
experimentally. Unfortunately, in order to create turbulence in which
there are a great many inertial eddies, a very high initial R is needed.
Such conditions exist in riptides in the ocean or in strong winds in the

A drop of food color, released gently onto the surface of water, will burst into a cascade of eddies as it descends. Although not turbulence, this flow possesses the basic elements of turbulence—eddies. It also is similar to turbulence in that it creates motion on a decreasing scale.

atmosphere. Testing in such conditions was no easy matter. But in recent years, fluid dynamicists have been able to confirm the Kolmogorov spectrum experimentally.

However, other experiments have shown one of Kolmogorov's basic hypotheses to be unfounded. They show that turbulence is never homogeneous, even at the highest R. It is very patchy and varies in intensity from place to place. Scientists cannot explain this phenomenon, called intermittency. Why Kolmogorov's original prediction is so accurate remains a mystery.

While theorists grapple with this dilemma, engineers face a practical consequence that results from the erratic behavior of inertial eddies. When turbulence breaks out, a fluid behaves as though its viscosity has suddenly increased. For example, fluid flow in a pipe slows down when it becomes turbulent, even though the pumping pressure on the fluid remains the same. It is as if the fluid has suddenly changed from water to honey and its viscosity has jumped to a larger value, the turbulent viscosity.

On a large scale, the chaotic whirling about of eddies in turbulence vaguely resembles the random motion of atoms in a fluid on a microscopic scale. In this similarity between the two lies the origin of the notion of turbulent viscosity. Just as the exchange of atoms, hence momentum, between adjacent layers of a fluid produces ordinary viscosity, the exchange of eddies between regions of turbulent fluid produces the far more powerful turbulent viscosity.

Although this analogy, which goes back to Reynolds himself, greatly simplifies what is going on, it enables workers in many fields to calculate the effective mixing effect of turbulence. For example, engineers use the turbulent viscosity of water to gauge the influence of turbulence on the drag encountered by a fast-moving ship. To determine the brightness of X rays produced when matter falls onto a compact star, astronomers must estimate the rate at which matter can reach the star's surface. Such matter is often turbulent, so a turbulent viscosity is often used.

To estimate turbulent viscosity, engineers and astrophysicists alike often rely on formulas that were worked out from experimental data about 50 years ago by German aerodynamicist Ludwig Prandtl. From his work has grown the approach to turbulence research of those less interested in turbulence than in its effects. At the other extreme are those like Kolmogorov who try to distill the essence of turbulence. They ask: What is common to turbulence in pipes, wakes, jets, oceans, and stars? In this approach, the study of turbulence becomes a discipline in itself, or at least a special branch of physics. A number of physicists have proposed this idea.

Workers at the two extremes often differ strongly today, but their work appears to merge in the study of large eddies. The motion of the largest eddies in turbulent flow is being studied intensively with computers. Even though the computers' memories are usually too small to allow scientists to follow the progress of all the eddies in turbulence, there is an exception. This is two-dimensional turbulence, where all the eddies have axes that lie in the same direction. This reduces the number of eddies, permitting large computers to keep track of them.

Some of the most important turbulent flows are almost two-dimensional. For example, the earth's rotation creates a force, called the Coriolis force, that tends to line up the axes of very large eddies. Hence, large eddies in the atmosphere and oceans are approximately two-dimensional and are being studied effectively with computers. Such studies may teach us about the behavior of great eddies, like those seen in satellite pictures of the earth's atmosphere. Perhaps we may also begin to learn more about the immense eddies that might have helped to form planets in the primordial disk of gas that once surrounded the sun.

Unfortunately, the Coriolis force hardly affects the small eddies, and they tend to be much more disorderly than large eddies. So much information is needed to describe their behavior that even the largest computers cannot keep track of them in detail. But they are very much there, operating in three dimensions. Because of the effect of small eddies, forecasting the weather with computers can be done for only a very few days.

Yet the success with studies of two-dimensional turbulence is encouraging and leads us to hope that the three-dimensional problem of weather behavior may be solved by some combination of different techniques for different eddy sizes. We will probably continue to use large computers to monitor large eddies. How to allow in computer studies for the effects of the many small eddies on the few larger ones is a problem that requires both practical understanding and advanced mathematical techniques. If a solution is found, we may be able to make accurate long-range weather forecasts.

Understanding the influence of small eddies on larger ones might also help us to fathom another aspect of turbulence, one that seems quite astonishing and that is barely understood: In the most intensely turbulent flows, we can often discern a semblance of order through the disorder of the eddies. For example, great hot masses of gas soar upward in the sun's atmosphere at speeds of 2,000 miles (1,200 kilometers) per hour. Their Rs are astronomically high, yet photographs of the solar surface show patterns that are astonishingly regular. The circulations in the oceans have huge Rs. Yet, we find sharply defined currents like the Gulf Stream. The earth's magnetic field is almost surely produced by the motions in its liquid, electrically conducting core, with an R well beyond 2,000. Yet these motions produce a reasonably regular magnetic field that permits us to tell easily which way is north. Instead of destroying these regular structures, the vigorous whirling of turbulence actually seems to help shape them.

Somehow, when turbulence destroys the order in a fluid flow to create its own peculiar brand of chaos, it re-creates a new pattern with its own embellished form of order. That is a phenomenon that cries out to be understood. Rarely does a physical process blend such tantalizing beauty with such extreme complexity that it challenges both pure mathematicians and practical engineers. Yet, despite the intensive efforts of both groups, the mystery of turbulence persists.

And therein lies the allure of turbulence research. Perhaps the problem may be solved by a fresh viewpoint on the mathematics. Or, some experimentalist may suddenly see an underlying order in nature's most puzzling process. The solutions to the difficult problems of science often seem strange and complicated when they are first discovered. It takes boldness and, above all, great mastery to find them. Turbulence will be no exception. Probably whoever first glimpses the new way will experience the excitement and even fright that comes to most discoverers. Perhaps the insight—the thrill—will come to you.

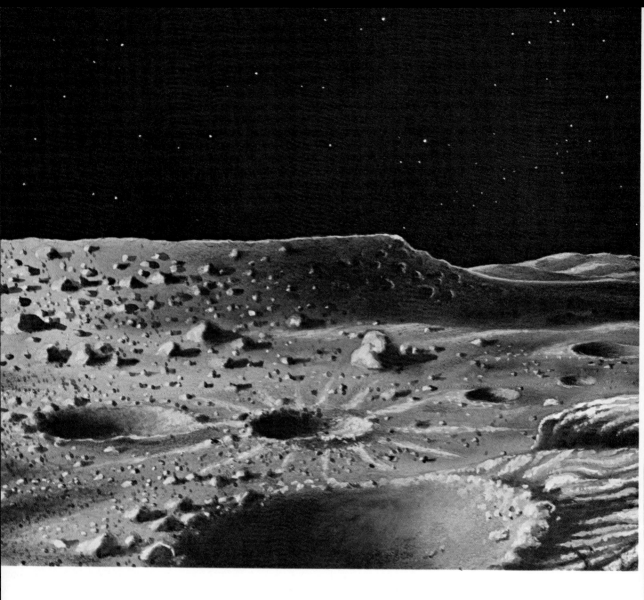

Asteroids: The Missing Planet?

By Joseph Veverka

Modern astronomical techniques are answering a number of questions about the small objects that wander between the orbits of Jupiter and Mars

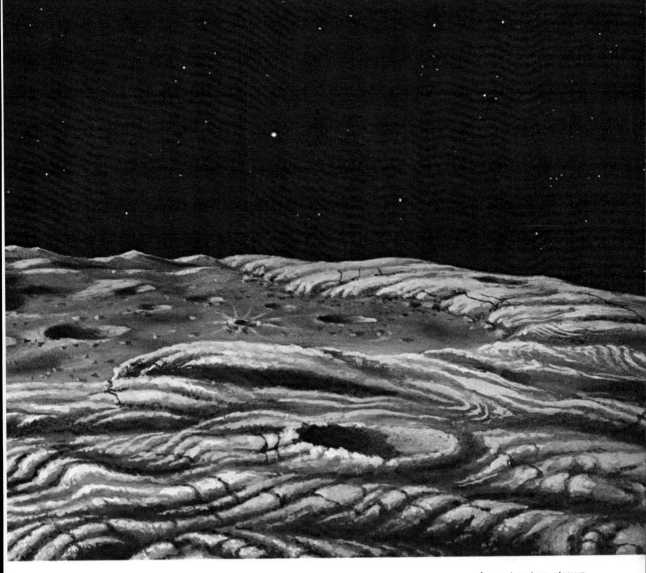

Impact craters, strewn rocks, and eons-old hardened lava flows dominate the surface of the asteroid Vesta.

If you plan to visit Vesta wear a sweater. A heated space suit would be better. Vesta, the third largest asteroid (from the Greek "starlike"), is a very cold place. The mean surface temperature is about −80°C (−112°F.). Since Vesta is about 2.4 times farther from the Sun than is the Earth, it receives only about one-sixth of the light and heat that we do. Your supplies would also have to include oxygen. The asteroid is too small and its gravity too weak to retain any atmosphere.

Walking on Vesta would be somewhat like walking on the Moon. The surface is scarred with craters of all sizes created by the impacts of innumerable meteoroids. These impacts have pulverized the surface into a layer of rubble and dust called a regolith, probably very similar to that which the Apollo astronauts found on the Moon. However, the landscape, although gray, would not be as dark as that of the Moon. Vesta's albedo, the fraction of sunlight that its surface reflects, is 23 per cent, compared with 12 per cent for the lunar surface.

You could easily explore large areas on foot without getting tired because Vesta's gravity is less than one-sixth that of the Moon, which is only one-sixth of the Earth's. The landscape might appear similar to that of the Moon, but the horizon would be much closer and more curved, because Vesta's diameter is only about one-sixth that of the Moon. Perhaps the single most interesting surface feature to explore on Vesta would be its hardened lava flows. Although no one has yet set foot on Vesta, and no spacecraft has been near, planetary scientists have obtained conclusive evidence during the last decade that cold, silent Vesta was once the scene of volcanic activity.

Vesta is in the asteroid belt, a vast space between the orbits of Mars and Jupiter that contains tens of thousands of asteroids, or minor planets. Despite this great number, the asteroid belt is a fairly empty place. This fact was dramatically illustrated in 1972 when National Aeronautics and Space Administration (NASA) scientists could find no trajectories that would take the *Pioneer 10* and *Pioneer 11* spacecraft close to any known asteroid on their journey from the Earth to Jupiter.

Compared to the nine major planets, or even to our Moon, asteroids are minuscule. The biggest of them, Ceres, is only about 1,000 kilometers (620 miles) in diameter, or less than one-third as big as our Moon. Its volume is less than one two-thousandth that of the Earth. Only about 200 asteroids have a diameter larger than 100 kilometers (60 miles), but there must be several tens of thousands that exceed 1 kilometer (0.6 mile) in size. The total mass of material in asteroids is very small, no more than one-tenth of the mass of our Moon.

Since asteroids are very small they are also very faint. Even the brightest, such as Ceres and Vesta, cannot be seen with the naked eye, but about a dozen can be observed as points of light through binoculars. Ceres and Vesta are just a little dimmer than the faintest stars visible to the naked eye, but most asteroids are considerably fainter, and large telescopes and accurate star charts are needed to locate them. By making long time exposures through large telescopes, astronomers have photographed asteroids 1 million times fainter than Ceres and Vesta. The orbits of such faint asteroids are not yet known.

The first asteroid was found in 1801, but the idea that the space between Mars and Jupiter might not be empty goes back at least as far as the 1600s and Johannes Kepler, a German astronomer and mathematician. Kepler's keen sense of symmetry was bothered by what appeared to be too large a gap between the orbits of Mars and Jupiter. He thought something must be there, probably one large planet waiting to be discovered. Then, in 1766, Professor Johann Daniel Titius of the University of Wittenberg proposed a numerical scheme for representing the distances of planets from the Sun. When the German astronomer Johann Elert Bode published the proposal in 1772, it became known as Bode's law. According to the law, a planet should exist at 2.8 astronomical units (AU) from the Sun. An astronomical unit is a measure of distance equal to about 150 million kilometers (93 million

The author:
Joseph Veverka is associate professor of astronomy at Cornell University.

miles), the average distance between the Earth and the Sun. Therefore, 2.8 AU is about 420 million kilometers (260 million miles). The discovery in 1801 of Ceres, whose average distance from the Sun is about 2.8 AU, seemed to be a remarkable confirmation of Bode's law. But then three more small planets were found within the next five years, and things have been getting worse ever since; by 1978, over 2,000 asteroids had been discovered.

Why are there so many small objects rather than the one large planet that Kepler expected? Originally, astronomers thought that these objects were fragments of some ill-fated large planet, or perhaps a pair of large planets, which had been shattered by an ancient cataclysm, such as a collision. This theory provided a plausible explanation for meteorites, those "stones from the sky" which occasionally fall to Earth. The meteorites were regarded as the small pieces left over from the catastrophe.

Astronomers now believe that no large planet ever did form in the asteroid belt. Modern theories of planetary formation suggest that the planets formed by condensing from a disklike nebula of gas and dust having the same chemical composition as the Sun. This condensation occurred quickly at the very beginning of the solar system some 4.6-billion years ago. Small bodies, or planetesimals, formed first, and some of the larger ones began to sweep up their neighbors. In this manner, Jupiter apparently grew to its immense size very quickly, and the smaller bodies that were still forming in what is now the asteroid belt began to feel its tremendous gravitational pull. Some of their orbits were changed from circles to ellipses. This change increased the bodies' velocities relative to each other so that if by chance they collided, as often happened, they were moving too fast to stick together. Instead, they struck each other with such force that they shattered into even smaller pieces.

Even under these unfavorable conditions, a few objects apparently managed to grow to a respectable size and survive essentially intact. The largest asteroids, such as Ceres, Pallas, and Vesta, seem to fall into this category. It is unlikely that they are fragments of much larger bodies because their shapes are almost round, like those of big planets, and not irregular like those of many small asteroids.

We can only guess at the original number of such large objects. There may have been several dozen of them at the beginning. Collisions have since reduced most of them to innumerable fragments of various sizes and shapes. Fortunately, some of the small fragments occasionally strike the Earth—as meteorites—and provide us with invaluable samples of asteroid materials.

Observers have determined accurate orbits for more than 2,000 asteroids. Most of these orbits are concentrated within the asteroid belt between 2.2 and 3.5 AU, but there are several groups of stray asteroids with unusual orbits. For example, there are some asteroids whose orbits extend from the asteroid belt to inside the orbit of Mars.

Asteroids in Collision
Traveling at immense velocity in orbits that cross, two asteroids collide with great force. The energy of the impact heats them and splits them into thousands of fragments.

These asteroids are called Amor asteroids. There are also two groups of asteroids moving in Jupiter's orbit at 5.2 AU from the Sun. These are the Trojans; one group moves 60 degrees ahead of Jupiter, the other 60 degrees behind.

There is also a group of very small, very faint asteroids in orbits that cross that of the Earth. These are called Apollo asteroids. Only about two dozen have been discovered so far, although it has been estimated that there must be many, many more. Several new ones have been found in the last two years, the latest by Hans-Emil Schuster of the European Southern Observatory in Chile on Feb. 8, 1978. This object, called 1978 CA, came within 19 million kilometers (12 million miles) of the Earth. At the time of its discovery, it was about 10,000 times fainter than Ceres.

Even though asteroids are very small and very faint, astronomers have learned a great deal about their sizes, shapes, and composition by using a variety of direct and indirect techniques. For example, it is known that the brightness of many asteroids varies periodically. These variations can best be explained in terms of the spinning of an irregular body around its axis, the changes in brightness being caused by changes in the projected area seen by the observer. Thus, the period over which the light fluctuations are observed to repeat must equal the rotation period of the asteroid. Typical rotation periods for asteroids are close to 6 hours, but range from 2.3 to at least 30 hours. Most asteroids vary in brightness by 10 to 20 per cent, indicating that, as they spin, their projected area varies by that amount. Some asteroids, however, are much more irregular. For example, Hektor, Eros, and Geographos show light variations of 250 per cent, 400 per cent, and 600 per cent, respectively, indicating that they have highly irregular shapes. The brightness of other asteroids, such as Ceres, varies much less, proving that they are essentially spherical.

Until about 10 years ago we did not know the true sizes of asteroids very well. Asteroid size cannot be measured directly because no asteroid is big enough to show a measurable disk in a telescope. It is easy to tell that one asteroid appears brighter than some other asteroid, but is it because it is bigger or because its surface material reflects a larger fraction of incident sunlight? The reflecting power of a surface is measured by its albedo, or reflectivity, which is simply the fraction of incident sunlight that it reflects. A perfectly white surface has an albedo of 100 per cent; a perfectly black surface has an albedo of 0 per cent. The Moon's albedo is 12 per cent.

During the last decade, two techniques—polarimetry and radiometry—have been developed that make it possible to measure the sizes and albedos of asteroids accurately.

With polarimetry, we measure the polarization of light. Sunlight is unpolarized; that is, the light waves vibrate in many directions. When sunlight is scattered from a surface, it becomes partially polarized, that is, the light waves vibrate in a limited direction. For rocky surfaces such as those of asteroids, the degree of polarization is inversely proportional to the surface's albedo. A dark surface polarizes light more than a bright one. I first made polarimetric measurements for a few asteroids in 1968. Since then Benjamin Zellner of the University of Arizona and his colleagues have measured almost 200. Not only have these measurements been used to calculate precise asteroid sizes and albedos, but their detailed interpretation has demonstrated that the surfaces of even small asteroids are covered by regoliths.

Radiometry of asteroids was developed independently in 1970 by David Allen, who was then at the University of Minnesota, and by Dennis Matson of the California Institute of Technology (Caltech). It has been applied to a large number of asteroids by David Morrison of the University of Hawaii. The idea is to measure not only the visible, but also the infrared, brightness of an asteroid. The visible brightness depends on the diameter of the asteroid and on its albedo. The infrared brightness depends on the diameter and temperature of the surface. The temperature depends on the fraction of sunlight that the surface absorbs, that is, on its albedo. Thus, the infrared brightness also depends on the two parameters, diameter and albedo, but not in the same mathematical way as does the visible brightness. By measuring both the visible and infrared brightness, we can determine both mathematical unknowns: diameter and albedo. The radiometric and polarimetric results agree very well and prove that the surfaces of all asteroids are not alike. According to Morrison, the darkest known asteroid is Arethusa whose albedo is about 2 per cent, while the brightest is Nysa with an albedo of 38 per cent.

Most asteroids in the main belt fall into two major groups: black asteroids with albedos of only 3 to 5 per cent, and gray asteroids with albedos of 12 to 20 per cent. The data indicate that there are more black than gray asteroids, especially in the outer half of the asteroid belt, closest to Jupiter. All of the Trojan asteroids studied so far are black, and some of them are quite large. For example, irregularly shaped Hektor has an albedo of 4 per cent and is 260 kilometers (160 miles) across its widest part. All of the Apollo asteroids are tiny objects and most are gray. Icarus, for example, has an albedo of 17 per cent and a diameter of 1 kilometer (0.6 mile).

The range of asteroid albedos suggests that asteroid surfaces vary in composition. The best way to study these differences is to analyze asteroid spectra. Just as we can identify gases in a laboratory by the characteristic wavelengths of their emitted light, we can also identify solids—including the rocks and minerals on a distant body—by the way in which they reflect light of different wavelengths.

In the late 1960s, John Adams, Clark Chapman, Torrence Johnson, and Thomas McCord, then working at the Massachusetts Institute of Technology (M.I.T.), began to study the spectra of asteroids. They noticed that these fell into several well-defined groups, some of which closely resembled the spectra of meteorites.

For instance, spectrophotometry of the surfaces of many black asteroids has shown that they are similar in composition to black meteorites called carbonaceous chondrites—stony meteorites that are rich in carbon. Since black asteroids predominate in the outer half of the asteroid belt, we conclude that this is where carbonaceous material was formed most abundantly. This finding is consistent with current theories about how the planets and asteroids condensed out of gas and dust to form the solar system. Such theories maintain that because temperatures were highest near the center of the developing solar system—close to the forming Sun—and decreased toward the edges of the solar nebula, the materials that condensed at various distances from the Sun should be chemically different. What we know about the chemical composition of the major planets and their satellites appears to support these predictions. As for the asteroid belt, carbonaceous material should be more common at the outer edge where it was cooler. Typical carbonaceous material, such as that found in the meteorite Murchison, which fell to earth in Australia in 1969, could not form at temperatures higher than about 130°C (260°F.).

One of the most striking spectral matches between asteroids and meteorites is that between Vesta and eucrites, meteorites that are

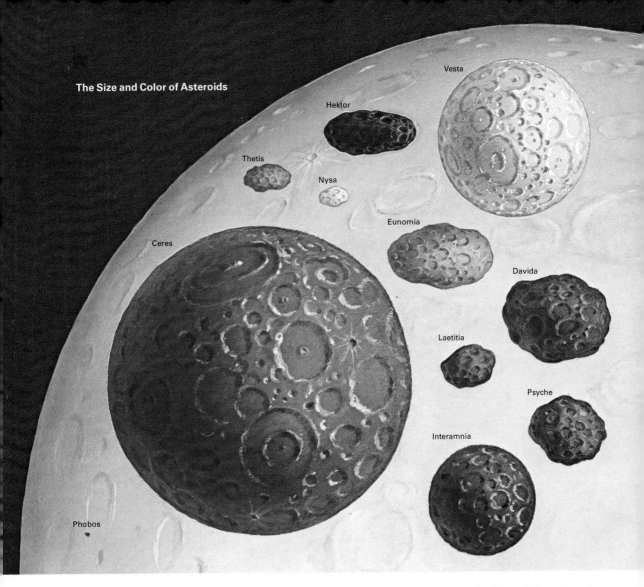

Vesta

Hektor

Thetis

Nysa

Ceres

Eunomia

Davida

Laetitia

Psyche

Interamnia

Phobos

similar in composition and texture to solidified lava. This spectral match is proof of volcanic activity in Vesta's past. But Vesta appears to be unique among asteroids in this respect. We are quite certain that volcanic eruptions did not occur on most large asteroids. For example, there is no evidence of lava on the surface of Ceres. On the contrary, spectral data obtained in 1977 by Larry Lebofsky of the Jet Propulsion Laboratory at Caltech tells us that material on Ceres' surface is similar to the Murchison material. Any large-scale volcanic activity on the surface of Ceres would have been accompanied by intense heat, which would have destroyed such low-temperature material.

Although surface eruptions were a rarity, we know that many asteroids did become hot enough to melt on the inside. We can tell this from the abundance of meteorites made of iron-nickel alloy. When a planet gets hot enough to melt inside, it probably forms a metallic core rich in this alloy by a process called differentiation, or separation into

An Asteroid Assortment
Shown to scale against a quadrant of the moon, asteroids vary in size from tiny Nysa to huge Ceres and in color from Nysa's light gray to Interamnia's jet black. Minuscule Phobos, lower left, a captured moon of the planet Mars, may also be an asteroid.

layers with different density and composition. The heat source is probably natural radioactivity.

Clark Chapman, now at the Planetary Science Institute in Tucson, Ariz., has suggested that some asteroids whose surface spectra indicate a rich iron-nickel content may be the stripped-down cores of differentiated parent bodies whose outer, rocky surfaces have been almost completely whittled away by collisions. To test this theory we could measure the mass of one of these "metallic" asteroids by sending a spacecraft close enough to feel the asteroid's gravitational pull. Gravitational pull is directly proportional to mass, which, divided by the asteroid's volume, would give the average density. An average density near 8 grams per cubic centimeter (0.25 pound per cubic inch) would indicate an asteroid made of iron-nickel.

But there is an easier way of finding out whether these asteroids, suspected of being stripped-down cores, actually have metallic surfaces: We can bounce radar waves off them from Earth. Metals reflect radar waves much better than do rocks; therefore, the stripped-down-core asteroids would send back much stronger radar signals than would rocky asteroids. As of 1978, radar signals have been bounced off several Apollo asteroids when they have come close to the Earth. These include Icarus, Geographos, and Toro. The only asteroid in the main belt observed successfully by radar so far is Ceres. None of these were suspected of being metallic objects, and not surprisingly all returned only weak signals. Using the newly upgraded radar in Arecibo, Puerto Rico, we should soon be able to study more asteroids, including some of those suspected of being metallic.

At present we know the masses of only the three largest asteroids, Ceres, Pallas, and Vesta, since these objects are the only ones big enough to cause visible changes in the motions of their neighbors. From these masses, we can calculate the average densities. For example, Vesta's average density is about 3.5 grams per cubic centimeter (0.13 pound per cubic inch)—consistent with that of the eucritelike rocks that cover its surface. Ceres has a mean density of about 2.5 grams per cubic centimeter (0.09 pound per cubic inch)—consistent with the density of an object made entirely of carbonaceous chondrite material. The low average density of Ceres suggests that no large-scale melting and differentiation ever occurred within Ceres. The fact that Vesta melted on the inside but Ceres apparently did not indicates that radioactive elements, the probable source for the heat, were not uniformly distributed throughout the solar system.

If past experience is a valid guide, our understanding of asteroids should improve tremendously once we have explored a few directly by spacecraft. Although the first asteroid mission is still at least a decade away, we may already have had a glimpse of two small asteroids. *Mariner 9* in 1971 and 1972, and *Viking 1* and *Viking 2* between 1976 and 1978 sent us numerous pictures of Phobos and Deimos, the two minuscule moons of Mars that were probably once small asteroids.

The *Mariner 9* data, a by-product of the exploration of Mars, showed that both Martian moons are irregular in shape and heavily cratered. Both Phobos and Deimos are made of a dark material that is perhaps similar to that found on carbonaceous, or black, asteroids. Phobos is about 25 kilometers (15.5 miles) and Deimos about 12 kilometers (7.5 miles) in diameter.

Astronomers have long wondered whether these bodies formed in the orbit of Mars or were captured by the planet. *Viking* data suggest strongly that they were captured. The spectrum and the average density of Phobos are characteristic of low-density carbonaceous chondrite material. Such material is believed to have condensed only in the outer half of the asteroid belt, so Phobos almost certainly did not originate near Mars.

Current theories suggest that both Phobos and Deimos probably were captured by the planet early in its history and may be typical of the primeval building blocks that went into the last stages of the formation of Mars. Evidently some of these final pieces, including Phobos and Deimos, came from the asteroid belt. So the two moons of Mars

Murchison, *above,* is a carbonaceous chondrite, a rare kind of black stony meteorite that contains carbon. Ordinary chondrites, such as Bruderheim, *above right,* resemble light-colored stones. A typical iron meteorite, *right,* is rust colored because 90 per cent of its content is iron.

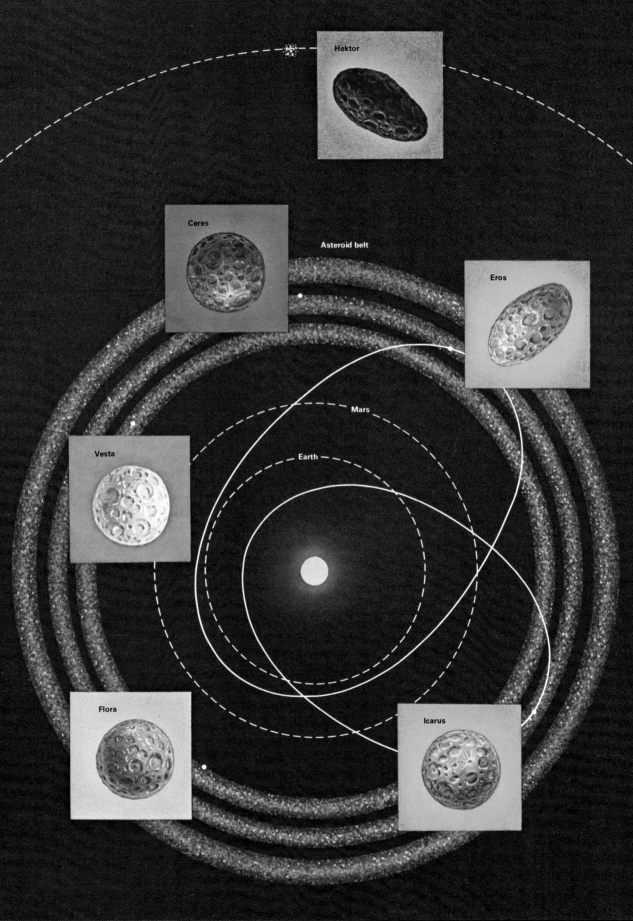

Hektor

Ceres

Asteroid belt

Eros

Mars

Earth

Vesta

Flora

Icarus

Orbits, Spectra, and Asteroid Types

Asteroids orbit the Sun in a variety of paths, *left.*
Most, including Ceres, Vesta, and Flora, lie between
Mars and Jupiter. Eros, in the Amor group, crosses
Mars's orbit. Icarus, an Apollo asteroid, crosses
Earth's orbit. Matching asteroid and meteorite
spectra, *below,* shows that asteroids in the same
orbit are usually made of the same material. Ceres
is a carbonaceous chondrite, Flora is stony-iron,
and Eros and Icarus are ordinary chondrites. Vesta,
however, is a eucrite, and because no match has
been found for Hektor, its composition is unknown.

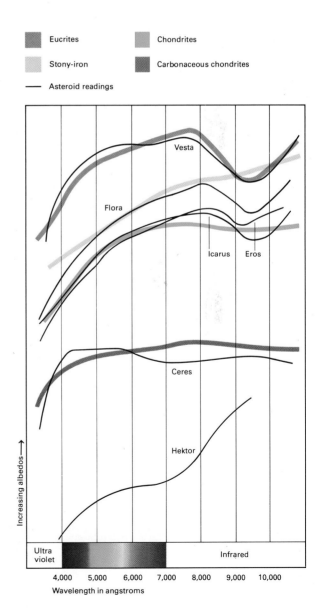

Jupiter

- ▮ Eucrites
- ▮ Chondrites
- ▮ Stony-iron
- ▮ Carbonaceous chondrites
- — Asteroid readings

Vesta

Flora

Icarus   Eros

Ceres

Hektor

Increasing albedos →

Ultra violet   Infrared

4,000   5,000   6,000   7,000   8,000   9,000   10,000
Wavelength in angstroms

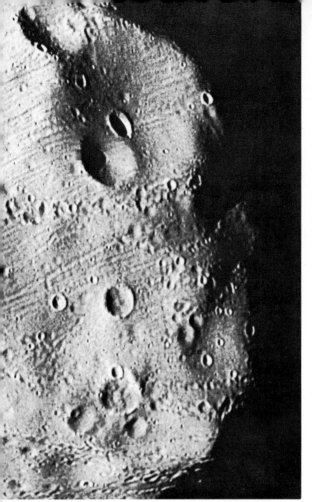

The surface of "ex-asteroid" Phobos, *left,* is heavily cratered and grooved, a sign of its besieged past. On Deimos, *above,* Mars's other moon, a layer of dust has apparently filled many craters and grooves, smoothing out the surface of the satellite.

may be good examples of small asteroids in general, and a close study of their surfaces should give us a good idea of what to expect in the asteroid belt once we begin full-scale exploration.

The biggest surprise in the *Viking* pictures was to find the surface of Phobos covered not only with craters but also with swarms of strange grooves that look very much like fractures. Most of the grooves are about 100 meters (109 yards) wide and 10 to 20 meters (11 to 22 yards) deep. Many of the grooves have pitted segments, and some of the pits have raised rims. The grooves begin near the rim of Stickney, the largest crater on Phobos, and fade away near the point exactly opposite the crater on the other side of Phobos. Astronomers wondered what could have caused them.

The accepted explanation is based on the fact that many carbonaceous chondrites are brittle. The severe impact that produced Stickney was apparently strong enough to crack Phobos, producing this remarkable pattern of grooves. At the same time, the impact energy evidently heated up the interior enough to release some of the water that is present in low-density carbonaceous chondrite material. This water could then make its way to the surface along the cracks in the form of vapor, carrying some solid material with it and enlarging some of the cracks. Such "outgassing" probably explains the pits in the grooves and why some of the pits have raised rims. Since similar events could take place on any small object made of weak, water-rich carbonaceous material, our study of Phobos indicates that swarms of pitted grooves may be common features on many small asteroids.

We know, however, that such features are not always present. Another *Viking* surprise was that the surfaces of Phobos and Deimos are quite different. Deimos has no grooves. The absence of grooves may be due to Deimos' greater strength—that is, it may consist of denser carbonaceous material than Phobos—or to the fact that it did not suffer impacts as strong as the one that produced Stickney. So far, we have examined only half the surface of Deimos. The largest craters on that half are about 2 kilometers (1 mile) in diameter, almost certainly too small to have caused cracking, whereas Stickney, by comparison, is 10 kilometers (6 miles) across.

Another remarkable difference is that the surface of Deimos, unlike that of Phobos, is littered with boulders 10 to 20 meters (11 to 22 yards) high. Also, many of the craters on Deimos, unlike those on Phobos, have been filled in conspicuously with fine-grained material. Both the boulders and the fine-grained material are probably ejecta—material thrown out when craters are formed. Usually we expect a body that is larger and hence has more gravity to retain more ejecta than a smaller body. Thus, it is puzzling that Deimos should have retained much more material than Phobos. When this puzzle is solved we will know much more about how craters and their ejected material are produced on small asteroids. The remarkable differences in the small-scale surface characteristics of Phobos and Deimos emphasize the fact that we should expect to find great variety when we finally can explore the surfaces of asteroids in the main belt.

Even unmanned-spacecraft exploration of asteroids should provide crucial and probably spectacular information. For example, such close-range study should tell us which small asteroids are fragments of much larger bodies and which are not. We will certainly be able to tell which asteroids have had their surfaces modified by internal processes such as lava flows. Most important, spacecraft fly-bys should give us the asteroid's mass and average density. Then we can infer the internal composition of the asteroid and compare it with what we see on the surface in order to determine which bodies have differentiated.

No one can predict exactly what the surface of any particular asteroid will look like in detail, and it is reasonably certain that the first close-up pictures will contain some surprises. By studying these, we will not only learn more about asteroids, but about the solar system as a whole. There is a growing realization among astronomers that the study of asteroids may provide essential clues to the processes of evolution during the earliest stages of our solar system. Thus, they could be the keys for unlocking important details of how the major planets—including the Earth—were formed.

Greening the Brown Lands

By Norman J. Rosenberg

By altering plants and their environments, scientists seek better ways to use the abundant sunlight and the sparse, uncertain rainfall in the world's dry regions

In a sun-drenched field of sugar beets near Scottsbluff, Nebr., University of Nebraska graduate students record wind speeds and air temperatures. In Montana, plant breeders trying to develop hardier grains painstakingly transfer pollen from one strain of barley to another. In California's heat-soaked Mojave Desert, botanists study the desert primrose, which has successfully adapted to that barren land. The information this research produces will answer some small questions. But combined with research in other parts of the world, it is helping to answer one of this century's biggest questions: How are we going to feed a world population that keeps growing and demanding more and better food? Furthermore, where can we grow this food?

Short growing seasons and poor soils limit production in the far northern latitudes and irrigation on a gigantic and impractical scale would be required to make large areas of the deserts fertile. When rain forests in tropical areas are cleared for agriculture, the soil deteriorates

Green and productive, irrigated farm fields flourish amid the scrubby semiarid plains of eastern Colorado.

quickly. In addition, the high concentration of aluminum in these soils may be toxic to many plants.

Many geographers, soil scientists, and agricultural climatologists think that the semiarid and subhumid regions of the world are the best places to increase food production quickly. These regions range from the middle latitudes to the tropics and include the Great Plains of the United States and Canada, the steppes of Russia, the Pampa in Argentina, part of northeast Brazil, large areas in South Africa and Australia, parts of northwestern India and Sahelian Africa south of the Sahara, and certain areas of dry summer Mediterranean climates, such as parts of Italy, Spain, and North Africa and some coastal regions of the United States and Australia. Although some of the greatest grain- and meat-producing areas in the world can be found in these regions, many scientists think that they can be made to produce much more. They generally have abundant sunshine and wind–both important for growing crops. The sunlight provides energy for photosynthesis and air turbulence keeps the plants supplied with carbon dioxide which is used in the same process. But these areas are named for their major deficit–water.

Geographers define semiarid and subhumid regions with complex mathematical formulas that relate rainfall and the potential water loss from the soil due to the effects of sun and wind on vegetation. In general, the annual rainfall in these regions is less than the annual water loss by evaporation.

In addition, the rainfall is usually distributed unevenly during the year. For instance, Scottsbluff, in the Great Plains, gets 70 per cent of its annual precipitation from May to October. In Niger, in Africa's Sahel region, almost all the annual precipitation falls between May and September. Jerusalem, Israel, gets 95 per cent of its annual precipitation between November and April.

The quantity of precipitation varies greatly from year to year in these regions. For example, Scottsbluff averaged 370 millimeters (14.6 inches) from 1941 to 1970, but in 2 out of 3 years, rainfall varied by 25 per cent above or below that figure. Rainfall at Niamey, Niger, shows a similar year-to-year variability. By contrast, the annual precipitation in the humid region around Columbus, Ohio, generally varies by only 15 per cent in 2 out of 3 years.

Much of the land in semiarid and subhumid areas is already being used for food production. If we can save and use more of the uncertain and sometimes inadequate water supply and also develop plants that use it more efficiently, we can produce more and better crops.

For centuries, farmers in dry lands have conserved and managed sparse rain water for their crops. The Nabataeans who inhabited what is now the Negev desert of Israel more than 2,000 years ago were particularly successful in such efforts. Avdat, one of their major settlements, receives only about 86 millimeters (3.4 inches) of rain per year; rain falls infrequently but intensely there. The soil crusts over after

The author:
Norman J. Rosenberg
is professor of
agricultural meteorology
at the University of
Nebraska in Lincoln.

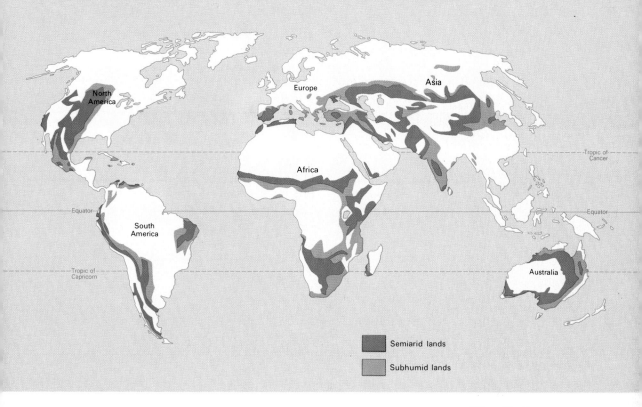

North America

Europe

Asia

Africa

South America

Equator

Tropic of Cancer

Equator

Tropic of Capricorn

Australia

Semiarid lands

Subhumid lands

**Where the Dry
Lands Are**
Semiarid and subhumid
regions are found on
all inhabited continents.
Some areas, such as the
Great Plains of North
America and the Russian
steppes, are vital to
the world's food supply.

absorbing only a little moisture and most of the water runs off in flash floods. During the 1960s and 1970s, botanist Michael Evenari of Hebrew University in Jerusalem reconstructed the catch basins, runoff channels, and other techniques that the Nabataeans used to conserve and spread precious water over their fields. His successful experimental farm at Avdat shows how these ingenious desert people grew fruits and vegetables, and developed pastures for their livestock.

The prolonged drought that parched the Great Plains in the 1930s triggered soil- and moisture-conservation research that continues to change the way we manage water. Many farmers now use terrace and contour farming to retain water and reduce soil erosion. Leveling hilly land into terraces, which slows the rate of runoff, allows more water to soak into the soil. Contour plowing on hilly or sloping areas also slows runoff and decreases soil erosion.

Strip farming also became important, especially to grain farmers in the western Great Plains. Fields are divided into strips 30 to 90 meters (100 to 300 feet) wide; half the strips are planted each year while the other half are left fallow to collect rainfall for the following year. In this way, farmers have enough moisture to produce a grain crop in each strip every other year. The strips are oriented perpendicular to the prevailing winds so that the planted strips protect the others.

When soil is turned over by plowing, loose moist soil is brought to the surface and the top 15 to 30 centimeters (6 to 12 inches) is exposed

A lone figure struggles against the dust-laden wind during the great drought of the 1930's that ruined thousands of farmers in the Great Plains of North America.

to drying by the sun and wind. To save moisture, more and more farmers are using minimum-tillage – that is, they slice through the soil, planting seed and applying fertilizer and herbicides in one operation without overturning the soil. A similar system – stubble-mulch farming – is used in growing some grains, such as wheat. To protect the soil, the stalks are left in the field after the grain is harvested. At planting time, the soil is not plowed but merely loosened and thin slices are made to receive the seed. After the 1974-1977 drought in the Great Plains, University of Nebraska agricultural engineer Howard Wittmuss reported superior yields of corn grown under these conservation methods compared with yields on conventionally tilled land.

Irrigation helps stabilize crop yields in regions of variable rainfall, and its use has greatly expanded. For example, in Nebraska, while irrigated corn land increased from 1.26 million to 1.5 million hectares between 1974 and 1976, there was a decline in unirrigated land planted in corn from 1.07 million to 1.01 million hectares.

Until the 1950s, most farmers in the Great Plains irrigated with water from rivers, ponds, and reservoirs. This water was distributed to and over the fields primarily by gravity flow. In the last 20 years, farmers in the Great Plains have turned increasingly to underground water that must be pumped to the surface and spread over the fields either by gravity flow or huge sprinkler systems. But higher petroleum prices have greatly increased the costs of pumping irrigation water. In 1972, the diesel fuel needed to power sprinkler irrigation for 0.4 hectare (1 acre) of corn in Nebraska cost $11.50 per year. In 1977, it cost $31.00. While the cost of fuel tripled, other irrigation costs, such as well drilling, rose 60 to 80 per cent. So, farmers are not likely to turn increasingly to irrigation for developing semiarid lands.

Scientists are looking for other ways to help farmers deal with the uncertainties of farming in these areas. Plant physiologists and soil specialists are studying the relationships between plants and their environment, especially the "microclimate" near the ground. They hope to improve the plant's use of sunlight and water, either by altering the environment or the plant itself. Plants waste a great deal of water. On subsistence farms in less developed countries, 1 metric ton (1.1 short tons) of water extracted by the plant from the soil produces only about 120 grams (4.2 ounces) of plant material. Intensive farming techniques such as heavy fertilizing and extensive weed control may produce 1 kilogram (2.2 pounds) of material with the same amount of water. Plants use only 1 or 2 per cent of the water in the internal chemical processes that keep them growing. The rest passes through the roots to the stems and leaves and evaporates into the air in transpiration, which cools the plant. At theoretical maximum photosynthetic efficiency, plants might produce as much as 10 kilograms (22 pounds) of plant tissue per metric ton of water.

Some scientists are also trying to make crop plants use sunlight more effectively. These plants are also quite inefficient in this respect. Un-

Plowing with the slope contours of the land, *top,* slows runoff, increasing water retention in the soil and reducing erosion. Small irrigation channels, *left,* provide water for a Texas soybean field. In strip-farming, *above,* half of the land is planted each season while the other half replenishes its water supply for the next year.

der subsistence farming conditions, they make use of only about 0.04 to 0.1 per cent of the available sunlight in photosynthesis, the process by which plants convert light, carbon dioxide, and water to plant material. With the use of fertilizer, hybrid seed, herbicides, and other modern intensive-farming techniques, the figure can rise to about 1 per cent. In test fields, agricultural scientists have done somewhat better. Healthy crops that are well supplied with nutrients and water can fix or "harvest" 1.5 per cent of the sun's energy in a good week – as much as 4 per cent on a single day. But botanists believe that the maximum photosynthetic efficiency is 8 to 10 per cent, so there is clearly room for improvement.

Plant scientists compute a plant's water-use efficiency as the ratio of crop material produced by photosynthesis divided by the amount of water consumed by transpiration. Scientists are trying to increase that ratio. There arc a number of ways to do this. One is to reduce water loss from transpiration without affecting photosynthesis. Another is to increase photosynthesis without increasing water loss.

However, one problem in manipulating photosynthesis and transpiration is that the two processes occur simultaneously, involve some of the same structures in the leaf, and are affected by the same environment. The surface of a leaf contains stomata, small openings through which carbon dioxide enters the plant in photosynthesis and through which water vapor exits in transpiration. The stomata operate like valves that open and close in response to environmental stimuli. For example, at nightfall when the light becomes insufficient for photosynthesis, the guard cells that surround and control the stomata close the pores. When the sun rises, the guard cells inflate and bulge to open the stomata, and photosynthesis begins. Carbon dioxide moves through the stomata into the substomatal cavity beneath, then to the grana, the structures where photosynthesis takes place. At the same time, water vapor moves out of the cavity and the stomata.

An array of instruments, *below,* rates humidity, temperature, and wind speed from ground level up to about 16 meters (52.5 feet) above a field of alfalfa. A scientist checks data on a spectroradiometer, *below right,* that tells the amounts and wavelengths of the sun's rays reflected by crops.

Both the water vapor and the carbon dioxide move by diffusion—they go from areas of greater concentration to those of lesser concentration. The greater the concentration of carbon dioxide in the air near the plant, the greater the rate of diffusion into the plant. At the same time, the more humid the air, the less transpirational water loss will take place from the plant, because the humidity in the air more nearly equals the humidity in the substomatal cavity, which is essentially 100 per cent.

Environmental changes that affect one process usually affect the other. For example, turbulent air brings carbon dioxide molecules to leaf surfaces, increasing the rate of photosynthesis. But the same turbulence carries off water molecules from the surface and allows greater diffusion of water molecules from the plant's interior, increasing water loss. Thus, as scientists try to manipulate the rates of photosynthesis and transpiration in the semiarid and subhumid regions, they must try to strike the balance best suited to the environmental stresses.

It is not likely that the day-to-day weather or the long-term climate of these regions can be changed by weather modification in the near future. However, it may be possible to change the microclimate. Temperature changes drastically in the first few centimeters above and below the surface of the soil. And the temperature there varies more during a day than in the air above and below. Changes in hu-

Agricultural researchers use a "pressure bomb" to determine how much water a plant contains. They place plant leaves in an aluminum capsule, pressurize it with gas, and then measure the water that is forced out of the plant leaves.

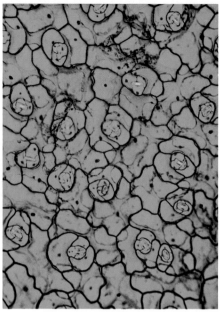

To find sorghum plants that conserve water best, scientists attach sensors to leaves, *above left,* to check stomatal openings. The most water-thrifty plants will be crossbred. They are bagged to prevent breeding with less desirable plants. The porelike stomata, *above,* are opened and closed by kidney-shaped guard cells.

midity are also greatest near the surface. Wind speed decreases markedly close to the surface and large quantities of energy in evaporation and condensation are exchanged in this zone.

To get the best ratio between photosynthesis and transpiration, we must know more about how wind, air temperature, humidity, and carbon dioxide concentration change with height above the surface. We can measure temperatures with thermometers and wind speed with anemometers; there are other instruments to measure humidity and carbon dioxide. We can find the rate at which a leaf loses water by clamping sensors onto it. But the interactions of plant and environment are so complex that more and more we must use computers to interpret them. We must develop a model that can tell us what will happen when we vary any factor in the environment or in the plant.

In one such project under my supervision at the University of Nebraska in the late 1960s, agricultural students Kirk W. Brown, Richard E. Felch, David W. Lecher, and David R. Miller studied the effect of windbreaks on the microclimate and plant growth. Brown later developed a computer model based on the data accumulated in these studies. Windbreaks are an age-old farming strategy, of course. For a long time, farmers protected their fields by planting tall shrubs or trees perpendicular to the prevailing winds. If you fly over the Great Plains, you can see thousands of windbreaks on the north and south sides of fields, because the prevailing winds come from those directions.

My students studied in detail what a windbreak does to the climate of the sheltered areas and how it affects productivity. They planted sugar beets, dry beans, snap beans, and soybeans and protected parts of the fields with movable wooden windbreaks and tall plants. They measured temperature, wind speed, water loss, and other factors during the whole growing season. They compared their figures with conditions in the unprotected parts of the fields. They found that the barriers clearly reduced wind speed and air turbulence. This, in turn, reduced the transport of heat and water vapor to and from the plant. The air temperature above the protected crops was warmer by day and colder at night compared with the unprotected fields, but the humidity was greater all the time.

The measurements showed that windbreaks do not greatly reduce transpiration when temperatures are reasonably moderate and the air not too dry. However, the shelters reduced water use by as much as 20 to 30 per cent on clear days with the stresses of strong very hot or dry winds. Our research also showed that, despite the lower turbulence, there was very little influence on the movement and concentration of carbon dioxide and thus on photosynthesis. The protected plants remained unwilted and continued to photosynthesize during such periods of atmospheric and moisture stress and had greater yields.

Windbreaks are a way to modify the microclimate and improve water-use efficiency. There are also ways to modify the architecture of the plant itself for better adaptation to environmental stress. For example, soybean breeders James H. Williams and James E. Specht of the University of Nebraska at Lincoln have been breeding plants to develop a short strain primarily to resist "lodging," the breaking or flattening of plants by wind. But in semiarid lands, where the wind is hot and dry, such shorter plants will also consume less water, since they are exposed to less wind.

The shape and the arrangement of leaves on a plant—the plant canopy—can also be bred into plants to provide "architectures" that can improve the plant's water-use efficiency. In the 1960s, agriculturists David M. Gates of the University of Michigan, Edward T. Linacre of Macquarie University in Australia, and others used rectangular plates as models of leaves in order to calculate how leaf shape affects the efficiency of heat exchange between the leaf and the air. The amount of heat absorbed by the leaf determines its temperature and how much water can be transpired. They found that narrow leaves exchange heat more efficiently per unit of area because the leading edge presents the first change in conditions that the wind encounters.

As the wind advances along the leaf from the leading edge, it adjusts more and more to the temperature of the leaf. If the leaf is hotter than the air, the air will be warmed as it moves over the leaf. Consequently, the temperature difference is lessened and heat exchange is reduced.

Aside from heat exchange, which affects water loss, the shape of the leaf also affects the way in which light penetrates plant canopies. Tropical grasses, with long thin leaves such as corn, sorghum, and sugar cane make use of increasing quantities of carbon dioxide by photosynthesis as solar radiation reaches its summer maximum. In fact, researchers have demonstrated that corn can continue to increase its photosynthetic rate under artificial radiation that is stronger than normal full sunlight. Most other plants reach maximum photosynthesis at light levels less than full sunlight.

The amount of light reaching a plant's leaves depends on how the leaves are arranged in the plant's canopy. That distribution is difficult to determine precisely. The color of the leaves, their thickness and density, and other factors complicate efforts to determine which canopy parts receive insufficient light for maximum photosynthesis.

My University of Nebraska colleagues Blaine Blad and Raoul Lemeur have determined the major computational methods to use in such studies. Some geometrical models are based on the idea that each leaf is a flat surface characterized by its shape and the angle between that surface and the direction of the sun's rays. Other models are based on mimicking the shape and arrangement of different plant types. For example, a corn crop can be modeled with an array of cylinders that roughly describes the shape of the individual plants. A pine forest might be modeled with cones placed at various spacings.

If we could design a plant with an ideal canopy, what would it be like? Tightly bound, abundantly leafed plants will absorb almost all the sunlight at the outer edge of the canopy; interior leaves will be short of light. The most efficient plants would have open canopies that

A windbreak of tall corn shelters a field of sugar beets in western Nebraska, *below,* and increases beet output by reducing wind-caused water loss. Soybeans bred shorter than standard varieties, *below right,* suffer less wind damage and also lose less moisture.

allow light to reach the lowest and most central leaves. Upper leaves that are upright permit light to penetrate to the lower leaves. Lower leaves that are horizontal absorb the penetrating light. Plants with leaves that fold down at night present a smaller surface to the night skies, so they do not cool as quickly as do other plants.

It may also prove useful for the plant to be able to reflect solar radiation that is not useful in photosynthesis. Agricultural engineer Ido Seginer of the Israel Institute of Technology in Haifa calculated that an increase in the plant's ability to reflect solar radiation would significantly reduce the amount of energy heating the plant and causing transpiration. Agricultural researchers Antoine Aboukhaled, Robert M. Hagan, and David C. Davenport of the University of California, Davis, put coatings of kaolinite, a natural clay, on the leaves of Valencia orange, lemon, kidney bean, and rubber plants to reflect light. They grew the plants in growth chambers so that they could measure photosynthesis and transpiration. They reported that transpiration was reduced in all cases and photosynthesis was reduced only when the plants were grown under very low light levels.

Using a different model, our Nebraska group calculated that the net radiant energy at the leaf surface could be reduced by 15 to 20 per cent with reflective coatings on crops under semiarid conditions and that similar reductions in water use would result. We also speculated that such a reflective coating on soybean plants would not appreciably decrease photosynthesis because soybeans reach their maximum pho-

Ancient ruins look down on green fields in the Negev desert where the water-conserving techniques used by the Nabataeans more than 2,000 years ago have been re-created.

tosynthetic rate at a relatively low level of illumination. With support from the National Science Foundation, we undertook a series of field experiments in which we coated large acreages of soybeans with kaolinite and Celite, a material used commercially in water-filtration plants. We measured the incoming solar radiation, and the radiation reflected by natural and coated plants. We also determined how light of different wavelengths was reflected and transmitted into the canopy and the temperature of the canopies in natural and treated plants.

These studies indicated clearly that the materials increased reflectivity. Transpiration was reduced by about 15 per cent, as the computer model had predicted. Photosynthesis was unaffected. Although some reduction in photosynthesis might have been expected, light penetration to the plant was actually increased because the reflective material bounced light rays into the canopy.

Except in such emergencies as a drought, coatings of reflective materials are likely to be too expensive for widespread use on field crops.

But the physical principle can now be used in developing new varieties more suited to the dry areas of the world. Agronomist Hayden Ferguson of the University of Montana in the early 1970s studied the "Golden Betzes" and "Golden Liberty" varieties of barley. These are identical in every respect with other varieties except that they are yellow. Ferguson reports that the plants produce as well as their normal cousins but use less water because they reflect away a significant portion of solar radiation that would otherwise heat the plant.

High reflectivity can be bred into plants in many ways. The sheen we see on very shiny house plants is usually due to natural waxes on the plant surface that reflect light. Physiological ecologists James Ehleringer, Olle Bjorkman, and Harold Mooney of the Carnegie Institution and Stanford University believe that pubescence, or hairiness, also is a mechanism for adaptation to aridity, decreasing the absorption of solar radiation. They found that pubescence in the desert shrub *Encelia farinosa* is greater in the dryer parts of the desert. Agronomist S. R. Ghorashy and his associates at the University of Illinois in Champaign-Urbana found in 1971 that pubescence in the "Clark" soybean lowers transpiration but photosynthesis is apparently unaffected.

Ehleringer and his associates reported in October 1976 on the behavior of the desert primrose *Cammissonia claviformis*, a winter annual that grows in Death Valley, California. This plant grows exceptionally rapidly after rainfall. The researchers measured its photosynthetic rate at these times. They found it to be 8.5 per cent in noon sunlight—80 per cent of the theoretical maximum possible and far above the performance of crop plants.

In the late 1960s, West German botanists O. L. Lange, W. Koch, and E. D. Schulze measured the photosynthetic and transpiration rates and compared the water-use efficiency of a number of cultivated and wild plants at Avdat, the site of Evenari's reconstruction of Nabataean agriculture in the Negev desert. They reported that two native plants used water extremely efficiently. *Citrullus* grows in the gullies that carry the runoff from the rare rainfalls in the area and produces abundant vegetation, while *Artemisia*, a dwarf bush, uses very little water but unfortunately produces very little plant material.

Many other desert plants have characteristics that fit them for survival and for efficient growth in extreme aridity, and scientists are studying these various plant strategies, evolved over millions of years. Agricultural plants may someday be developed from these species and much that we know about these plants can be used to guide us in modifying or managing cultivated species.

Plant breeding and water and land management, and microclimate modification cannot, of course, provide the full answer to the world's food problems. Questions of nutrition and food distribution, of economics and politics, remain. But this agricultural research will help us to use the dryer parts of the world to feed the human species and it may even allow us someday to farm the deserts.

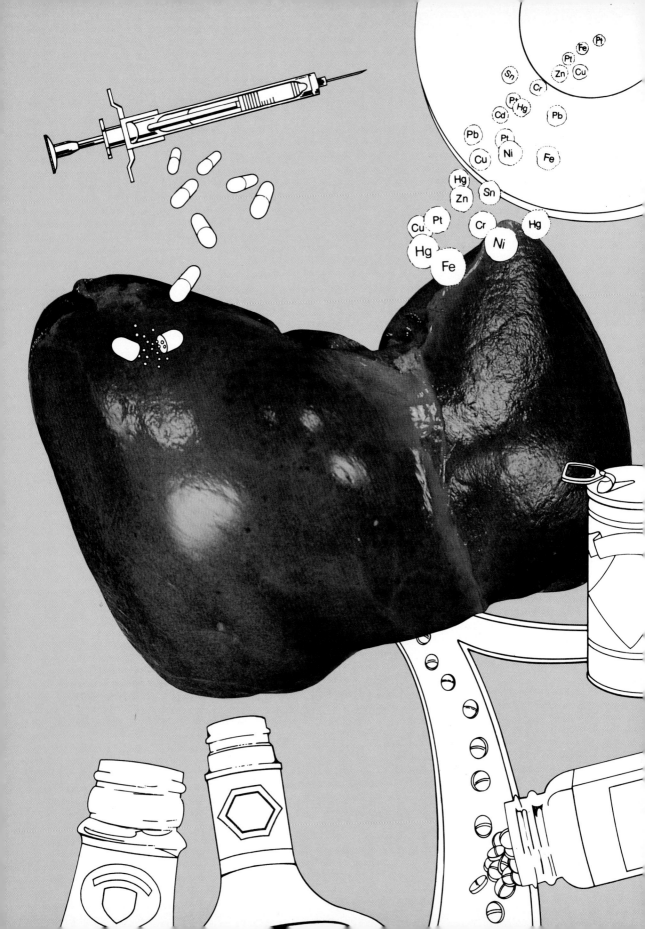

The Liver's Many Roles

By Ben Patrusky

**Scientists are seeking a better understanding
of how our largest internal organ protects
our body from a variety of external assaults**

At the dawn of history, people viewed the liver as the organ best representing life. They considered it the seat of the soul, an entity of magic, mystery, and myth. Why? Because the liver is the organ most drenched with blood—and blood and life were seen as one.

Archaeologists still find clay models of animal livers, inscribed with sacred texts of long-forgotten civilizations, in the sands of the Middle East. The models, left by priest-physicians of ancient Babylon, show that they studied the shapes and wrinkles in sheep livers for clues to the future and other signs from the gods.

Eventually, the liver lost its privileged position in folklore to an organ that broadcasts its life force with audible beats, the heart. It became the seat of the soul; modern love ballads testify to this. It is not the liver that sings, dances, or gets left in San Francisco.

Biologically, the liver has never given up its central role, for it is the body's master chemical factory. In recent years, stepped-up research has shown that this unromantic organ is essential to dozens of life processes. Moreover, new-found knowledge of how the liver works has produced a wondrous roster of medical advances—along with a worrisome list of newly recognized health hazards.

The liver, weighing about 1.4 kilograms (3 pounds) in an adult, is the largest internal organ of the body. Lying mainly on the right side of the abdominal cavity, it functions as a manufacturing center, as a storehouse for body nutrients, and as a neutralizer of drugs and other

A terra-cotta model of a sheep's liver helped Babylonian priests teach students where to look on an animal's liver for the markings that were sometimes used to predict the future.

The author:
Ben Patrusky is a science writer who specializes in medical topics.

foreign chemicals. "You can think of the liver as a magnificent metabolic sorting system," says Attallah Kappas, physician-in-chief at Rockefeller University Hospital in New York City, and long active in liver research. "It processes an astonishing number of substances, good and bad, selects what the body needs and doesn't need, and knows what to do with them and when to do it."

Blood, laden with nutrients and other substances absorbed from the small intestine, travels directly to the spongelike liver through the portal vein. Smaller veins then distribute the blood to the individual liver cells, which are clustered in tightly knit groups called lobules.

The liver cells process nutrients in several ways. They convert sugar from the diet into a starchlike carbohydrate, glycogen, which the liver then stores for ready release as glucose when the body needs energy. Liver cells also produce bile, which works in the small intestine neutralizing acids and breaking down fat. Liver cells use other nutrients in manufacturing vital blood proteins, such as serum albumin, serum globulin, and fibrinogen. And they also make cholesterol, which is essential for the production of sex hormones. In addition, liver cells store vitamin A and certain minerals that the body needs.

One of the liver's most important functions is to inactivate or detoxify a wide variety of potentially harmful chemicals. The liver cells take such chemicals out of the circulation, and enzymes in the cells transform them into less toxic substances. These enzymes form the mixed function oxidase system, which processes more than 80 per cent of the drugs, pollutants, insecticides, and other foreign chemicals that invade the body. The system makes these chemicals soluble in water and thus easier to transport for eventual excretion through the kidneys and lower intestines. The system acts on useful medications in the same way as it does on poisonous substances. This activity must be taken into account by physicians when they are determining dosage levels and methods of administering a drug.

Biochemists have had a reasonable understanding of how the mixed function oxidase system operates only since about 1964. The key enzyme in the system is called cytochrome P-450, a technical name derived from the way it is measured in the laboratory. Cytochrome P-450 is vital primarily because it releases oxygen atoms that attach to and inactivate the chemical to be eliminated. The oxygen in cytochrome P-450 comes from heme, its main active component. Heme is an iron compound that is also important in red blood cells as the material that carries oxygen.

The activity of the mixed function oxidase system increases or decreases dramatically in response to the concentrations of various drugs

All blood circulates in the liver, entering from the heart through the hepatic artery and from the small intestines through the portal vein, and afterwards exiting to the heart through the hepatic vein. Within the liver, the blood circulates in sinusoids, or spaces, formed by the interlacing liver cells. Here it deposits harmful wastes for disposal and picks up chemical substances produced by the liver.

Channels in the Liver Factory

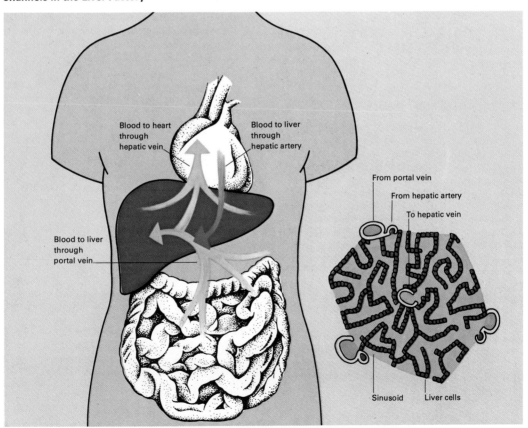

Blood to heart through hepatic vein

Blood to liver through hepatic artery

From portal vein

From hepatic artery

To hepatic vein

Blood to liver through portal vein

Sinusoid   Liver cells

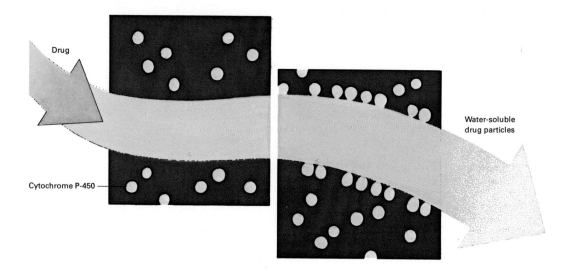

Drug

Cytochrome P-450

Water-soluble
drug particles

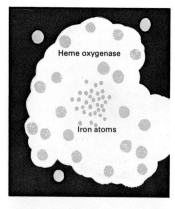

Heme oxygenase

Iron atoms

Dealing with Drugs

When the blood brings a drug to the liver,
it is processed and disposed of by a series
of enzymes, primarily cytochrome P-450,
which transfers oxygen atoms to the drug and
makes it water-soluble and easy for the body
to eliminate. But trace amounts of metals,
such as iron, disrupt this normal activity.
Iron increases the production of another
enzyme, heme oxygenase, which destroys a
chemical in cytochrome P-450. This chemical
then cannot do its work properly and greater
concentrations of the drug stay in the blood.

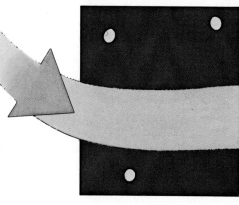

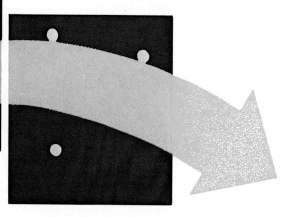

or chemicals. This sensitivity helps to explain the unpredictable and often nettlesome effects that can occur when several drugs are administered at the same time. For example, prolonged use of the sedative phenobarbital causes the liver to produce large quantities of cytochrome P-450, and this, in turn, affects the metabolism of other drugs taken at the same time as the sedative.

Consider the case of a patient who is taking drugs to prevent blood clotting and who has been using phenobarbital for a long time. The patient's level of cytochrome P-450 will suddenly drop if he stops taking the phenobarbital. Less of the enzyme will then be available to handle the metabolism of the anticoagulant drugs. And, unless his anticoagulant dosage is lowered to appropriate levels, he stands a very serious risk of hemorrhage.

Certain food constituents can also affect the rate at which drugs are processed by the liver. Kappas and his colleagues showed, in a study in 1976 on human volunteers, that eating moderate amounts of charcoal-broiled beef could significantly diminish the biological activity of certain widely prescribed drugs and speed up their elimination in body wastes. One such drug is theophylline, used to treat heart ailments. Another is the pain reliever antipyrine. Apparently, some chemical in the charcoal-broiled beef triggers increased production of cytochrome P-450, thereby speeding up the removal of these drugs.

Trace amounts of metals can also disrupt the cytochrome P-450 balance. Rockefeller University biochemist Mahin D. Maines, working in association with Kappas, discovered this fact in 1974. Cadmium, chromium, copper, iron, lead, mercury, nickel, platinum, tin, and zinc, which are widespread in our industrial environment, often enter our bodies in the air we breathe and the food we eat. These metals tend to accumulate in the liver and elsewhere in the body, and as they do, their potential for damage grows.

The contaminating metals tend to increase the production of one enzyme, heme oxygenase, in the mixed function oxidase system. This is the enzyme that breaks down the heme molecule in cytochrome P-450. At the same time, the trace metals tend to block the synthesis of another enzyme, ALA-synthetase, which is needed to manufacture additional heme for cytochrome P-450 and for hemoglobin.

This action on the two enzymes depletes the supply of cytochrome P-450 and may seriously impair the system's ability to inactivate drugs and other chemicals. There is no way to gauge how much the trace metals are currently affecting human beings. But, to the prescribing physician, this subtle, new-found danger can spell real trouble.

Not all of Maines's news is bad, however. Out of her work in mapping the biochemical routes by which trace metals lower heme levels has come an unexpected strategy for treating jaundice and drug toxicity in infants. All babies are prone to jaundice, or yellowing of the skin, during the first two weeks of life. This is because, as the infant makes its own red blood cells, its liver breaks down the heme-rich blood cells

Alcohol and the Fatty Liver

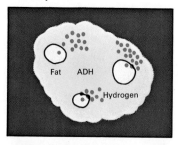

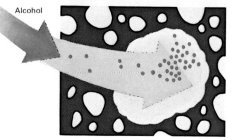

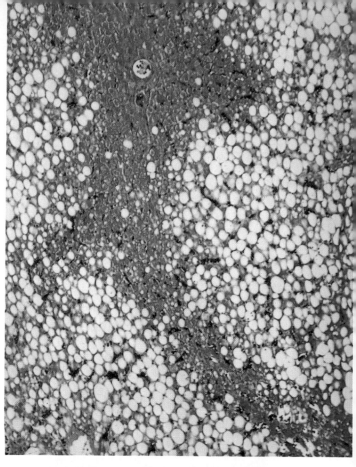

In the human liver cell, alcohol dehydrogenase (ADH) breaks fat down to get hydrogen for cell use. An alcoholic's liver gets hydrogen from alcohol, and white fat globules accumulate in the liver tissue, *right* (magnified 500 times).

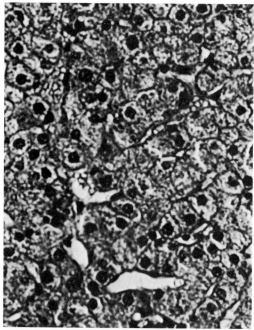

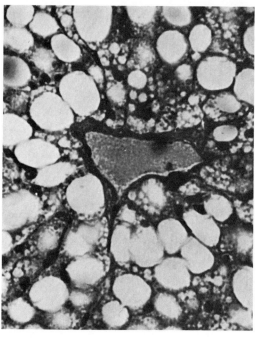

Needle biopsy section of a healthy baboon's liver, *above,* enlarged about 300 times, has none of the fat globules, *above right,* found in the same animal's liver after 15 months of heavy alcohol consumption.

that were acquired from the mother. Bilirubin, a product of heme breakdown, accumulates and spills over into the baby's bloodstream during this process. The bilirubin causes the yellowing of the skin. And, if the bilirubin overload is great enough, it may damage brain cells, giving rise to kernicterus, a grave neurological disorder that causes convulsions, mental retardation, and cerebral palsy.

In adults, the enzyme glucuronyl transferase transforms bilirubin into a water-soluble substance and transports it to the intestines for excretion. But this chemical transformation is no easy task for the infant liver, which does not yet have an abundant supply of the necessary glucuronyl transferase. And, as if the enzyme deficiency were not enough, the heme breakdown releases iron, one of the trace metals that speeds up the production of heme oxygenase, the enzyme that breaks down heme. This increases the bilirubin in the blood.

To get rid of the excess iron and prevent bilirubin build-up, Maines suggests using chelating agents—compounds that combine with, and thus deactivate, metals. She conducted experiments on newborn mice in 1977 and confirmed the soundness of this procedure. When fed to the animals, the chelating agents reduced the production of bilirubin.

Maines believes that chelation therapy might also effectively treat drug toxicity in newborn infants. This condition is common in babies born to women who are taking certain drugs. Maines reasons that removing iron would increase the levels of both heme and cytochrome P-450 by decreasing production of heme oxygenase and by speeding up the synthesis of ALA-synthetase. As a result, the infant's liver should more easily eliminate the drug overload. Maines drugged the newborn mice with hexobarbital, a sleep-inducing sedative, and showed that chelation therapy is effective in this way.

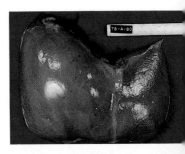

Compared with smooth and normal-colored healthy human liver, *top,* the diseased liver of an alcoholic is knobby and ravaged by scar tissue.

Alcohol puts the liver through some of its toughest, most elaborate paces. Liver cells are the only ones in the body with the chemical artillery needed to metabolize ethyl alcohol (drinking alcohol). This makes the liver the most vulnerable of all our organs to alcohol's ravages. The most common of these ravages is alcohol-induced cirrhosis. Cirrhosis, a chronic disease characterized by a degeneration of the liver cells, is the fifth leading cause of death in the United States.

Scientists thought for a long time that excessive drinking was bad for the liver because of the malnutrition that almost always accompanies it. They now know that the alcohol directly damages liver cells. Experiments reported in November 1977 by biochemist Charles S. Lieber and his associates at the Veterans Administration Hospital in the Bronx, N.Y., showed how the damage is done.

Lieber put baboons on a diet in which alcohol accounted for 50 per cent of the total calories. The baboons developed all the alcohol-related liver diseases, including cirrhosis, in two to four years.

Lieber found that the liver tissues developed all the symptoms that ordinarily precede cirrhosis. He also showed that the breakdown of ethanol in the liver involves the same biochemical machinery that is used to metabolize fats. An important product of the process is hydrogen, which is used by the mitochondria, tiny sausage-shaped structures within the cells, to produce energy. The mitochondria ordinarily get all the hydrogen they require from the breakdown of fats. But the liver will take the hydrogen from alcohol first, because fats can be stored in the liver while alcohol cannot. The unburned fats begin to accumulate and engorge the liver cells.

Fatty liver is generally a reversible condition–up to a point. If heavy drinking persists over many years, the liver cells may lose their ability to use fats as a source of hydrogen for the mitochondria, and the drinker develops cirrhosis.

Not all heavy drinkers or alcoholics–or, for that matter, alcohol-fed baboons–develop cirrhosis. The majority do not, though no one can tell who is a high-risk candidate for advanced liver damage. Lieber discovered what may be a way of predicting which baboons are most susceptible to extensive alcohol damage. He used needle biopsy, the insertion of a needle into the liver tissue to withdraw cells for examination. He found that the baboons most vulnerable to cirrhosis developed lesions in cells around the liver's central vein. Lieber's co-workers are now trying to determine if the same thing happens in humans.

Learning how the mixed function oxidase system works has enabled biochemists to understand the quirky, sometimes topsy-turvy reactions that result when alcohol is mixed with drugs. Heavy drinking apparently boosts the level of the drug-dismantling enzymes. This causes drugs taken at the same time–barbiturates or tranquilizers, for instance–to be inactivated far more rapidly than they are in nondrinkers or light drinkers. But this only happens when the drinkers are sober and the liver is not having to deal with both the alcohol and the drugs. If drinking is resumed, the alcohol competes with the barbiturates or tranquilizers for the same metabolizing enzymes. Then, the drugs remain in the body longer, and the combination of alcohol and drugs may have a lethal effect on the centers of the brain governing respiration or other vital processes. The deadly combination of drugs and alcohol has been implicated in many deaths, including those of such celebrities as Judy Garland and Janis Joplin.

In most instances, however, the mixed function oxidase system works to benefit people because it rids the body of many unwanted compounds. But the system sometimes backfires disastrously. Hitching an oxygen atom to certain substances can set the stage for a dire biological double cross. In such cases, otherwise harmless chemicals can become carcinogenic and lead to liver cancers.

"It's taken about two decades, but we now have a reasonable idea of how cell metabolism turns on the chemicals so that they do their dirty work," says Allan H. Conney, a biochemist at Hoffman La-Roche Incorporated, in Nutley, N.J., and an authority on chemical carcinogenesis. As a result of acquiring an atom of oxygen, the substances become electrophilic, or "electron-hungry." What happens

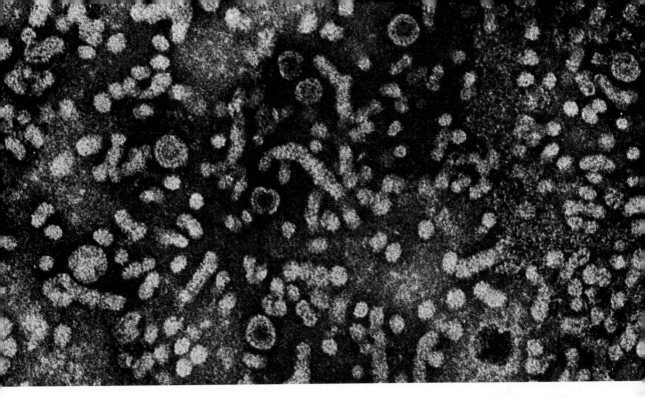

next is a matter of speculation, but researchers suspect that the electrophilic chemicals home in on electron-rich sites in molecules of deoxyribonucleic acid (DNA), the cell's hereditary material. These chemicals may then alter the genetic makeup so that the cell becomes malignant.

Perhaps the most remarkable chapter in liver research is that describing another major liver disease, viral hepatitis. Until about 1967, virus-caused hepatitis was classified as either infectious hepatitis, transmitted from person to person through poor hygiene, or serum hepatitis, thought to be caused by unsterile injections or transfusions of infected blood. But in the late 1960s and early 1970s, evidence began to accumulate suggesting that serum hepatitis was communicable through more than contaminated needles and blood transfusions. A person could get the virus through a kiss, a shared fork or toothbrush, or sexual contact. In a word, serum hepatitis was also infectious.

As a result of this discovery, the old infectious hepatitis was renamed hepatitis A and serum hepatitis became hepatitis B. Then, in 1974, a third kind of hepatitis was discovered. This form is now recognized as the one that is most common after a transfusion with infected blood. Because little else is yet known about this form except that it definitely is neither hepatitis A nor B, it is called non-A, non-B hepatitis.

Each type of hepatitis poses a different medical problem. Physicians do not consider hepatitis A a serious disease. It is never transmitted by transfusion, and it is contagious only during its acute stage, after incubation. Most victims recover quickly and are immune to further assaults by the hepatitis A virus. Hepatitis B and, from indications, non-A, non-B hepatitis are more significant health hazards. Most victims recover from acute attacks of either disease. But later some of them

Blood of hepatitis B patients contains three different particles — string-shaped objects, small spheres, and the telltale doughnutlike hepatitis B virus. (Magnification is more than 200,000 times.)

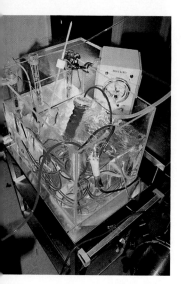

Modified kidney dialysis machine uses suspended layers of rabbit liver tissue in one design of an artificial liver.

may become carriers and transmit the disease. Potential carriers of hepatitis B can be identified by a viral "fingerprint" in the blood, the shell or envelope of the hepatitis B virus. Its presence indicates that surviving whole viruses may be present. Baruch S. Blumberg, associate director of the Institute for Cancer Research in Philadelphia, discovered the particle in 1963 and named it the Australian antigen. An antigen is any agent that invades the body and triggers production of protective antibodies. Alfred M. Prince, a virologist at the New York City Blood Center, showed in 1968 that the Australian antigen, now called hepatitis B surface antigen, is a mark of hepatitis B.

Armed with this knowledge, Prince developed a screening test that could detect the antigen to determine if would-be blood donors were hepatitis B virus carriers. Such screening is now mandatory at blood banks. Possible carriers are advised never to give blood.

Discovery of the antigen also opened the way to the development of hepatitis B vaccine. Researchers have been unable to isolate and grow the virus in a laboratory. But when it was discovered that blood contaminated by the B virus produced no disease in recipients whose blood contained antibodies to the B surface antigen, the possibility arose that the antigen alone might serve as a vaccine. It was based on the assumption that antibodies that would attack the virus shell would also destroy the virus in it. Three new vaccines based on this principle have effectively protected chimpanzees against infection when they were given live hepatitis B virus from the blood of hepatitis victims.

Two of the vaccines were developed under the direction of Robert Purcell, a virologist at the National Institute of Allergy and Infectious Diseases in Bethesda, Md. The third was prepared by Maurice R. Hilleman and his associates at Merck, Sharpe, and Dohme, a pharmaceutical company in West Point, Pa. All these vaccines are now being tested on human volunteers–Purcell's on a small number of consenting Trappist monks in a Georgia monastery and Hilleman's on a group of company employee volunteers. These studies are aimed at determining the safety of the vaccines as well as their ability to stimulate the production of antibodies to the antigen. These will be followed in 1979 by more extensive trials.

Ultimately, the vaccines may have a lifesaving potential beyond their powers to protect against hepatitis; they may also reduce the incidence of cancer of the liver. Several studies in the mid-1970s have turned up a startling correlation between the presence of the B surface antigen in a person's blood and liver cancer. For instance, about 80 per cent of the liver cancer patients tested in Taiwan had the antigen. If there is a direct relationship between hepatitis B and liver cancer, then the vaccine preventing hepatitis may also prevent the cancer.

The success of the artificial kidney, or dialysis machine, in keeping chronically ill kidney patients alive has led researchers to speculate that an artificial liver might be developed to support a diseased human liver. The liver, unlike the kidney, has enormous regenerative powers, so an artificial liver would only have to be used for a few days or weeks until the natural organ could heal itself.

Researchers are evaluating several methods. One is to adapt an artificial kidney to cleanse the blood of such toxic compounds as ammonia and bilirubin, which the healthy liver would normally process. Another is to pass the blood of patients through an adsorbent compound such as activated charcoal, synthetic resins, or special gels, to remove unwanted substances. These methods have been used on a few mortally ill patients with disappointing results.

Hematologist Paul Berk of New York City's Mount Sinai Hospital, a close observer of artificial liver development, is not surprised at the lack of success. "The problem is that we really don't know what an artificial liver is supposed to be doing," Berk says. He adds that it is wrong to compare kidney dialysis with artificial liver development. Dialysis machines, he points out, were designed only after researchers had worked out the basic metabolic problems that must be corrected in order for a kidney patient to survive. And the artificial kidney, much like the real organ, is little more than a garbage-disposal unit. However, removing toxic compounds is only one part of the liver's many vital functions.

A promising approach is the use of living liver cells taken from animals. A "device" composed of such cells would presumably serve the required dual functions of manufacturing life chemicals and trash removal. However, the major obstacle is to find a way to allow the animal liver cells to do their work while minimizing or eliminating direct contact between the patient's blood and the cells or tissues. Otherwise the patient may reject the immunologically "foreign" liver cells just as he would most transplanted organs.

A device developed by Kenneth N. Matsumara of the Immunity Research Center in Berkeley, Calif., combines layers of rabbit liver cells with a modified artificial kidney machine. The cells are separated from the blood by a semipermeable membrane through which waste products can pass and be taken up by the cells. Meanwhile, such liver-made products as albumin move in the opposite direction. The liver cells are kept alive by blood-borne oxygen and other nutrients that diffuse through the membrane, but antibodies and cells that normally police the body against foreign materials are too large to get through the barrier. This system successfully reversed liver failure in a cancer patient in its first clinical test in Berkeley in 1977.

Clearly, the story of the liver is far from over. Despite astonishing research progress, there is still much about liver function that puzzles scientists. Perhaps this is symbolic of how our view of the liver has come full circle. Once, as a kind of biological divining rod, the liver mystified. Deposed, it went unsung. But this marvel of chemical manipulation is center stage once again, sparkling with new mysteries that command the attention of modern-day descendants of those ancient, sign-seeking priest-physicians.

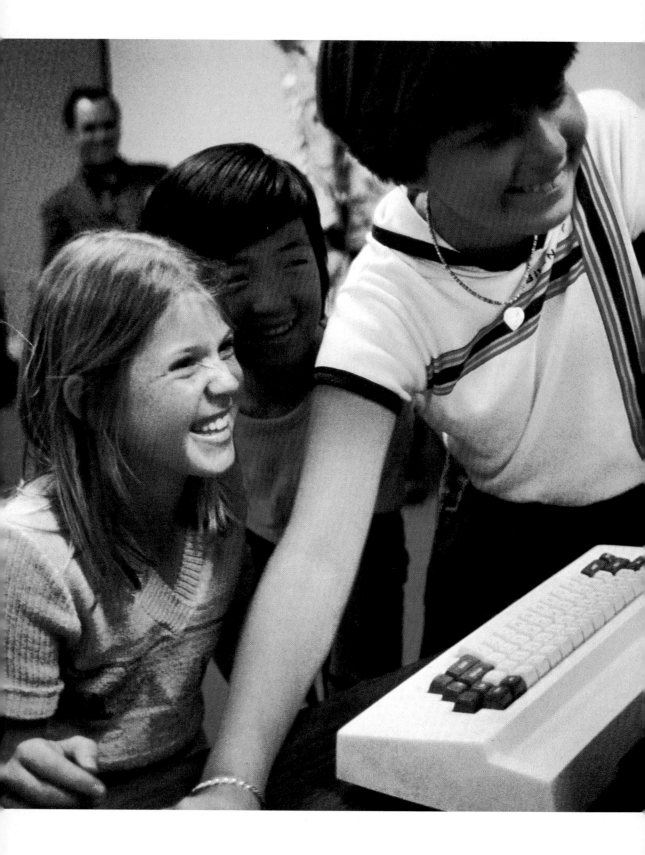

Programming Your Own Computer

By Alan C. Kay

The computers of the 1980s will be easy to use and inexpensive, yet powerful enough to let us do things we have yet to imagine

Beth, a 14-year-old junior high student, lounged in the grass under a tree, enjoying the sunshine. She was watching pictures move about on the televisionlike display screen of a curious gadget she held in her lap. Her mother called from the house, "Beth, time to do your homework."

"I'm doing it, mother," Beth answered.

She began striking keys on the typewriterlike keyboard below the display screen. Part of a composition about space travel that she had begun the previous day appeared on the screen, along with a half-finished illustration and some references.

An awkward sentence caught her eye. She pointed a pencillike stylus at the sentence, typed a revision, and watched the sentence change to her new phrasing. Then she finished the illustration with a drawing tool, filling in tone and drawing straight lines. When she made a mistake, she typed out instructions to undo what she had done, and then tried again.

Another of Beth's illustrations was a shuttle docking to a space station. She decided to animate it and began to grapple with the problem of how a spacecraft's position can be controlled if the simulated rocket can only be turned on and off. Soon, she had an image of a shuttle moving on the screen in response to her controls. It did not look quite right, but she was sure that she could correct it with a bit more thought.

When Beth was satisfied with her work, she filed the composition away by pressing a key and turned to more personal pursuits. For fun, she had been working on an elaborate horse-racing animation for some time. It was now time to think about making betting on the horses a part of the game.

Beth was working with her personal computer. Although she is a fictitious teen-ager living in the future, hundreds of students like her have already had similar experiences with personal computers at the Xerox Palo Alto Research Center in California. They have been part of a 10-year program, begun in 1971, to develop and test the personal computers of the 1980s. By mid-1978, about 100 adults and more than 300 young people between the ages of 6 and 15 had learned to use these computers to write and illustrate reports, create drawings, compose music, and bring their own ideas to life through animation.

Each of them has learned how to instruct, or program, computers to create new tools and new effects. For example, 12-year-old Susan designed a drawing tool that would help her form and manipulate geometric shapes and textures on the television display. Dennis, an 11-year-old, created his own version of a space-war game in which spaceship fleets he designed battled on the display screen. Twelve-year-old Joan adapted a tool built by professional animators to produce a beautifully animated horse race.

My interest in personal computers follows a dream I have had since I was a graduate student in the 1960s. Thanks to some far-sighted professors, I realized that computers were not just huge, clanking, million-dollar arithmetic gadgets that had to be constantly fed punched cards by highly trained experts. Instead, they had the potential to be a fantastic tool with which ordinary humans could communicate. Moreover, the room-sized equipment of that time was being replaced by much smaller and faster models. In a few years, it would be possible to package the computer power–represented by the amount of information per unit time that it can handle–of the million-dollar machines of the 1960s in inexpensive containers as small as an ordinary three-ring notebook. The technology that has already made possible devices such as pocket calculators or digital watches would bring forth the personal computer.

This meant that everyone could soon have a personal computer. But what could they do with it? It is not enough to have a machine with all its circuits, storage, and memory facilities–the hardware–compacted into a small but mighty computer. We also need a way to communicate with and control it–the software. In present computers, software systems are unwieldy, to say the least. They require expert program-

The author:
Alan C. Kay is principal scientist and head of the Learning Research Group at the Xerox Palo Alto Research Center.

mers to bludgeon them into more-or-less working order. Obviously, personal computing in the 1980s would be impossible if softwares were not drastically improved.

In 1971, my company provided the kind of long-term research support that the problem demanded, and a group of us interested in personal computers began to work on them. We visualized the personal computer of the 1980s as a notebook-sized package whose front side was a flat-screen reflective display, like a liquid-crystal watch face. The surface of the screen would be sensitive to the touch of a finger or a stylus. It would contain miniature computer circuits that could carry out millions of instructions per second, and there would be enough storage capacity to retain several months worth of projects. The machine would be completely self-contained. However, it also could be connected to hi-fi sets to create music, to other personal

The ENIAC, a 1946 vintage computer, *top left,* has given way to increasingly smaller and more powerful machines such as the PDP 11/45 text and picture layout minicomputer, *top right,* and the Alto, *above left,* used to develop programs for personal computers. Such power will soon be contained in the notebook-sized Dynabook, *above.*

computers for group projects, and to external information sources such as the computerized libraries of the future. We called this visionary computer "Dynabook."

To work on the software of the 1980s, we had to design and build a computer with the hardware of the 1970s. Miniaturization of computer components had just begun, so we had to make our computer the size of a desk to be powerful enough for our purpose. It also had to have a high-resolution television screen instead of a flat reflective display which does not yet exist. In addition to a typewriter keyboard, we provided a movable device—we call it a "mouse"—that controls an electronic pointer on the screen. It also has push buttons to indicate commands to be carried out.

Meanwhile, the first of the microcomputers, or microprocessors, began to appear on the market. Engineers were designing integrated circuits with thousands of transistors on single silicon chips. Several of these chips can be connected to perform all the operations of a digital computer in a very small space. This development triggered a commercial explosion in calculators, control devices, and video games. This was encouraging because it confirmed our projections about the future of computers. It also meant that more people would be getting interested in personal computing.

The first microprocessors were generations away from the kind of computing power that would be needed for the personal computers of the 1980s. By 1978, a second generation of microprocessors had become available that are about 10 times as powerful as their predecessors. If the trend continues, the next generation of microprocessors, in the early 1980s, will be powerful enough for our personal computer. By packaging several microprocessors together, we can get the tens of millions of executions per second Dynabook will require.

A set of instructions on how to perform a process that can be recalled and carried out later is called a program. Movie scripts, football plays, and musical scores are all programs written by humans to be followed by humans. Only in the past few decades have machines been constructed that can also store instructions and later recall and follow them, although these programs are much simpler than the programs that humans can handle.

Most computer programming is done using lists of commands in a sequence. This is often described as using ingredients in a recipe. For example, to make cookie batter, you follow a recipe that tells you first to mix the ingredients flour and water. If the batter is too sticky, add more water. If the batter is too thin, add more flour. If the batter is just right, do not do anything. The task is ended.

Recipes get very complicated when many things have to be coordinated simultaneously, such as in planning a banquet. A banquet "programmer" is responsible for hiring the hall, the cook, and the waiters; ordering the table settings; planning the menu; and inviting the guests. Since many of these activities happen at the same time, he

Editing a Composition

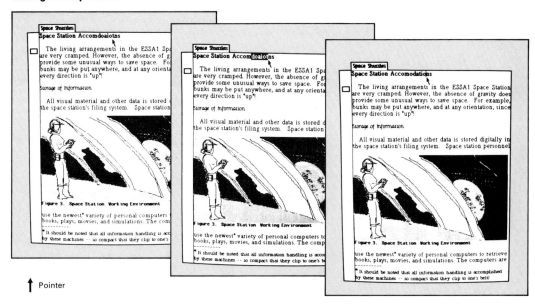

You can write and edit an illustrated composition on your personal computer. After writing and storing a story on the space shuttle, for example, you can type instructions to call up any part of the story for checking. If you discover a typographical error, you can use the "mouse" control device to correct it. When you guide the electronic pointer under the error, the screen behind this section goes dark. You type the correction, push a button on the mouse, and it appears in place. To edit the illustration, push another button on the mouse and a "painting palette" will appear on the screen. After selecting a "paint" with the pointer, you take it to the area to be painted. After pushing a button on the mouse, you can color in the desired area by moving the mouse.

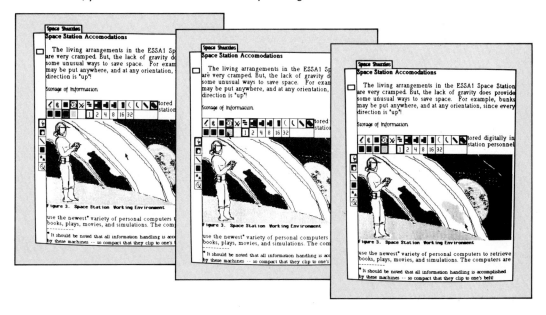

Programming a Player

To direct a player on your personal computer, you first call up the player and its associated list of commands, with the keyboard, or with the mouse. A command is chosen by moving the mouse to bring the electronic pointer to the command on the screen. It is executed by pressing a button on the top of the mouse. The computer acknowledges the command by responding to the words — the screen behind them goes dark.

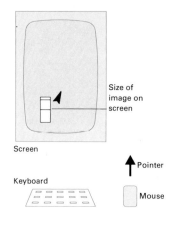

Size of image on screen

Screen

Pointer

Keyboard

Mouse

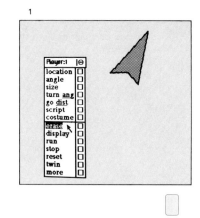

To make the player disappear, bring the pointer to "erase," and press mouse button. The screen responds.

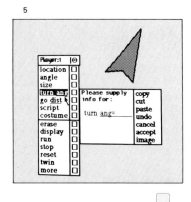

To begin programming, move pointer to "turn angle." An information slate appears requesting a specific number.

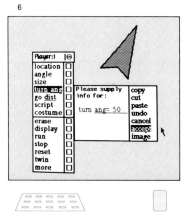

Type in degrees player is to turn (50) and move pointer to "accept" on editing list. Push mouse button.

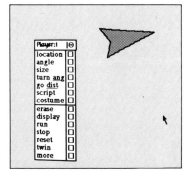

The information slate disappears and the player turns 50 degrees.

needs to coordinate them. In computer programming, such complications require skilled programmers.

Fortunately, there are ways to think about programming other than in terms of recipes and ingredients—ways that allow neat systems to be described compactly by nonexpert programmers. Some of these techniques have been developing since the early 1960s. For Dynabook, we designed a programming system based on one of these models. We called it Smalltalk. Instead of manipulating inert ingredients with recipes, Smalltalk's programs proceed like stage directions or football plays that coordinate active, independent players.

Smalltalk's world is like a computerized version of show business. We see a play on a television screen and hear the sound through speakers. But we can also communicate with and manipulate this miniature universe through typewriterlike keyboards for text, piano-like keyboards for music, and pointing devices that allow us to isolate

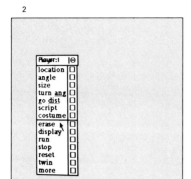

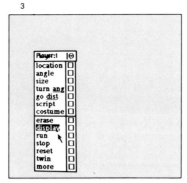

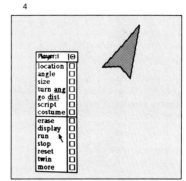

The player disappears and the command clears.

Move pointer to "display," and press the mouse button. The screen responds.

The player reappears and the command clears.

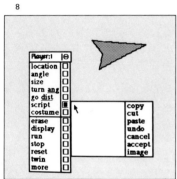

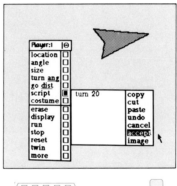

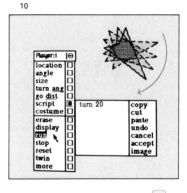

To program a general task, move the pointer to "script." A blank information slate will appear.

Type the command "turn 20" and move the pointer to "accept."

Move pointer to "run" and press the mouse button. The player will turn in 20-degree steps.

and work with pictures on the television screen. People learn Smalltalk by first directing an already written play. Next, they add their own modifications to the play. Finally, they are ready to write and produce a play of their own. They are then programming.

The production of a Smalltalk play begins with the author–the programmer–visualizing various scenes, then writing them down for the players. Rehearsals follow. "Bugs" are eliminated. Then the costumes and sets are added and the show is ready to be performed.

The display screen is the theater. The play consists of the intentions of the programmer. The show is how any one performance turns out. For example, Beth's horse-racing theater could produce many different races from the same play and players.

Smalltalk's program is unique in that each player can produce many offspring, or new players who inherit their characteristics from their parent. The characteristics can then be modified by program-

Programming a New Game

You can program a player on your personal computer to move around the screen in response to movement of the mouse. Using the command "twin," you can bring forth a second player with abilities identical to the first. Introducing a second mouse and transferring the commands for the twin to it enables two people to play a game of "Chase."

Keyboard — Pointer — 1 Mouse 1 — 2 Mouse 2

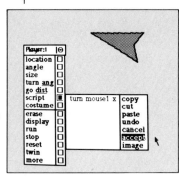

1

Move pointer to "script." Type "turn mouse1 x." Execute "accept."

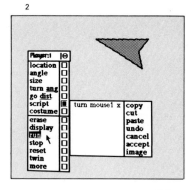

2

Move pointer to "run."

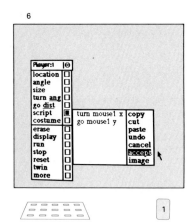

6

Type in "go mouse1 y" on the slate and move the pointer to "accept."

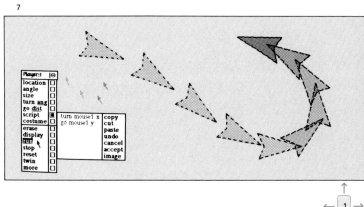

7

Move the pointer to "run" and move the mouse in vertical and horizontal directions. The player will then travel about the screen like a car.

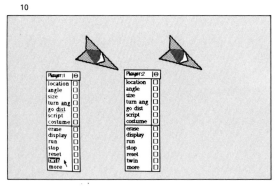

10

Commanding and executing "twin" on original player list causes identical player, with its identical list, to appear on the screen. The palette disappears.

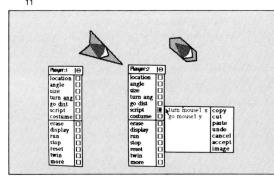

11

Redesign player 2 with the costume routine. Next, call up "script." Mouse 1 instructions will appear on player 2's slate.

3

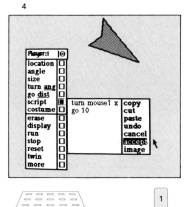

Control the player's rate of turn
by moving the mouse horizontally.

4

Point to "stop," type "go 10," and
move pointer to "accept." The player
can then move forward in 10-unit steps.

5

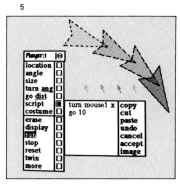

Execute "run" and move mouse
to the left. The player will move
forward, turning right gradually.

8

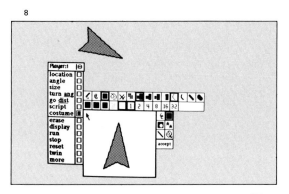

To change the appearance of the player, bring the
pointer to "costume." The painting palette and
the master image of the player will appear on the slate.

9

Use the pointer to pick lines and tones from
palette with which to paint the player image.
"Accept" transfers the costume to the player.

12

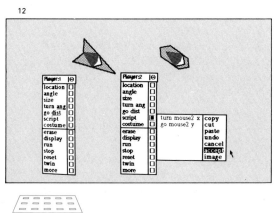

Edit the text on player 2's slate, changing 1 x
and 1y to 2x and 2y. Execute "accept."

13

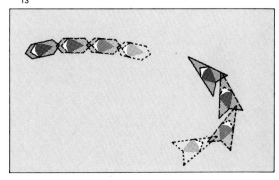

Execute "run" on both player lists and key
instructions to remove the lists. You and a
friend now have the total screen to play "Chase."

ming to give birth to still more new players. The players in Smalltalk are quite versatile. The number 3, an arrow shape, a car, a musical instrument, a spaceship are all players.

We learn to program in Smalltalk by first typing in commands that permit us to communicate with a single player. For example, let us communicate with a player dressed as an arrow. We call up the arrow on the screen with the keyboard. It appears on the screen along with a list of commands that the arrow will obey. This list is the arrow's repertoire. It contains words such as "erase," "display," "turn," "go," "run," "script," and "costume," which are performed when we point at them and operate the mouse's push buttons. To the right of the repertoire is a "how" column that is used when we want the computer to report in detail how it will follow the commands.

For example, the command "erase" makes the arrow's image disappear and "display" makes it reappear. With other commands, such as "turn" and "grow," the computer must ask questions. For example, when the pointer is brought to "turn," an information window appears on the screen with words that ask how many degrees the image is to be turned. The number must be then typed in. Similarly, "go" will request and be told how far the image should move.

When the item "script" is selected, the window appears blank; the computer waits for specific instructions. After selecting "script," we use the keyboard to enter a simple combination from the player's list of commands, such as "go 10" and "turn 10." When we point to the command "run," and press the push button on the mouse, the script is performed over and over. The arrow goes forward 10 spaces, then turns 10 degrees, then repeats the sequence.

The command "stop" is selected to make the player stop performing the script. Thereafter, we can do many things. The script can be modified, for example, by changing "go 10" to "go 15." Or we can devise an entirely new command. For example, the program we wrote drives the arrow in a circle. Using the keyboard, we can add this new command–"circle"–to the arrow's repertoire.

Issuing previously programmed commands to a single player in the computer theater is only the beginning. Next, the users learn how to work with several players and plays. After that, they are ready to do their own programming, writing new scripts and teaching new tricks to the players. They can change costumes by calling up a "palette" from which they choose lines and tones to "paint" illustrations with the electronic pointer. They can animate–train a player to move while changing its size and shape as it encounters different objects. To write music, players can be made to follow scripts in the form of tunes and given costumes that are the sounds of musical instruments. The users can simulate systems that exist in the real world such as drawbridges, electrical circuits, or rides at the amusement park.

Animated games are particularly instructive and fun to do. For example, a game in which one player chases another around the screen can be programmed in a few minutes. We write a script that hooks up the "turn" direction to the horizontal axis of our mouse and the "go" distance to the vertical axis of the mouse. When "run" is selected and executed, the player can be driven like a car by moving the mouse forward and to the sides. The next step is to select the list item "twin" in order to produce another player with the same script. The new player's script can be modified to respond to a second mouse. Now two people can drive independent players about the screen. We can change each player's costume into an individual car shape with Smalltalk's painting capability, and the simplest version of the game is ready to be played.

The important difference between being able to program one's own video game and obtaining a canned version from a game company is that new variations can be added to the homemade program as the participants think them up. For instance, what can be done about obstacles and collisions? How about putting the cars on a track? Besides being more fun, programmable games also help the programmer learn how complex situations can be modeled.

How can all these things be done with something as small as the proposed Dynabook? How are the electronics arranged inside the computer so that you can control the images on the screen with the keyboard and the mouse?

To learn something about this, we must first realize that computers deal only in symbols—a pattern, or structure—with which a sender (the programmer) communicates with a receiver (the program). A concept may be represented by many symbols. For example, a device used to close off an opening is called "door" in English, "porte" in French, and "Tür" in German. These words are meaningless, however, to anybody who does not understand the particular language, or symbol system, to which the words belong.

There is a simplest way to represent symbols. German philosopher Gottfried Wilhelm Leibniz in the 1700s discovered that all conceivable symbols could be formed from combinations of just two indivisible marks. The form of these marks is unimportant. Leibniz used "God" and "void." Morse code uses "dot" and "dash." In computer terms they become "on" and "off," or sometimes 0 and 1. These are the familiar "bits" of computer terminology.

Leibniz discovered that any number of symbols can be formed from patterns of these two marks. The greater the number of bits in a pattern, the more symbols can be formed. For example, a two-place pattern can form four different symbols. A three-place pattern can form eight symbols. A pattern 20 places long can form more than 1 million symbols.

Computers can hold millions of bits that can be used by a programming system to represent anything a programmer understands. A computer's power depends on how many bits it can store and how fast it can manipulate them. The Smalltalk system, for example, has a

The color and detail of a computer-drawn animated film suggest how powerful computers have already become.

storage capacity of about 21 million bits. One million of these are fast and used for the display, and as a scratch pad. The rest are used for long-term storage.

The simplest use of bits to represent information is to store display images for the television screen. About half the primary memory, some 500,000 bits, is used for this purpose. From the point of view of the display programs, the screen is a configuration of 800 rows of 600 bits each. As the electron beam of the television tube scans the face of the tube, the display programs reach into this memory and pick up the bits row by row, painting an image. The image changes whenever Smalltalk's graphics programs change the bits in the display memory. Then the next time the beam sweeps through the changed area, a new picture appears on the screen. It looks somewhat like a high resolution version of the electronic signs that display time and weather and advertising messages on top of buildings or beside highways.

This manipulation of bits is the bottom layer of many levels of complexity in programming a computer. These levels are like those required in designing, building, and using a theater. A construction architect designs the building. He is responsible for its structural integrity and aesthetics. A theater architect is concerned with the design as it supports different kinds of artistic productions. Together they will work out the interior design—such as the stage, lighting, and seats. In the computer world, the construction architect is the chief hardware designer; the theater architect is the chief software designer.

The theater manager, who handles stagehands, scenery designers, costume makers, and the lighting and maintenance people, is comparable to a computer's operating and programming system. Smalltalk is, in effect, the theater manager.

A new show is put together by a production team composed of the playwright, composer, producer, director, and people in charge of the music, sets, costumes, lighting, choreography, and properties. In the computer world, the production team is the one or more programmers who build environments for document and image handling, animation, music, information retrieval, and simulation.

Finally, the stage performers—the actors and musicians—are assembled and rehearsed. In Smalltalk, these are the players.

Every major new technology has changed people's lives. What is the onrush of computerization doing to us in 1978? There is no doubt that it has already changed our lives. The personal computers of the next decade will change them even more.

I think that the impact on human life will resemble what happened after the invention of movable printer's type in the 1400s, but in a much shorter time. When books became readily available, the concept of literacy arose and people who could not use books were labeled "illiterate." The illiterate was soon left behind by those who could read and write. The primary function of tutors, and later of schools, was to "teach" literacy.

To meet the challenge of the new technology, many schools are now conducting courses in "computer literacy." In addition, young people visit research centers like ours to see what computers can do. As they learn by doing, they also have a lot of fun. Computer literacy will become more widespread as more schools add computer classes to their curriculums. This will be an absolute necessity if people are going to understand their technology.

Today's students have not progressed much beyond computer kindergarten. They are still primarily involved with video games. The usage that will probably follow video games is both exciting and disturbing. It is exciting because of the artistic possibilities. It is disturbing because what may develop could be more mind-numbing than most of today's commercial television.

The next step in personal computing will probably be do-it-yourself cartoons. It is already possible to represent and animate stylized color images, applying techniques similar to those employed in Smalltalk. Soon after that, the first participatory drama systems will appear. Imagine a full-color James Bond movie in which you can insert a character representing yourself. You can be the hero, the villain, or one of the minor characters, with the plot controlled by decisions you make during the course of the action. Your family or friends can also assume roles. The story will be the result of your combined decisions.

The artistic possibilities are tremendous. Instead of a James Bond story, imagine manipulating a Shakespearean play. Or, working with your personal computer and a music synthesizer, you could create your own sonata, or the next rock-and-roll hit. If your taste runs to art, your computer can become a canvas on which you can experiment with a realistic sunset, or the most inventive abstract painting.

With your personal computer, you can do as much as your imagination will allow.

Science Fights Fire

By Lee Edson

From analyzing the chemical intricacies of flame to burning down buildings, researchers seek ways to make our lives more fireproof

At 1:30 A.M., Valerie Costello awoke with a start. The bedroom of her suburban Boston home felt unusually hot. She ran toward the kitchen and saw flames shooting up from the floor. "I told her to go for help," her husband, Howard, recalls, "then I headed for our 2-year-old son's room on the other side of the kitchen."

But Howard never quite made it. "I tried to reach him repeatedly," he says, "but I couldn't hold my breath and had to go back for air. There was a wall of flame. I just couldn't see. I was peeking out through small slits, because my eyes were all but burned closed. There was tremendous heat, the smell of oil burning, and the roar of walls cracking. It was deafening. I started wandering in a daze. I found myself outside getting into the car. I started to cry and wondered what was going on and why this was happening to me."

The fire burned down the Costellos' house and killed their son. Howard had burns over 65 per cent of his body. That was in 1967. Since then, Howard has recovered, and the Costellos have built a new life. However, they will never forget the horror of the blaze.

That sense of horror is shared by an unfortunately large number of Americans. According to the latest available figures from the National Fire Prevention Association in Boston, $2.7 billion worth of buildings in the United States went up in smoke in 1976, and 8,800 Americans died in all types of fires.

Fire losses in the United States rank among the highest in the world. Yet at the time of the Costello home fire, no one knew with certainty what characteristics would qualify materials as flame-retardant and little was understood about how fire behaves in a building or how people behave in a fire. Since then, the U.S. government has made a major commitment to cutting the fire toll through research.

Backed by federal funds, scientists in university and government laboratories are developing tests for evaluating fire hazards in construction materials, building designs, and home furnishings. They are also developing techniques for measuring levels of toxic gases given off by burning materials. Some scientists are studying the way fire spreads and the chemistry of such aspects of fire as spontaneous combustion and smoldering, while others are testing smoke detectors, sprinkler systems, and other safety devices.

In 1974, Congress set up the National Fire Prevention and Control Administration (NFPCA) in the Department of Commerce and the Center for Fire Research of the National Bureau of Standards (NBS) in Gaithersburg, Md. "We have a clear mandate from the Congress to cut the horrible loss due to fire in the United States by at least 50 per cent," says chemist Frederic B. Clarke, acting director of the center.

In working toward this goal, the teams of fire researchers have had to look at fire more closely than ever before. Fire itself, the rapid and continuous combination of combustible substances with oxygen to release heat and light, has not changed its character since its discovery in prehistoric times. The elements that start and sustain a fire are oxygen from the air, heat, and fuel. Air has always been everywhere in our environment, and heat has always been provided by a spark or a small flame. But the fuel that feeds the fires that gut modern homes and other buildings has changed radically. Today's new plastics and synthetics used in furnishings are symbols of the high living standard of industrial society. But they burn much more rapidly than natural materials, such as wood, cotton, and burlap.

The reason lies in the chemical nature of the materials. Fire is a complex of chemical reactions. As a substance grows hotter, its atoms and molecules begin to vibrate rapidly, breaking the chemical bonds that hold them together and giving off gas that can burn.

The author:
Lee Edson is
a free-lance
science writer.

When heat is applied to wood, moisture is driven off. For a short while, this staves off fire. But as the wood becomes drier it gets hotter, and the heat penetrates deeper. The wood breaks down into simpler chemical compounds, some of which become combustible gases. As the wood's kindling temperature–the point at which it will burst into flame–of 190° to 266°C (375° to 510°F.) is approached, the gas molecules mix with oxygen in the air and begin to burn. The gases continue to be driven off and the layer of wood under the flame chars. This char layer acts as an insulator, temporarily slowing the combustion of the underlying wood. Many plastics do not develop this intervening char layer, so they burn more rapidly.

But not all modern materials increase fire hazard; some decrease it. For example, gypsum wallboard, a fire-resistant material used in building construction, contains a great deal of water locked in the gypsum crystals. The ability of gypsum to resist fire depends to a great extent on how long it takes the heat to drive off the moisture.

Minerals in a burning substance also affect the rate of combustion and can be added to make materials flame-retardant. Glass fibers in gypsum, for example, delay its disintegration under further heating even after the moisture is gone. But the fact that small amounts of a foreign substance can radically alter a material's flammability makes the researchers' complex task of analyzing the chemical processes involved in burning even more difficult.

Scientists working under the direction of chemist Richard G. Gann, chief of the Program for Chemistry at the Center for Fire Research, are developing sophisticated laser techniques for studying the chemistry of burning materials. A laser is a device that emits an intense, highly concentrated beam of light. The scientists pass a laser beam through a flame to analyze temperatures and chemical substances in the flame. By observing characteristics of light given off, as well as the electrical properties of the flame, the scientists can determine what kinds of chemical molecules are in the flame, how concentrated they are, and even their temperature. Once the scientists have identified the particles and gases in the flame of a burning material, they can analyze changes in the chemical reactions when a flame retardant is added.to it. In this way, they can learn how the retardant works.

The bewildering array of modern materials is being studied at the center both individually and in combinations to determine how they contribute to halting or spreading fire. One of the most interesting areas at the center is a concrete and steel-walled building containing a maze of enclosures that duplicate the areas where most home fires occur. There are simulated attics, a kitchen, and bedrooms.

In these "burn rooms," scientists test the ignitibility, smoke production, and burning rate of a wide variety of objects made of various materials. Mattresses, a major source of fire in homes and institutions, have come in for special attention. Engineer Vytenis Babrauskas and his colleagues in 1976 furnished experimental areas to simulate hospi-

tal rooms, using the types of mattresses commonly found on hospital beds. For each test, they mounted thermocouples—electrical devices made of wires that produce electricity proportional to their temperature—in strategic spots around the room to measure temperature variations. They installed smoke-density meters in the doorway and placed the mattress on a special scale that would automatically record its weight loss as fire reduced it to ashes. The scientists also used probes that measure airflow and radiometers, instruments that measure radiant heat, to trace the heat radiated to different points in the room.

The researchers tested more than 20 mattresses of various materials. They set each one afire with burning trash in a wastebasket and recorded the time it took to burn by simply checking a clock mounted nearby. The results of the tests indicated that latex and polyurethane foam mattresses burned fastest. Neoprene-core mattresses burned much slower but, except for the newest types, produced dense smoke. The least hazardous mattress in these tests proved to be the old-fashioned cotton-batting type.

But scientists testing mattresses set on fire with a lighted cigarette rather than a large, open flame found that cotton batting poses the greatest hazard. It smolders, producing large quantities of smoke and toxic gas that can overcome people before they are aware that a fire exists. Synthetic foams are much less likely to catch fire from cigarettes, the most common cause of bedroom fires. This points up a serious problem plaguing fire researchers—no single test can determine how a material will behave in all types of fires.

Different solutions are needed for these varied fire problems. Cotton batting can be treated with flame retardants to pass government cigarette-ignition tests now required of all new mattresses. One possible solution to the flammability of foam mattresses exposed to open flames has been provided by E. I. Dupont de Nemours & Company, which in 1977 introduced a flame-retardant lining material for these mattresses. It retards burning by first releasing water vapor, then a chemical

A grease fire in a pan, *top,* flares in a test fire in a mobile-home kitchen. The fire spreads to wooden cabinets, *center,* and within minutes, the cabinets above the stove are engulfed in flames, *left.*

flame retardant. Then it forms a char layer. Manufacturers can install this material under the fabric covering to prevent fire from penetrating to the foam mattress core.

The development of more sophisticated measuring techniques has allowed scientists to focus on how fire spreads within an enclosure. "When fire departments were first being established, people worried about stopping fire from spreading from building to building as it did in the Great Fire of London in 1666, which burned down 13,000 buildings," says chemical engineer Robert S. Levine, chief of the Fire Science Division at the center. "In the last 100 years or so, fire fighters have tried to keep the fire from spreading throughout the building. Now we are able to concentrate on ways to halt fire in the next smaller unit of the building, the room."

Important information about how a room fire grows and spreads has emerged from the work of engineer Howard W. Emmons and his colleagues at Harvard University in Cambridge, Mass., and Factory Mutual Research Corporation in Boston. Since the early 1970s, these researchers, under the sponsorship of the NBS and the National Science Foundation, have been gathering data from experimental bedroom fires and using it to construct a computer model for predicting how a fire will behave.

The scientists built a bedroom with walls and ceiling of gypsum wallboard on 2- by 4-inch studs and furnished it with a bed, a polyurethane mattress, a desk, bookshelves, carpeting, and drapes. They linked instruments that measure temperature, heat radiation, gas composition and movement, and weight of the bed to a computer so the measurements could be recorded and checked every few seconds.

Emmons' team conducted three tests between 1973 and 1975 to observe how fire spreads. In each test, they set their fire in the middle of the bed by igniting a fuel-filled capsule. As the flame grew, heat and smoke rose and spread along the ceiling. The air got hotter near the ceiling, and the instruments recorded radiant heat lines creeping like fingers along the walls, working down lower and lower into the room.

Early in the fire, most of the heat was radiated from the flames, but later the hot smoky layer above became the greatest source of radiated heat. Emmons' research team found that this layer has a great effect on the fire's duration and severity, because it plays a major role in a phenomenon called flashover. This occurs when the heat in a room gets so intense that something flammable, perhaps the drapes, bursts into flame—even though it may be across the room from the initial flames. Within seconds, one object after another catches fire and the entire room becomes a raging inferno.

Before flashover occurs, a person in a burning room may crawl to safety along the floor. But Emmons observed that at flashover, the hot smoky layer instantly drops down, making escape impossible. This is an important reason why one should never enter a burning room or building, even if it looks "safe." In one of Emmons' studies, a bed was burning rather slowly. Suddenly, the fire flashed over, and in 40 seconds, flame was pouring out the open door.

Even though Emmons and his team tried to make all three of their bedroom setups as similar as possible, they found that the time before flashover varied greatly. The first test fire flashed over in 17½ minutes; the second in 7¼ minutes; and the third in 6¼ minutes. Emmons theorizes that flashover was delayed in the first test fire because it was raining lightly outside and the furnishings had absorbed moisture from the air. But, assuming that this was true, the scientists were surprised at the length of the delay—up to 10 minutes—that such a small change in the fire environment could make.

Flashover-delaying materials and devices can be built into homes and offices. This will give people more time to escape and fire departments more time to respond. For example, Emmons found that only 1.9 liters (0.5 gallon) of water from a small ceiling sprinkler extinguished the raging flames of his third test fire in five seconds. This indicates that simple automatic-sprinkler systems installed in homes could be of great benefit in halting fire.

Emmons' team also investigated various physical factors, such as airflow, that can change the course of a fire. If a door is suddenly opened, for example, the rush of cool air going into the room at the bottom generally sends the flaming gases back out at the top. For this reason, doors must be kept closed to contain fire.

According to Emmons, most doors leak air. If the leak is under the door, the pressure of the heated gases forces cooler air out of the burning room, and the fire soon consumes all the available oxygen.

This stops the combustion, but the room is still filled with hot gases that may burst into flame if a door or window is opened. If the leak is at the top of the door, the pressure may force hot gas out and spread the fire to other areas outside the room.

Emmons suggests that the flow of hot gases could be controlled by vents installed in each room near the ceiling, leading outside the building. The vent would open automatically in case of fire, allowing the hot gases to flow out. This would control the spread of fire and lessen the danger of filling hallways with toxic gas.

Emmons and his colleagues have made computer programs of the behavior of component parts of a fire. The programs include the behavior of flame, composition and movement of gases, and air-circulation patterns. A great deal more data is needed on factors ranging from burn rates of various materials to the pressure at which windows break out. But the Harvard researchers hope eventually to develop a

In an experiment to determine how fire behaves in a room, a test fire set in the middle of a bed grows slowly for about six minutes, creating a hot, smoky layer near the ceiling, *opposite page.* Then, flashover occurs and within seconds, *left,* flames have engulfed the entire test area.

Attached row houses, *above,* share a cockloft, space under the roof through which fire can spread rapidly. Blankets of mineral fiber, *top right,* are hung in the cockloft between two abandoned row houses to test the fiber's effectiveness in halting the spread of fire. One house is set ablaze, *center.* Even after fire consumes the top floor, *bottom,* the adjoining house is unscathed.

master computer fire model that will enable them to predict how any fire will behave in a given building. They could also program in data on various changes in design and furnishings to predict how these would affect the building's overall flammability.

Tests of fires in entire buildings have been carried out by civil engineer Paul R. De Cicco, director of the Polytechnic Institute of New York's Center for Urban Environmental Studies. De Cicco began his tests in abandoned residential buildings in Brooklyn, N.Y., in 1974 for a study sponsored by the New York City Fire Department. He concentrated on wood-frame row houses, two- or three-story residential buildings that are attached to each other and have a connecting space, called a cockloft, between ceiling and roof. Such buildings are known to pose a special type of fire hazard, because flames can spread to adjoining residences through the cockloft.

Row houses dating from around 1900 account for a large percentage of lower-income housing in older U.S. cities. This type of architecture is also being revived for new residences, such as town houses and senior-citizen dwellings. De Cicco wants to determine exactly how fire spreads to and through the cockloft in these structures and how older row houses can be modified and new ones designed to eliminate this danger of rapid fire spread.

D e Cicco and his team began by studying 18,000 fires that had occurred in Brooklyn from 1972 through 1974. They found that most of these row-house fires started in the kitchen or bedroom, followed by the basement, living room, and hallway, in that order. De Cicco set test fires that duplicated the accidental ones as closely as possible. "We found condemned buildings that were similar in structure to the burned buildings," he says, "furnished them with second-hand furniture, fitted them with instruments to measure temperature, smoke, and pressure, then set them on fire with a match."

De Cicco found that flashover occurred much faster in rooms in his test buildings than in the Harvard bedroom-fire experiments. In some of his tests, the fire flashed over in only four minutes. Temperatures in most of the rooms climbed to 149°C (300°F.)–hot enough to cause irreversible skin damage–in less than three minutes. De Cicco explains that his fires were set in very old buildings where walls were covered with many layers of combustible paint and wallpaper and floors were layered with rugs and other flammable materials. Broken windows, false ceilings, and old furniture with exposed, flammable stuffing also contributed to more rapid flashover.

De Cicco also confirmed what many experts had long thought but never tested–fire spreads more rapidly in a building that contains a dumbwaiter, elevator shaft, or light and ventilation shafts. In one test, the instruments recorded temperatures of more than 815.5°C (1500°F.) at the top of a 9.8-meter (32-foot)-high light and ventilation shaft only one minute after the fire was set. In a test fire in a ventilation shaft between two attached residences, temperatures in a third-

A model of a stairwell in a high-rise building provides scientists with a convenient way to chart the circulation patterns of lethal smoke.

floor living room soared to more than 704°C (1300°F.) in 7½ minutes. Such a rapid rise in temperature on the top floor would quickly spread the fire to the cockloft. Consequently, De Cicco recommends that such shafts in existing row houses be kept free of rubbish in which a fire could start. He also suggests that this type of construction be avoided in newly constructed row houses.

De Cicco and his team devoted a series of tests to keeping fire from spreading through the cockloft to adjoining residences. In one case, they hung a blanket of mineral fiber 5 centimeters (2 inches) thick to separate the cockloft space between two buildings. Temperatures in the cockloft of the burning building reached 927°C (1700°F.), but the cockloft temperatures on the other side of the blanket reached only 65.5°C (150°F.). De Cicco also tested gypsum board nailed to the ceiling as a barrier to prevent fire from reaching the cockloft. Although temperatures ranged up to 871°C (1600°F.) in the burning room, they never rose above 38°C (100°F.) on the other side of the gypsum-board ceiling.

De Cicco plans to install such fire-prevention devices as aluminum siding, smoke detectors, and minisprinkler systems hooked into a building's plumbing system in 80 residences. He has also selected four groups of 80 buildings each to serve as controls. He will compare future fire statistics among all the groups to observe how well the fire-prevention devices perform in real-life situations.

Equally as important as the fire is the smoke it produces. Smoke inhalation causes most deaths in fires. To find out why smoke is so deadly and what to do about it, the Center for Fire Research is sponsoring projects devoted to analyzing combustion products in smoke. This is an extremely complex task. For example, in the smoke from cellulose, which is present in paper, wood, and many fabrics, scientists have identified about 175 organic compounds.

In one project, researchers at Johns Hopkins University studied toxic-gas levels found in the blood of 421 persons killed in fires in Maryland between 1970 and 1976. The Maryland State Medical Examiner's Toxicology Laboratory cooperated with the project by analyzing the victims' blood. The Johns Hopkins scientists were particularly interested in hydrogen cyanide levels. The burning of certain materials that contain nitrogen in their structure, such as wool or nylon, will result in chemical changes that produce hydrogen cyanide. There is little reliable data on cyanide-gas poisoning. Hydrogen cyanide reacts with biochemicals in the blood and is therefore difficult to separate out and measure.

However, cases in which the Maryland laboratory workers carefully analyzed blood of fire victims for cyanide revealed levels too low to be deadly yet high enough to suggest that cyanide played some part in preventing the victims from escaping the fire. The researchers theorize that the small quantities of cyanide gas may have caused the victims to lose consciousness or become physically weak or mentally confused.

In the Johns Hopkins study, the most deadly component of smoke proved to be carbon monoxide gas. The scientists found that half of the 421 deaths were clearly due to carbon monoxide poisoning. Another third died because carbon monoxide aggravated heart ailments.

Other researchers are seeking ways to keep these deadly gases from spreading throughout a building or to divert their flow so that people can escape before being overcome. Stairwells, a major escape route, also carry smoke and fire to upper areas. De Cicco and other researchers have conducted studies indicating that one way to curb this flow of smoke is to install equipment that will pressurize the stairwells as soon as a fire breaks out. Smoke and hot air at a lower pressure than the air in the stairwell cannot enter even when several doors are open.

De Cicco ran his experiments in an abandoned New York City office building in 1972. He placed blowers below the stairs to blow in outside air, raising the pressure in the stairwell. Even when a corridor was filled with smoke, De Cicco reported that the pressurized stairwell remained clear.

One modern type of construction that creates unique patterns in the travel of smoke is atrium buildings, such as the Bobst Library of New York University and hotels in various U.S. cities. Atrium buildings consist of huge enclosed and covered central courtyards surrounded by various facilities—five floors of books in the Bobst Library and tiers of guest rooms and restaurants in the hotels.

De Cicco knows a great deal about this kind of building and its fire characteristics. He has found that smoke and toxic gases can be transported swiftly up through the atrium. At the request of an architect wanting to design an atrium hotel that would be as safe as possible from fire, De Cicco created a model of the planned hotel and injected either smoke or the buoyant gas helium at various points. Using sensitive probes to trace their progress, he found that smoke and gas could rapidly reach areas of the building far from the site of a fire. De Cicco suggested a careful ventilation design, in which numerous exhaust fans in ducts around the atrium would blow smoke and gas out of the building before they could circulate upward.

The overall research battle against fire does not end with safeguards built into structure and materials. It also involves the fire fighter and fire-fighting equipment, which is being virtually remodeled.

The breathing apparatus that fire fighters use to enter smoke-filled areas has drawn criticism for being too bulky and heavy. So the National Aeronautics and Space Administration (NASA) in the mid-1970s applied its space age technology to the problem and developed equipment that is smaller, 40 per cent lighter, yet still carries an adequate air supply. It features a tank that is made of aluminum and fiberglass rather than only metal. NASA has made details about the

A small, lightweight air-supply tank that was developed by NASA, *below,* and a "flying fire engine" for use in high-rise fires, *below right,* join the arsenal of modern fire-fighting weapons.

system's development available to manufacturers, who are now producing improved breathing equipment.

More changes are underway. The fire-fighter's clothing is being revolutionized through a collaborative NASA-NFPCA program. This program's designers are producing a protective "envelope" that will fully encase the fire fighter from boots to helmet in a one-piece uniform made of lightweight, fire-retardant fabric.

In a sense, even the water from the hydrant has been improved, thanks to a liquid polymer, a substance called rapid water. The liquid polymer is stored in a container in the fire truck and pumped into the water that will travel through the hose. It cuts down the friction of the water on the hose lining so that the water can travel more quickly. Greater quantities of rapid water than of untreated water can be poured on a fire in a given time.

One of the most spectacular developments underway is a "flying fire engine" being designed by the McDonnell Douglas Aeronautics Company in St. Louis. This aerial unit, an open cage suspended from a helicopter by a cable, will be used in fighting high-rise fires. It will hold up to 16 persons and either carry its own water supply or draw water from the building's pipes. While the helicopter hovers overhead, an engine and four jetlike exhaust vents atop the cage will maneuver it horizontally to dock against a window, for example. The helicopter will maneuver the cage up and down. A gangplank extended from the cage will allow fire fighters to enter the burning building or occupants to escape. The unit was test-flown for the first time in May 1978.

Of course, even with the best-designed systems, the number of people injured or killed in a fire still depends on how they behave. A study published in late 1977 confirmed that most people do not act intelligently during a fire. Psychologist David Canter and his colleagues at Surrey University in England reported that their study of four major fires showed that most individuals did not use or even look for the fire escape. They simply rushed to the nearest exit. People who found fire extinguishers did not know how to use them. A substantial number of people either did not notice signs that the fire was beginning or ignored them until the fire was raging.

Canter also contends that many fire regulations are based on false assumptions about how people will behave. For example, designers base the width of fire exits on the space required for two average-size adult males to move side by side through the opening. But people tend to walk so that they will not touch one another. As a result, it is possible to overestimate the speed with which people can leave a building by at least 50 per cent.

So the human factor adds yet another complicating element to the already complex fire story. But scientists hope that learning more about all the physical, chemical, and human factors that are involved in a fire will enable them to find ways of making our life in the modern world more fireproof.

A New Light
On Chemistry

By Richard N. Zare

**The laser is illuminating the world of atoms
and molecules in ways that will ensure a better
understanding of the fundamentals of matter**

My introduction to chemistry took place some 25 years ago in the basement of my parents' home in Cleveland. There I began to experiment on various fiery displays, such as burning magnesium ribbon and making molten iron out of thermite. These colorful pyrotechnics brought me a certain measure of neighborhood recognition, as well as one visit from the local fire department. My experiences also whetted my curiosity about the role of color in chemical change. Little did I know then that this fascination with flames and flares would lead directly to my present research with lasers, devices for projecting colored light of the purest and most intense hue ever produced.

Lasers were a laboratory plaything about 15 years ago. But in 1978, they are being used in many everyday activities, from scanning and recording prices at supermarket checkout counters to attempts to harness nuclear energy in laser-fusion laboratories. Lasers find their widest application, however, in chemistry, where they are used to probe the structure of atoms and molecules, start chemical reactions, make

High-speed photography captures steps in a chemical reaction initiated by a laser beam. The monochromatic light converts the gas, chromyl chloride, into a green powder, chromic oxide, almost instantaneously.

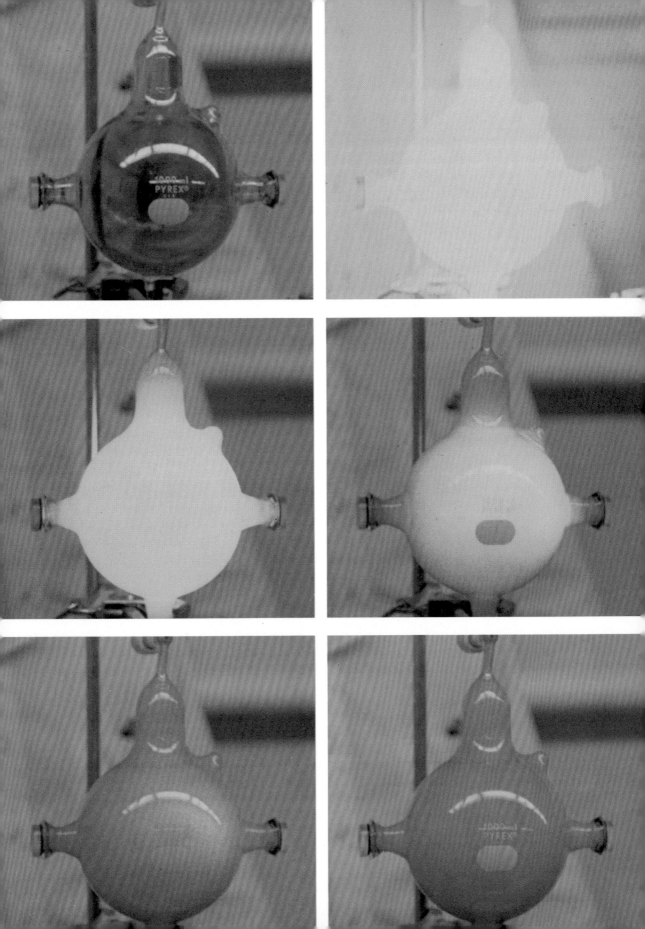

new compounds, remove impurities, separate isotopes—different forms of the same element—and detect minute quantities of substances that could not be identified in any other way.

To understand how lasers are used in chemistry, we first need to know a little about how they work. A laser is a device composed of a special material constructed in a special way so that it can generate and amplify light waves. Many materials, if given the proper energy, such as by heating, give off light. The tungsten filament in an incandescent light bulb, for example, emits light when its atoms are excited to high energies and then spontaneously radiates that energy.

The amount of energy radiated varies with the material. Atoms and molecules have discrete energy levels that vary from material to material. They all absorb or emit radiation in units called photons that correspond to the energy required to travel between levels, the transition energy. Most of the time, molecules are in their lowest, or ground, level of energy. The energy of the photon gives it its color, or wavelength. As the wavelength increases from the red to the blue, the energy of the photon increases.

In any transition, in any material, there are always more species—atoms and molecules—in lower than upper levels at a given temperature. When light passes through such material, more photons are absorbed than are emitted and the light is attenuated, or dimmed. In an operating laser, the population in the upper level is made greater than that in the lower level. Thus more photons are emitted than are absorbed and a light beam passing through the laser is amplified.

The laser material, or "active medium," can be a solid, such as a ruby; a gas, such as a combination of helium and neon; or a liquid, such as an organic dye solution. To "lase," or generate and emit an amplified wave, those materials must attain their excess of upper-level species, called an inverted population, through an external energy source. This energy source can be, for example, a powerful flash lamp, which produces short, high-energy laser pulses, or an electrical current, which produces a continuous beam but at lower energy.

The laser's basic structure, also called the resonant cavity, is essentially a long tube with mirrors at each end. In the presence of excited atoms, light waves of a single frequency are reflected back and forth along the axis of this cavity. As they travel, the waves increase in energy, eventually emerging from one end (which is only partially reflective) as a highly directed and powerful beam.

The author:
Richard N. Zare is a professor of chemistry at Stanford University.

Stimulating emission in a laser causes the excited atoms or molecules to emit light together not only in the same direction but also with the same phase—that is, the crests and troughs of the light waves travel together. This is called coherence and gives laser light some special properties that light from a noncoherent light source, such as an incandescent bulb, does not have.

Laser emission wavelengths span the spectrum from the infrared through the visible and ultraviolet to the soft X-ray region. The energy of photons from a laser increases as the wavelengths grow shorter. Most lasers operate at fixed wavelengths. There are some, however, that can be "dialed" to a number of wavelengths. These tunable lasers work on the principle that the energy levels of the lower transitions are spaced so closely together that they are essentially continuous. By inserting a selective element, such as a prism or a diffraction grating, in the light path, the laser can be tuned to operate over the wavelength region for which the laser material can amplify. The best tunable laser available at present is one that uses an organic dye solution as the active laser medium.

Lasers offer many unique advantages in chemical applications. To understand how, we need to understand the process of chemistry. Much of chemistry is concerned with observing and controlling the behavior of the basic constituents of matter—atoms and molecules. For purposes of understanding chemical change, we can picture a molecule as simply a collection of atoms of one or more different elements. The nuclei of the atoms in this model are held together by the atoms' electrons, which distribute themselves in a cloud surrounding the entire structure. This negatively charged cloud holds the positively charged nuclei together in a delicate balance. The nuclei can move slightly, but if they move too much, the balance is destroyed and the molecule may dissociate, or break up, into smaller fragments.

Because laser light operates at a single wavelength, it can deliver precise amounts of energy to a molecule. The directionality of the laser beam permits the energy to be delivered efficiently and easily to the sample. The coherence of the beam allows it to be focused to an incredibly small spot—the size of the wavelength of the light itself. All this energy in such a small volume can cause unusual effects.

In a chemical reaction, we generally know what we start with and what we have after the reaction is over. What we do not know is what happens in between—the intermediate steps that occur so rapidly that they cannot be observed, but are important to a complete understanding of the process. Here the pulsed laser can help enormously because, in addition to its other properties, it can be operated at intervals of a picosecond (trillionth of a second). In effect, the laser can catch a reaction in the act, and observe what is happening at each stage.

There is a meaningful connection between the laser medium and the materials that lasers are used to study—the existence of energy states. There are actually three types of energy states of interest to a chemist—rotational, vibrational, and electronic.

The smallest energy transitions are between rotational levels; the next smallest between vibrational levels. A molecule will respond, for example, to photons in the far infrared by changing its rotational level. It will respond to photons in the near infrared by changing a combination of rotational-vibrational levels.

At still larger photon energies—the visible or the ultraviolet—electronic transitions occur in which the electrons redistribute themselves,

Electronic Energy

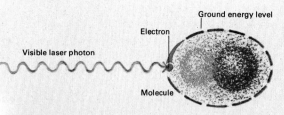

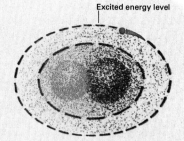

A high-energy photon from a visible or ultraviolet laser imparts its energy to the electron cloud around a multi-atom molecule at its lowest, or ground, energy level. The cloud takes on a new size and shape as the molecule goes to a higher electronic energy state.

Vibrational-Rotational Energy

Infrared laser photon

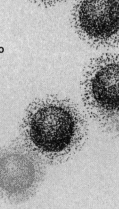

A lower-energy photon from an infrared laser affects the vibrating and rotating energy states of the molecule. When it absorbs the photon, the molecule's vibrational and rotational behavior changes from the ground state to a higher state, in which vibration and rotation increase.

changing the size and shape of the molecule. The new distribution of electrons may still bind the atoms together in the molecule or it may cause the molecule to dissociate into smaller fragments. At even higher photon energies, the electronic rearrangement may be so violent that one or more of the electrons is expelled. This is called photoionization.

What can examining molecules of a material with laser light tell us about the material? Because of its single wavelength, the laser permits the chemist to excite only those molecules in a gas sample that are in an energy state specified by that wavelength. Other molecules are unaffected. Furthermore, by polarizing the laser output–that is, limiting the direction of oscillations of the light wave–the spatial orientation of the excited molecules may also be determined.

After a molecule absorbs laser radiation and makes a transition to an excited state, it may lose its energy of excitation in one of three ways: It may collide with other molecules to form new compounds; it may collide in such a way that the energy is transferred to new excited vibrational-rotational levels within the same molecule; or it may spontaneously re-emit a photon of light, radiating its excess energy.

When a molecule re-emits a photon, the spectrum, or range of wavelengths, of the radiation is not continuous. It consists instead of sharp lines of different wavelengths, each corresponding to a transition from an upper vibrational-rotational level to a lower one. These lines, known as a molecular fluorescence series, can give us a detailed map of the molecule's energy levels, which shows us the molecule's structure– the average distances and angles between the atoms.

A practical example is the study of the nitrogen dioxide molecule (NO_2), a brownish-colored gas that is primarily responsible for giving smog its ugly appearance. In its ground state, the NO_2 molecule is shaped like a spread "V" with the N atom at the central vertex and the two O atoms at the outer ends. The angle between the two N-O bonds is about 135 degrees (°) and the length of the N-O bond is about 1.19 angstroms (0.0000000119 centimeter). The visible spectrum of NO_2 is so crowded with lines that no one had been able to recognize the pattern of upper-energy levels, which is the key to unlocking the structure of nitrogen dioxide.

At our laboratory at Stanford University in California, we have used a laser to tune to individual NO_2 lines and obtained its fluorescence spectrum and thus its excited state structure. We found that the electronic cloud rearrangement in the excited state causes the N-O bonds to lengthen by about 10 per cent, while the ONO bond angle decreases to about 110°. These structural changes agree well with the best theoretical predictions. By understanding the excited state structure of NO_2, we can take the first step to understanding how to control it in the atmosphere.

Lasers are also providing new insights into the motion of molecules in liquids, where most chemistry takes place. In a gas, the atoms or molecules are always random; in a solid, they form a rigid three-

Fluorescence

Excited molecules are unstable and will give up energy spontaneously in returning to lower energy states. In so doing, they fluoresce, or emit photons that correspond to the frequency (color) of the states that they are traveling between.

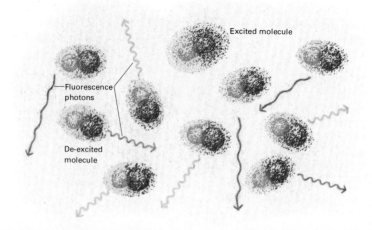

Excited molecule

Fluorescence photons

De-excited molecule

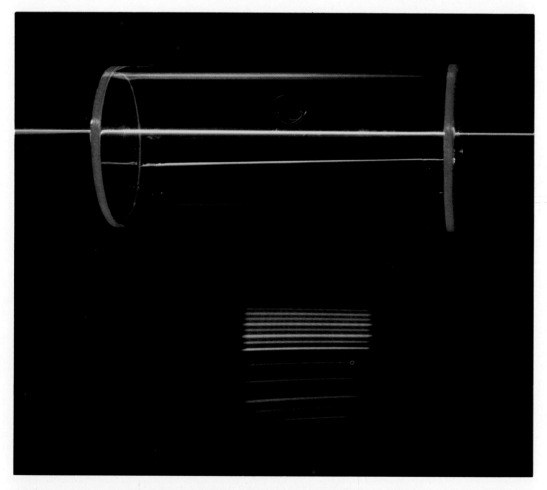

A green laser beam excites iodine vapor molecules which fluoresce a yellow light that represents many energy transitions, and colors. The colors are resolved by reflecting the beam from a diffraction grating.

dimensional lattice. In liquids, some molecules move randomly, but some are also held in local structures. For example, when iodine (I_2) is dissolved in the cleaning solvent carbon tetrachloride (CCl_4) the CCl_4 molecules tend to cluster about each I_2 molecule to form what chemists call a "solvation cage."

When we dissociate gaseous I_2 it is very unlikely that the original pair of I atom fragments from any one I_2 molecule would meet each other before combining with something else. However, if the same experiment is carried out in a liquid composed of I_2 dissolved in CCl_4, the two I atoms are much more likely to re-encounter each other and recombine because the CCl_4 molecules imprison the I fragments and hinder their escape.

Because the molecules in liquids are so densely packed together, the average time between collisions is a picosecond or less. This is much too fast to follow by conventional methods.

The picosecond laser has dramatically changed this picture. In the middle 1970s, Kenneth B. Eisenthal, now at Columbia University, and his co-workers at the IBM Research Laboratories in San Jose, Calif., measured the average time for the I atoms to recombine in CCl_4. They used two picosecond pulses separated in time by having the second pulse travel a slightly longer path.

The first pulse—an intense green flash of light—dissociates a large fraction of the I_2 molecules in its path. The second pulse has the same wavelength, but it is much weaker in intensity. Following the first pulse, the I atoms begin to recombine into I_2 molecules. Because the I_2 molecules absorb photons from the second pulse, its energy gives the number of I_2 molecules that have recombined in the beam path. As the time delay between the first and second pulses is lengthened, the energy of the second pulse diminishes, indicating that more I_2 molecules have recombined. The combination of energy measurement and time gives a direct measurement of the cage effect. Eisenthal and his co-workers found that it took 97 picoseconds for half of the I atoms in CCl_4 to recombine into I_2.

Chemists are using picosecond laser techniques in a number of other areas. For example, Peter M. Rentzepis and his co-workers at Bell Telephone Laboratories in Murray Hill, N.J., are studying the photochemical steps in rhodopsin, the pigment in the retina of the eye. This pigment is the primary photoreceptor in vision. Morris W. Windsor and his colleagues at Washington State University in Pullman are investigating the intermediate chemical stages in bacterial photosynthesis in which energy is stored by transferring an electron from a structure containing chlorophyll to an unidentified molecule.

Even shorter pulses are becoming available to chemists. In 1977, Eric P. Ippen and Charles V. Shank of Bell Telephone Laboratories discovered ways to shorten the duration of a pulsed laser to a few tenths of a picosecond. They did this with a continuously pumped dye laser. This technique is permitting chemists to look at nature in sub-

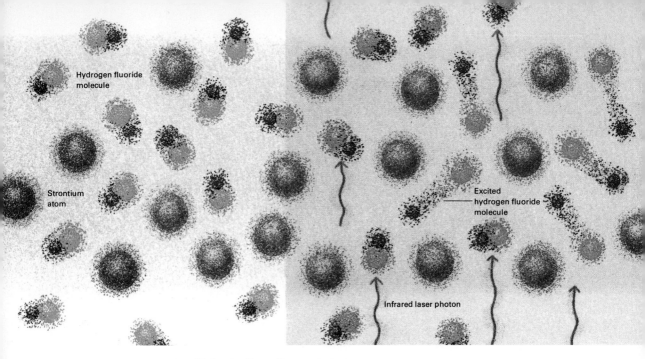

Hydrogen fluoride molecule

Strontium atom

Excited hydrogen fluoride molecule

Infrared laser photon

Molecular-Beam Spectroscopy

As a gaseous mixture of hydrogen fluoride molecules and strontium atoms travels from left to right, it is intersected by an infrared laser beam, bottom to top. The infrared photons excite the hydrogen-fluoride molecules vibrationally and rotationally. This promotes a reaction with the strontium atoms, forming new strontium fluoride molecules and leaving free hydrogen atoms behind. Photons from a second, visible, laser beam excite the strontium fluoride molecules which, in turn, fluoresce to provide a measure of their vibrational and rotational energy.

picosecond glimpses, which is certain to reveal even richer details of the dynamics of chemical change in liquids.

To study the behavior of single molecules, we must use gases at very low pressure. Most reactive studies of gases are carried out in evacuated glass bulbs. However, between the time the components are mixed and the time the product is sampled, many collisions occur. Furthermore, these reactions occur throughout the entire bulb, including the walls, which causes confusing surface effects. Thus, to study individual collisions, we must turn to molecular beams.

In an evacuated chamber of less than one-billionth of an atmosphere, gas molecules travel in straight lines and do not collide with residual background molecules. This permits chemists to direct two beams of molecules into each other. In these crossed-beam experiments, molecular reactions can be studied one collision at a time in about a tenth of a picosecond—the duration of a typical reactive encounter. The reaction zone is confined to the intersection of the two beams. The pressure in the chamber is so low that collisions do not disrupt the straight-line motion of the reactants as the two beams approach, or that of the products as they scatter away from the reaction zone at some angle.

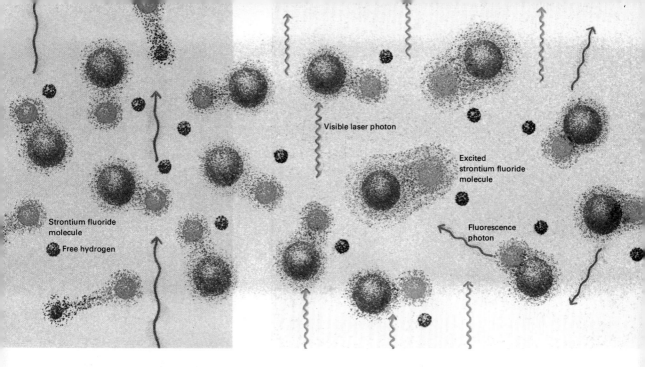

Strontium fluoride molecule

Free hydrogen

Visible laser photon

Excited strontium fluoride molecule

Fluorescence photon

These experiments require detection systems that are extremely sensitive to the small number of molecules produced. The detection systems must also be sensitive enough to identify the new molecules from the overwhelming background of molecules that have scattered but have not reacted.

In our laboratory, we have been developing a new detection technique based on fluorescence. We aim a laser at the reaction zone and tune it through its applicable wavelengths. Whenever the energy coincides with an absorption line of the reaction product, the molecules of that product make a transition to an excited electronic state from which they subsequently emit fluorescence. This fluorescence is detected by a photomultiplier. The intensity of the fluorescence is recorded as a function of the different laser wavelengths that produced it. The intensities may then be converted to figures that indicate the relative populations of the various internal energy states of the products. This procedure provides the most detailed description presently available of the nature of a single reactive collision.

Lasers can also be used to prepare reactants in specific energy states. For example, Ziv Karny has been studying the reaction of strontium (Sr) atoms with hydrogen fluoride (HF) in our laboratory. This yields an H atom and strontium fluoride (SrF), an intermediate step in the formation of the mineral SrF_2. The SrF product is detected by its visible excitation spectrum, which is the same color as the red flares used for emergency stops in road traffic.

An infrared laser is used to excite the HF molecules from their vibrational ground state to their first vibrational excited state. Karny found that the reaction rate of HF molecules with Sr is more than 10,000 times faster with excited HF molecules than with unexcited molecules. Moreover, he has learned which energy states of the react-

A laser beam passing through a methane flame containing sodium vapor causes the vapor to fluoresce (horizontal orange bar) and change ion concentration in the flame. Electrodes in the flame detect changes in an electrical current, providing an analysis of the sodium.

ants change into which energy states of the products, and how they do this. Such information brings chemists closer to achieving their goal of understanding the stages in chemical reactions.

Lasers are also changing chemists' concepts of how little they can detect of one substance in the presence of others. The analysis of elements at the part-per-million, or 10^6, level used to be considered exceptional. Analysis at the part-per-billion, or 10^9, level was considered beyond almost all instruments. However, the laser is shattering these barriers by making possible the detection in some cases of a single atom, the ultimate in chemical analysis.

Samuel Hurst, Munir Nayfeh, now at Yale University, and Jack Young of the Oak Ridge National Laboratory reported in 1977 that they were able to "tag" an individual atom of cesium with a laser against a background of 10^{19} argon atoms in a gas-filled chamber. They tuned a pulsed dye laser to excite an electronic transition in the cesium atom. Because of the immense power in the laser beam, the atom absorbed a second photon causing it to eject an electron. A voltage applied across the gas-filled chamber in which this takes place causes the newborn electron to accelerate and slam into other atoms, knocking out additional electrons. This avalanche process generates a pulse that can be counted in much the same way that a click of a Geiger counter signals the radioactive decay of a single nucleus.

The two-photon laser-ionization method only works for the atoms of the alkali metals because the energy of two photons from most lasers today is not powerful enough to ionize other elements. However, John Travis and his co-workers at the National Bureau of Standards have used the high temperature of flames to assist the laser-ionization process. Here, two electrodes are placed in the flame of a gas burner and a current passing between them is measured as a tunable laser beam is directed through the flame. Whenever the laser is tuned to the wavelength that excites the atoms of some element in the flame, the current increases. Single atoms have yet to be detected with this method and the results vary widely among the half-dozen elements they have studied. But there is promise in the ability of the laser to probe the hellish environment of a flame and give us a better understanding of combustion.

Most chemical analytical problems arise not in gases, but in solids and liquids. The task is much more demanding in these states and the limits of detection are generally poorer. However, Gerald J. Diebold and others in our laboratory have made notable progress using laser fluorescence to detect specific molecules in solution below the part-per-trillion level.

Fluorescence caused by a laser beam passing through a compound in water proves the value of lasers for trace analysis. The compound can be detected in decreasing amounts (left to right) of 0.1 parts per million, 0.1 parts per billion, and 0.1 parts per trillion. The latter is the smallest concentration ever photographed.

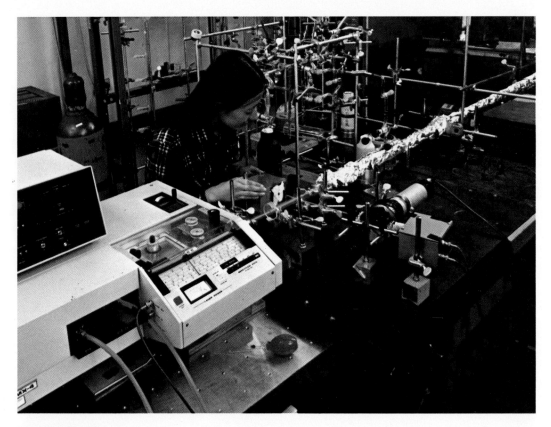

Ultraviolet light from a laser excites molecules of formaldehyde to produce hydrogen and carbon monoxide that contains carbon-14, an isotope used in radio dating. The carbon-14 is 100 times more concentrated in the carbon monoxide product than in the original formaldehyde.

Diebold and his colleagues are measuring the amount of aflatoxin in corn. Aflatoxin, a naturally occurring chemical residue left by mold on grains, is one of the most potent agents for causing liver cancer. The researchers grind the suspected corn samples to a fine powder and make a liquid extract. After some preliminary purifications, the extract is poured into a chromatography column filled with an absorbent material, such as resin or a polymer. A constant stream of solvent runs through the column. As the liquid passes down through it, molecules of the same type travel together at a specific speed. Therefore, as the droplets of liquid flow out the bottom of the chromatography column, aflatoxin can be detected by timing it and by its characteristic fluorescence stimulated by an ultraviolet laser. With present limits of detection, the number of aflatoxin molecules found in the droplets is a few parts per trillion.

Why do chemists want to analyze materials for such small quantities? For one reason, most biological effects operate at these, or lower, levels of concentration. There is an important use for detection techniques that could, for example, look at the hormone levels of newborn infants. Other examples would be to determine early warning signals of cancer from changes in certain protein levels in the body, or monitor how a patient responds to medication. Perhaps it may even be possible to discover what kind of chemicals are in the brain that transmit or store neural messages.

To synthesize new compounds, chemists have followed the time-honored recipe of stirring together the reactants and heating the resulting mixture. However, heating energizes the vibrational, rotational, and electronic motions all at once. Lasers can excite specific modes of the reactants. This puts the energy where it may be most effective for making a particular reaction occur and presents chemists with the opportunity to synthesize compounds in novel ways.

Producing laser photons is too expensive to make most compounds economically. However, it may be a practical way to make or isolate certain chemicals. One example is the use of lasers to separate isotopes. In nature, most elements are mixtures of isotopes—atoms whose nuclei have the same number of protons and electrons but different numbers of neutrons. Ordinarily, this mixture means little because the various isotopes are almost indistinguishable in most of their properties. For that reason, however, separating the isotopes of an element can be exceedingly difficult and costly.

The prime example is the element uranium (U), which occurs naturally as two isotopes—the lighter, fissionable U-235 and the heavier, nonfissionable U-238. Only 7 uranium atoms of every 1,000 are U-235. However, nuclear power reactors need uranium with U-235 at a concentration of 30 in 1,000. As a result, huge and expensive gaseous-diffusion plants have been built to enrich the uranium.

Lasers promise to change this by making isotope separation easier and cheaper. Because the isotopes have slightly different masses, their energy levels are shifted a little, causing their spectra to differ slightly. This spectral shift permits laser light to selectively excite molecules containing one isotope while leaving the molecules containing the other isotope undisturbed. There are several ways to separate excited from unexcited molecules, thus harvesting the desired isotope.

Lasers can also be used to purify materials. In this case, we do not want to collect some rare species, but rather to remove it. An example is silicon used in semiconductors. Ultrapure silicon (Si) is now produced by heating a gaseous mixture of silane (SiH_4), a molecule containing a central Si atom surrounded by 4 H atoms, to very high temperatures. In 1978, John H. Clark at Los Alamos Scientific Laboratories for the first time removed the common impurities of silane, such as phosphine (PH_3) and arsine (AsH_3), by irradiating the silane gas with a pulsed ultraviolet laser. The phosphine and arsine absorb the ultraviolet light much more strongly than does silane, causing them to be deposited out on the walls of the container.

There is no question that the laser will continue to revolutionize the field of chemistry. In industry, it has already provided new manufacturing techniques. In medicine, it will increase our knowledge of many important life processes. And in the research laboratory, the laser will give us a new understanding of the fundamental nature of matter.

Science File

Science Year contributors report on the year's major developments in their respective fields. The articles in this section are arranged alphabetically by subject matter.

Agriculture

Anthropology

Archaeology
Old World
New World

Astronomy
Planetary
Stellar
High-Energy
Cosmology

Biochemistry

Books of Science

Botany

Chemical Technology

Chemistry

Communications

Drugs

Ecology

Electronics

Energy

Environment

Genetics

Geoscience
Geochemistry
Geology
Geophysics
Paleontology

Immunology

Medicine
Dentistry
Internal
Surgery

Meteorology

Microbiology

Neuroscience

Nutrition

Oceanography

Physics
Atomic and Molecular
Elementary Particles
Nuclear
Plasma
Solid State

Psychology

Public Health

Science Policy

Space Exploration

Technology

Transportation

Zoology

Agriculture

Agronomist Henry Yokoyama and his associates at the United States Department of Agriculture (USDA) found a way in 1978 to increase the production of natural rubber in guayule, a desert shrub found in Mexico and Texas.

Working at the Fruit and Vegetable Chemistry Laboratory in Pasadena, Calif., the scientists sprayed young guayule plants with 5,000 parts per million of the hormone stimulator 2-(3-4-dichlorophenoxy)-triethylamine. They reported that two to six times as much rubber accumulated in the stem and root tissues of the sprayed plants.

Yokoyama estimated that about 2-million hectares (5 million acres) in Arizona, California, New Mexico, and Texas have soils suitable for guayule's growth. Scientists investigated guayule as a domestic source of rubber during World War II. However, the project was terminated when synthetic rubber was developed in the early 1940s. Since that time, the rising costs of synthetic rubber and U.S. dependence on foreign supplies have intensified the search for a domestic source of natural rubber.

Strawberry harvesting. Agricultural engineers Clarence M. Hansen and Richard L. Ledebuhr of Michigan State University demonstrated a new mechanical harvester and a fruit decapper in the summer of 1977. The machines effectively performed the many hand operations involved in strawberry harvesting.

Past attempts to develop mechanical strawberry pickers have failed because the berries mature on a single plant at different times and mechanical pickers were not selective, picking both ripe and unripe berries. The key to the success of the new machines is a new strawberry variety named Linn, developed by plant researcher Francis J. Lawrence of the USDA station at Corvallis, Ore., in 1976. About 85 per cent of its fruit matures at the same time.

Saltwater barley. Plant physiologist Emanuel Epstein and his associates at the University of California, Davis, obtained marketable yields of four genetic selections of barley grown in dune sand and irrigated with salt water from the Pacific Ocean. They rated the barley as

Snow-white sheep from St. Croix, Virgin Islands, and brown sheep from Barbados in the West Indies, breeds with hair instead of wool, are part of an Ohio Agricultural Research Institute experiment to improve lamb meat production.

Rows of barley varieties were irrigated with seawater to see which grows best in the dry and salty soils near the oceans. Barley heads of plants that thrive in seawater (bottom row) are as healthy as·those grown in fresh water (top row).

Agriculture

Continued

a satisfactory livestock feed. This development could open up vast new water and land resources for food production. It follows earlier work in which Epstein grew tomatoes under the same conditions. Similar possibilities exist for wheat, sugar beets, and alfalfa, all of which have salt-tolerant genetic strains.

Cattle growth. William E. Wheeler and Robert R. Oltjen of the USDA station at Beltsville, Md., added cement-kiln dust, a by-product of cement making, to cattle feed and found the cattle gained more weight than expected. The researchers reported that steers fed the cement-kiln dust as 3.5 per cent of their diet gained 28 per cent more weight and consumed 21 per cent less feed. The butchered meat was also of higher quality. The researchers obtained similar results with sheep.

Georgia cattle ranchers who limed their pastures observed the effects of cement-kiln dust, which contains lime and looks like talcum powder, some years ago. They inadvertently dumped some of the dust into their cattle feed and the cattle gained more weight than

expected. The dust has not been fed to dairy cattle, nor cleared by any regulatory agencies as an additive for beef-cattle feed.

A plastic vaginal insert called the HeiGro device was introduced by Agro-physics, Incorporated, of San Francisco to suppress estrus in cows. Cattle with the inserts reportedly grow faster on less feed.

Hog cholera. A landmark for U.S. agriculture and for disease eradication was announced on January 31 in Washington, D.C. Secretary of Agriculture Robert Bergland reported that the United States is now free of hog cholera. Success came after 99 years of hog cholera research and a 17-year, $140-million, federal-state inoculation program. The impact on animal health is comparable to eliminating polio in humans. In the early 1960s, hog cholera cost pork producers more than $50-million per year.

Twin calves. Embryo-transfer techniques improved for beef and dairy cattle during 1977 and 1978. A group of agricultural scientists at the University of California, Davis, led by Gary B. Anderson, substantially increased the number of twin calf births through bilateral surgical embryo transfer in beef cows. The researchers remove the embryos from the uterus by surgery and implant two embryos in each surrogate mother so that, if both survive, she gives birth to twins. Meanwhile, the cows from which the embryos are removed can continue to produce milk for human consumption. Twenty-six cows produced 16 sets of twins and 10 single calves through this process.

Other researchers at the USDA Meat Animal Research Center in Clay Center, Nebr., used a nonsurgical technique to transfer cattle embryos. They flushed the embryo out of the mother's uterus with a salt solution. This method is cheaper than the commonly used surgical technique, and does no damage to the uterus, so it can be repeated with more cows than can the surgical method. However, only about 40 per cent of the nonsurgically transferred embryos survived, compared with 70 per cent of the surgical implants.

Ralph R. Maurer of the USDA center said the isolated embryos are kept frozen at −190°C (−374°F.) until they are needed. They can be thawed later and transferred to a heifer.

Nonsurgical embryo collection, aided by extremely sensitive microscopic techniques for embryo sexing, freezing, and implantation, could revolutionize genetic improvement and productivity in both beef and dairy cattle. Embryo banks of sexed and frozen embryos may soon be available for cattle breeders to use with either surgical or nonsurgical implantation techniques. This development could mean twin males for each beef cow and twin females for each superior dairy cow.

Solar greenhouses. Reed E. Maes of the Environmental Research Institute of Michigan in Ann Arbor designed a large, solar-heated greenhouse for use in Michigan. The north side of this modified A-frame structure contains a layer of Styrofoam 10 centimeters (4 inches) thick that is covered on the inside with an aluminum-foil surface that reflects sunlight into the green-

A machine that strips grapes from their stems and then disposes of the stems undergoes a trial run at Michigan State University. It sorts leaves, stems, and other trash from grapes harvested mechanically.

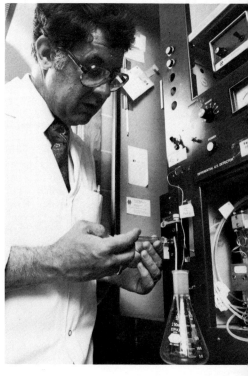

A housefly's ovaries are removed, *above,* to search for oöstatic hormones that could be used to disrupt egg development in flies. U.S. Department of Agriculture chemist J. George Pomonis, *right,* injects the ovarian extract into a liquid chromatograph as a first step in isolating the hormone.

Agriculture

Continued

house and onto the south side of the structure. The south side has an outer layer of polyethylene and an inner layer of fiberglass that are separated by 10 centimeters of air. Winter sunlight passes through the polyethylene and fiberglass into the greenhouse. A Styrofoam insulator reflector ceiling on the upper two-thirds of the south side is lowered at night and raised during the day. This conserves the heat in the greenhouse at night. Cool-season vegetables grew in this greenhouse with no supplementary heat during the 1977-1978 winter. Tomatoes required some supplementary heat.

Many new varieties of commonly cultivated crops appeared in 1978. The Michigan State Agricultural Experiment Station in East Lansing increased its roster of hybrid carrots to nine. Varieties developed during the past year include Spartan Winner, Spartan Delux, Spartan Fancy, Spartan Classic, Spartan Premium, Spartan Delight, and Spartan North. Michigan State also developed a new blueberry called Top Hat that is bred specifically as a

dwarf plant for ornamental gardens. And the agricultural experiment station at the University of Florida in Gainesville developed two new blueberries with good flavor for Florida gardens. They are called Avonblue and Alice Blue.

Wakefield, a new canning tomato, was developed at the Beltsville USDA station, and Brandywine, a new purple raspberry, was grown at Geneva, N.Y. The White House Pear was introduced by plant breeders at the U.S. National Arboretum in Washington, D.C. Tuskegee Institute in Alabama developed Carver and Rojo Blanco sweet potatoes. Carver is a moist-flesh type of potato that is good for baking and canning and Rojo Blanco is a prolific dry-flesh type.

The Canadian Agricultural Research Service in Summerland, B.C., introduced two grapes, the Sovereign Coronation and the Sovereign Rose. The first one is a pink grape that matures in October and the second one is a seedless black grape that matures in September.   [Sylvan H. Wittwer]

Anthropology

Rebel warfare in Ethiopia kept anthropologists out of the Afar region's rich fossil deposits in 1977 and 1978. However, anthropologists Mary N. Leakey and her son Philip reported an interesting find in Tanzania — footprints of a humanlike creature. The Leakeys found the prints in the Laetolil lava deposits south of Olduvai Gorge. They date from 3.59 million to 3.75 million years ago.

The footprints are 15 centimeters (6 inches) long and 11.5 centimeters (4½ inches) wide, much wider than those of modern man or Neanderthal man, the earliest known hominid prints before the Leakey discovery. Mary Leakey believes that the prints were made by a creature about 122 centimeters (4 feet) tall. Because the footprints suggest a plodding creature, she surmises it was an ineffective hunter that gathered plant products and scavenged dead animals. See OUR ROOTS GO DEEPER.

Pakistan finds. Members of the Geological Survey of Pakistan and anthropologists from the Peabody Museum of Natural History at Yale University in New Haven, Conn., have been collecting primate fossils in Siwalik geologic formations on the Patwar Plateau in Punjab Province, Pakistan, since 1973. They reported in December on 86 primate fossils from 18 Patwar locations, part of 13,000 fossils discovered at more than 300 sites. The primate fossils fall into three categories — a large form known as *Gigantopithecus*, an intermediate form called *Sivapithecus*, and a small form named *Ramapithecus*. They are dated from 9 million to 12 million years ago.

Three lower jaw bones, two adult and one infant, clearly distinguish the most humanlike of the forms, *Ramapithecus*. The jaw bones are narrow in the region of the incisor teeth, and have small canine teeth and a V-shaped palate. The teeth toward the back of the jaw have unusually thick enamel and are shaped like the back teeth of human and apelike australopithecines.

Sivapithecus and *Ramapithecus* fossil teeth were also discovered in a road cut near Pasalar, Turkey. Anthropologists Peter Andrews of the British Museum

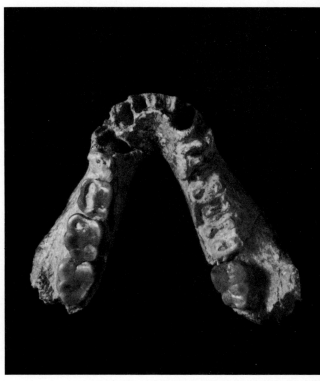

Yale University and Pakistani anthropologists search for fossils, *above*, in the Siwalik Hills of Pakistan near the spot where the first *Ramapithecus* bones and teeth were discovered in 1932. Teeth and jaw, *right*, were found at another Siwalik Hills site in 1977.

Anthropology

Continued

in London and Heinz Tobien of Johannes Gutenberg University in Mainz, West Germany, reported the finds in August 1977. Almost 100 teeth, representing at least 20 individuals, were collected. The teeth identified as *Ramapithecus* closely resemble some found in 1974 at Candir near Ankara, Turkey. Because of the age of these teeth and those found in Pakistan, anthropologists now think that the two forms may have evolved from a common apelike ancestor in Eurasia, not in Africa.

The common ancestor of apes and humans is thought to have been a member of the fossil genus *Dryopithecus*, dating to about 20 million years ago and relatively well represented in fossil records. Much less is known about the ancestors of *Dryopithecus*, an evolutionary line that diverged from a monkeylike animal to the earliest apelike creatures.

While working in the Fayum geologic deposits southwest of Cairo, Egypt, paleontologist Elwyn L. Simons of Duke University in Durham, N.C., discovered skull fragments several years

ago that he believed showed the earliest divergence toward the apes, a primate he named *Aegyptopithecus*. Returning to the Fayum in 1977, Simons and anthropologist John Fleagle of the State University of New York at Stony Brook found four fragments of upper-arm bones dating from 28 million to 30 million years ago. Simons' study disclosed that *Aegyptopithecus* walked on all fours like a monkey instead of swinging from branch to branch like the present-day apes.

Loss of fossils. Although scientists have now found thousands of primate fossils relevant to human evolution, such fossils are still quite scarce compared with the remains of other animals. The factors that determine what remains become fossilized after an animal dies are now being carefully studied by a new branch of science, taphonomy. For example, present-day orang-utan remains are seldom recovered, and those that are found are badly broken.

A fragment found by anthropologist Birute M. F. Galdikas of the Orang-

Anthropology

Continued

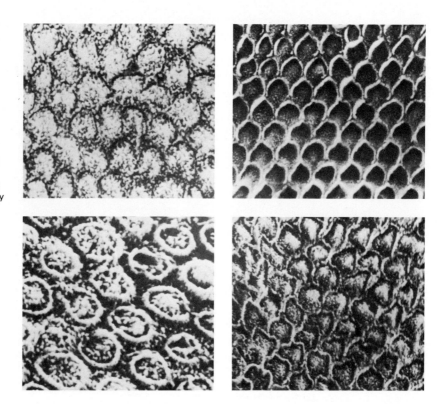

Natural patterns formed in tooth enamel and examined with scanning electron microscope may help anthropologists distinguish ape teeth from human teeth. The circle patterns in the baboon teeth, *above right,* and orang-utan teeth, *right,* differ from keyhole patterns in the *Ramapithecus* teeth, *above far right,* and those of modern man, *bottom far right.*

utan Project in Indonesia consists of only part of the forehead and face of an adult male orang-utan. According to a report published in April by Galdikas, the Bornean bearded pig (*Sus barbatus*) is primarily responsible for keeping the forest floor so clean of ape remains. Galdikas watched a pig capture and eat an infant orang-utan and consume the remains of an adult male orang-utan, leaving little of the bones.

Tartared teeth. Seventeen of 27 human skulls recovered from the Los Ceritos cemetery on the Santa Elena Peninsula in Ecuador had unusually heavy deposits of tartar on their teeth. Anthropologists Linda L. Klepinger of the University of Illinois in Champaign-Urbana, and John K. Kuhn and Josephus Thomas, Jr., of the Illinois State Geological Survey suggested in a report in October 1977 that the tartar was produced by chewing coca with lime, a common practice in that area today. Heavy tartar deposits have also been found on the teeth of individuals in Guam and India, where people chew betel nuts with lime.

The tartar-covered teeth from Los Ceritos, a site radiocarbon-dated to 840 B.C., were analyzed and the scientists found a high concentration of magnesium. A constituent of chlorophyll and some plant enzymes, the magnesium is thought to have come from the coca leaves. Although lime pots provide good archaeological evidence that earlier Ecuadoreans used coca, the absence of tartar on the teeth of earlier skeletons suggests that they used it sparingly, perhaps only on religious occasions. By Los Ceritos times, however, chewing coca appears to have become a common practice, especially among men.

Saint Francis. Physical anthropologists are frequently asked to provide information about human skeletal remains. The skeleton of Saint Francis of Assisi was exhumed while the grave at the basilica in Assisi, Italy, was being repaired. Pope Paul VI asked that anthropologists study the bones. Their March 1978 report described the saint, who died in 1226, as a short, frail man with porous bones, indicating malnutrition.   [Charles F. Merbs]

Archaeology

A gold casket believed to contain the bones of King Philip II of Macedonia, father of Alexander the Great, was unearthed near the village of Vergina in northern Greece.

Old World. Anthropologist Manolis Andronikis of the University of Salonika in Greece announced in November 1977 that he had unearthed a tomb he believed to be that of Philip II, king of Macedonia from 359 to 336 B.C. The tomb, near the village of Vergina in northern Greece, and its impressive contents, untouched by grave robbers, constitute a discovery of major importance. However, many of Andronikis' colleagues contend that it is premature to say it is the tomb of Philip II.

Nevertheless, there is reason to believe that Philip II may have been buried at this location 2,300 years ago. According to historical accounts, he went to the town of Aigai, which Andronikis believes stood where Vergina now stands, to attend his daughter's wedding before starting a military campaign against Persia. But he was assassinated. Philip's son, Alexander the Great, went on to carry out his dreams of conquest.

The tomb looks as if it was hastily built. The walls of the main room and the door to the anteroom are unfin-

ished. But the tomb's exterior is decorated in a brilliantly executed frieze depicting the turbulent finish of a lion hunt. This is the first complete painting ever found from the Hellenic period of Greek history.

The tomb contains many finely worked gold and silver objects, including a golden headband. Statues from this period show the Macedonian kings wearing such headbands. The bones were in a solid-gold casket, and the casket lid bears a stylized exploding-star symbol of the Macedonian royal house. There were also five figurines with heads of ivory that Andronikis believes represent the royal family, including Philip and Alexander.

"When I first looked at the bones," Andronikis said, "I saw something in a deep blue color, and another element which I thought should be some kind of fatty substance. Then I remembered the lines of Homer, telling how the bones of Achilles, after they were taken from the funeral pyre, were put in clear wine mixed with a substance Homer calls 'aliphar.' We don't know what this

Archaeology

Continued

was exactly, but we think it was something like butter. This is another indication that the remains are not of a common man. When I saw it all, I thought that we must be in some kind of royal tomb."

Andronikis' colleague, Salonika University archaeologist Photios Petsas, is not convinced that the tomb was Philip's, however. He points out that other tombs in the area, many larger than the one Andronikis found, have been plundered, so their richness cannot be compared with the new find. Petsas also believes that experienced grave robbers would surely have found Philip's tomb.

Other experts cast doubt on the significance of the exploding-star symbol. They say that perhaps the person buried there was merely a member of the royal court. And there are doubts about the identification of modern Vergina with ancient Aigai.

Egyptian city. University of Utah archaeologists found evidence of a lost city beneath the sands of Egypt's Nile Delta in December 1977. The team, headed by anthropologist Philip C. Hammond, reported that the site at Tell es-Shuqafiyah is littered with ancient coins and pottery fragments dating back to before 300 B.C. The archaeologists used such sophisticated electronic equipment as proton magnetometers and soil-resistivity instruments to scan the sand for evidence.

The electronic equipment detected probable evidence of buried buildings and other structures. The surface findings indicated that the site may have been associated with the Nabataeans, an Arab people who controlled some of the most important trade routes in the ancient world.

The surface material included stamped handles from large wine jars exported from the island of Rhodes to the Mediterranean basin; luxury earthenware from Italy and Asia Minor; and coins that came from the reign of the Ptolemy family of Macedonian kings who ruled Egypt from 323 to 30 B.C. The scientists also found some stone tools that may date back to the Middle Paleolithic Period, 65,000 to 35,000 years ago.

Surveyors map sandy terrain in Egypt's Nile Delta, *left,* that may cover the ancient city of Tell es-Shuqafiyah. Pottery, *above,* and ancient coins found at the site led archaeologists to dig in search of the lost city.

Archaeology

Continued

Turin shroud. Controversy raged among Italian archaeologists over the authenticity of an artifact probably discovered in the A.D. 500s, known as the shroud of Turin. The alleged burial cloth of Jesus Christ, housed in a chapel in Turin, Italy, since 1578, has been the subject of disjointed historical references since early Christian times.

The cloth bears the light yellowish-brown image of a man who had been beaten about the face, whipped, stabbed in the chest, and crucified. Unlike most such burial shrouds, there is no evidence of decay in the cloth. The image has been subjected to limited scientific testing by Italian criminologists, physicians, and pathologists. They have established that the images were not painted on the cloth but are the result of chemical changes due to intense heat or light or both, and resemble a photographic negative. A forthcoming 1978 exhibition in Turin may give other scientists the opportunity to examine the shroud and accurately establish its age and the nature of the image. [Carole L. Crumley]

New World. Archaeologists in Canada, the United States, and Peru continued to make important discoveries in 1977 and 1978. They found bones, tools, cooking utensils, and many other artifacts at a series of significant sites.

In Canada, Christopher J. Turnbull of the University of New Brunswick in Sackville excavated a prehistoric burial mound in east-central New Brunswick. The property owner found this site several years ago. He recovered more than 1,000 copper beads, fabric preserved by copper salts, a banded-slate gorget, or band worn around the neck, flint spears, and arrowheads.

Turnbull's digging turned up over 600 more copper beads, large stemmed and notched spears, a tubular pipe, a shell pendant, and chipped- and ground-stone celts and cache blades, both of which are cutting implements. One large spearpoint is apparently made of flint from Ohio Flint Ridge material, but most of the chipped-stone artifacts are made from local white quartz. Charcoal found in a subfloor central pit was radiocarbon dated at

Archaeology

Continued

about 380 B.C. The findings indicate that the prehistoric Indians of this coastal area lived much like those in the central and upper Ohio Valley and in the Northeastern United States.

A Royal Ontario Museum of Toronto field party, led by Walter A. Kenyon, excavated an early historic site in Grimsby, Ont., once occupied by the Neutral Indians, an Iroquoian group living in the Niagara Peninsula. They had up to 28 villages in the early 1600s, but the New York Iroquois drove them out of their territory in 1651.

Kenyon's team recovered 16 copper kettles that contained some fabrics and matting made from cedar, wooden spoons, and bowls with bird-shaped heads carved on them. They also found elaborate bone combs with handles shaped like animals; stone and clay pipes, some with cut-in patterns and bird effigies; gorgets; turtle-shell rattles; copper effigy rattles; iron axes; pottery vessels with cut-in Neutral designs; and beads.

Midwestern sites. Archaeologist David M. Stothers and his associates at the University of Toledo, Ohio, continued their excavation of the Williams site near Toledo. This is one of several prehistoric sites in the Great Lakes area dating to between 1000 and 500 B.C. They found many artifacts that are similar to those found at excavations from Illinois and Wisconsin to New York and southern Ontario.

The prehistoric people who lived at the Williams site cremated some of their dead and buried all of them in pits. Piles of bones from several individuals were found in a few pits. Stothers excavated tubular stone pipes with expanding bowl ends, shaped stones known as birdstones and bannerstones, a gorget, beads made from large sea shells, and arrowheads. Some of the flint and other artifacts were of materials that could not be acquired locally and must have been obtained through trade from hundreds of kilometers away.

At Phillips Spring in Hickory County, Missouri, archaeologists Marvin Kay and Christine Robinson of the Illinois State Museum in Springfield found evidence that plants were trans-

A prehistoric shrine dating to between A.D. 1264 and 1657 was discovered by archaeologists on top of Mauna Kea mountain on the island of Hawaii. It was apparently used by workers who made stone and shell tools at a nearby adz quarry.

Archaeology

Continued

Pottery made in about A.D. 1650 by a group known as the Neutral Indians is excavated and inspected at a site at Grimsby, Canada.

ported over long distances. In the summer of 1977, they excavated a site dated shortly after 2400 B.C. They found spearheads known as Sedalia points that had first been identified in central Missouri. They also uncovered empty storage pits and wooden implements.

The most important find at Phillips Spring was fragments of squash and bottle gourds that undoubtedly came from northeastern Mexico. Remains of such tropical gourd plants have also been found within the past five years in the Green River area of Kentucky and in the Tennessee River Valley in eastern Tennessee. These finds, dated to about the same period, suggest that such domesticated plants were brought into the Southeastern United States from northeastern Mexico about 3000 B.C. The seeds of the fruit of these plants have been found in dried human feces in caves in western Kentucky.

South America. William H. Isbell of the State University of New York at Binghamton conducted excavations at Jargampata and related sites in the central Peruvian highlands along the San Miguel River in Ayacucho Department. The Jargampata site was a prehistoric farming subsidiary of a major town called Wari from about A.D. 600 to 800. The Wari people conquered and occupied a large area in Peru. They were forerunners of the Inca.

One of the two groups of buildings at Jargampata was used for housing and the other was a storage and distribution center controlled by Wari overlords. Pottery vessels and fragments found at the site represent three different stages of ceramic development, each covering more than 50 years. The earliest is composed of pottery made locally and the latest has pottery made exclusively by the Wari. The farmers must have traded some of their produce for the Wari pottery.

The changes in building style over the three time periods also seem to indicate the influence of the Wari. The results of this archaeological study reinforce other studies of Wari archaeology that indicate the Wari came to dominate the area, both politically and economically. [James B. Griffin]

Astronomy

Planetary Astronomy. Phobos and Deimos, the two tiny satellites of Mars, yielded valuable information in 1977 and 1978. It was obtained by the *Viking 1* and *Viking 2* spacecraft, which are orbiting the planet. The National Aeronautics and Space Administration (NASA) scientists overcame difficult navigational and maneuvering problems to bring *Viking 1* to within 100 kilometers (62 miles) of Phobos and *Viking 2* less than 30 kilometers (18 miles) from Deimos. The scientific data obtained by the spacecraft included new information about the surfaces of both satellites and the mass of Phobos.

Grooves seen on early pictures of Phobos were mapped over the entire surface of the satellite. The age of the grooves, estimated from the number of small impact craters situated directly over them, is probably more than 1 billion years. They could date back to the time of the formation of Mars. Astronomers Peter Thomas and Joseph Veverka of Cornell University in Ithaca, N.Y., and Thomas Duxbury of the Jet Propulsion Laboratory (JPL) in Pasadena, Calif., concluded in a report published in May 1978 that Phobos must have collided with a large celestial body at some time early in its history, causing a deep-seated fracture of the satellite. The grooves are simply the surface sign of this fracture.

The observations of the satellites also showed that the surfaces of Deimos and Phobos are totally different. Phobos is heavily cratered and rough, while Deimos' surface is smooth, with only a few craters that appear to be buried in a mantle of fine debris. See ASTEROIDS: THE MISSING PLANET?

Viking 1 determined the mass of Phobos — it is 10^{19} grams (10^{13} metric tons) — by observing the satellite's effect on the spacecraft's orbit around Mars.

Once the project observers knew the mass and obtained precise knowledge of the satellite's volume from photographic data and descriptions of its color and brightness, they could show that Phobos has reflectance properties and a density similar to carbonaceous chondrite meteorites. If Phobos is composed of such chondritic material, then it probably was formed farther out in cooler regions of the original solar nebula, not near the orbit of Mars. The satellites Phobos and Deimos appear to be captured objects.

Auroras on Jupiter. Aurora borealis and aurora australis — the northern and southern lights — occur when energetic particles from the magnetosphere, primarily electrons, bombard the Earth's upper atmosphere, causing its atoms and molecules to glow. For example, oxygen molecules energized in this way produce the green color that is most often seen in auroras. Because Jupiter has an extensive and energetic magnetosphere, it should also have auroral displays. But scientists searched for evidence of this phenomenon for almost two decades without success. Then in 1978, three independent groups of researchers reported finding indirect evidence of auroras on Jupiter. Kenneth Fox of the University of Tennessee and D. E. Jennings of Goddard Space Flight Center in Greenbelt, Md., detected microwave emissions from methane molecules on Jupiter using the 11-meter (36-foot) radio telescope of the National Radio Astronomy Observatory in Kitt Peak, Ariz. They did not discover where the auroras originated on the planet, but they did show that the methane emission seems to occur when Jupiter also gives out bursts of longer-wave radio emission. Astronomers have known about the longer-wave bursts for a long time. Their occurrence is strongly correlated with the position of Jupiter's satellite, Io, in its orbit as seen from Earth. The methane emission could also be related to Io's position.

This fits in quite well with another set of observations made from data from the *Copernicus* satellite by S. K. Atreya and Thomas M. Donahue of the University of Michigan, Y. L. Yung of the California Institute of Technology, and W. S. Barker of McDonald Observatory at Mount Locke, Texas. These observers reported finding a greater number of glowing hydrogen atoms near the spot on Jupiter where the "tube" of magnetic lines of force, which passes through Io, originates. The glow appears exactly where strong auroras should occur at the end of this "flux tube," in which powerful electrical currents should flow.

Theodor Kiostiuk and his colleagues at Goddard Space Flight Center and at

A crescent moon above and beyond a crescent earth was photographed by cameras on *Voyager 1* as the spaceship sped away on its long journey to Jupiter and Saturn.

the Massachusetts Institute of Technology in Cambridge reported that they occasionally detect glowing ammonia gas near the north and south poles of Jupiter. This emission, too, is sporadic and appears to be highly localized.

Thus Jupiter must have at least two types of auroras. One may be the result of emissions from methane, ammonia, and atomic hydrogen that are concentrated in regions of the atmosphere connected magnetically with the satellites. The second type is similar to the Earth's northern lights and is concentrated in Jupiter's polar regions.

Uranus and Neptune. New observations by Robert F. Loewenstein, Doyal A. Harper, and Harvey Moseley of the University of Chicago have shattered the assumption that Uranus and Neptune are physically identical. Astronomers had assumed that the planets were "twins" because of their remarkable similarity in mass, size, and appearance. The latest studies, made by NASA's Gerard P. Kuiper Airborne Observatory, show that Neptune, like the other outer planets Jupiter and Saturn but unlike Uranus, is radiating more than twice as much energy into space as it receives from the Sun. Neptune apparently has a massive internal heat source that Uranus lacks. Balloon observations reported by G. Fazio at the Center for Astrophysics in Cambridge, Mass., and astronomers at the University of Arizona have confirmed this surprising result. It is clear that the internal structures of Uranus and Neptune are quite different.

Observations relating to the structure of their stratospheres supported the new discoveries. Just as ozone heats the Earth's stratosphere by absorbing solar radiation in the upper atmosphere, methane gas can heat the stratospheres of the outer planets. For some time, astronomers have had direct evidence of this in strong infrared radiation emissions at wavelengths characteristic of methane and ethane from Jupiter and Saturn. Observers did not expect to find strong emissions of this kind from Uranus and Neptune because their lower atmospheres are cool enough to condense methane gas into vapor. However, Fred C. Gillett of Kitt Peak National Observatory and George Rieke of the University of Arizona

239

The fly's eye telescope, a lightweight multilens instrument on Mount Haleakala in Hawaii, detects laser light that is reflected from the moon. Researchers will use the telescope to measure continental drift, North Pole "wobble," and lunar motion and mass.

Astronomy

Continued

found that Neptune is radiating very strongly in the methane and ethane bands, and they concluded that the planet must have an exceedingly hot stratosphere. Uranus has no such emissions, however. These surprising and perplexing observations were confirmed by an independent research group at the University of Hawaii. Researchers believe that these differences are caused by either Neptune's internal heat source or the fact that Neptune, unlike Uranus, is orbited by a massive satellite that raises tides in the planet's atmosphere and so heats it.

Uranus' rotation. Two independent groups of observers reported in 1977 that the period, or time of rotation, of Uranus was 23 to 24 hours, almost twice as long as astronomers previously believed. Then, using the newest equipment and largest telescopes, Robert Brown and Richard Goody of Harvard University measured a period of almost 15$\frac{1}{2}$ hours, while Guido Munch of the California Institute of Technology and John Trauger and Fred Roesler of the University of Wisconsin in Madison

reported a period of 13$\frac{1}{2}$ hours. All four studies seem to have been carefully done, so the period of rotation of Uranus apparently has yet to be properly determined.

Neptune's rotation period seems to be better understood. Spectroscopic results obtained in 1977 indicated a period near 22 hours, but it is difficult to get precise data from such a faint and distant object. Dale P. Cruikshank of the University of Hawaii determined the planet's rate of rotation by measuring the periodicity of its light curve. He looked for repeated sequences in light intensity, and took one sequence to equal one revolution. If a series of observations is made over a sufficiently long time, this method can be highly accurate. Cruikshank's best results indicate a period of 18 hours 10 minutes, with an uncertainty of only about 18 seconds. He tried to determine Uranus' period by this method also, but has not come to any conclusions yet because the light curve from Uranus is not as variable as is the light curve from Neptune.   [Michael J. S. Belton]

Astronomy
Continued

Stellar Astronomy. In 1977 and 1978, astronomers found the remains of an exploded star, learned more about radio galaxies, discovered that the sun may be cooling as its sunspots grow, and studied several new stars and a new nebula.

Supernova remnant. A supernova, or exploding star, first seen in 1182 by Chinese astronomers, was discovered again. In February, Sidney van den Bergh of the University of Toronto in Canada reported finding the nebular remains on photographs that were made with the Hale Observatories' 508-centimeter (200-inch) telescope on Palomar Mountain in California.

Radio galaxies. Anthony C. S. Readhead, Marshall H. Cohen, and Roger D. Blandford of the California Institute of Technology (Caltech) in Pasadena reported on March 9 that they had found an emission core and associated jet 5.5 light-years long in the nucleus of the radio galaxy NGC6251. This elliptical galaxy was known to have a narrow jet that extends out about 650,000 light-years from the nucleus toward one of the radio lobes.

A typical radio galaxy consists of two zones, or lobes, of radio emission on either side of the associated visible galaxy and at equal distances from it. Often there is a third radio component, a small emission core at the nucleus of the galaxy, and there also may be a jet of emission from the core. In NGC6251, the relatively short jet is aligned with the longer one, and energy appears to be streaming out from the nucleus and from one jet to the other. This discovery supports the theory that a radio galaxy's lobes get their power from beams of energy from the nucleus.

Cygnus A, the best-known radio galaxy, until recently was thought to have a pair of powerful lobes but a weak central component. However, Robert W. Hobbs and his associates at Goddard Space Flight Center in Greenbelt, Md., reported on March 15 that the central source in Cygnus A may be the dominant emitter. They deduced that this would be true if allowance is made for radiation in the presently unobserved region of submillimeter and far-infrared waves.

This possibility provides additional support for the theory that the bulk of a radio galaxy's energy is stored in the nucleus. But A. G. Willis and Richard G. Strom of the Leiden Observatory in the Netherlands reported in January that they found strong evidence that the radiating electrons in the lobes of the giant radio galaxy 3C326 are energized by an unexplained process that occurs within the lobes themselves.

Sunspots and climate. Solar activity increased during 1977 and 1978, as was expected for the ascending phase of the 11-year sunspot cycle. William C. Livingston of Kitt Peak National Observatory near Tucson, Ariz., reported in February that the sun seems to be cooling as the number of sunspots increases. The 6°C (11°F) temperature decrease during 1977 is small compared to the sun's surface temperature of 5500°C (9900°F). And the decrease may be only apparent, because the energy decrease in the visible light wavelengths may be counterbalanced by an increase in solar emission at unobserved wavelengths. Still, this is the first modern evidence for theories that solar variations cause climatic change.

In a related study based on historical research, John A. Eddy, Peter A. Gilman, and Dorothy E. Trotter of the University of Colorado's High Altitude Observatory in Boulder reported on Nov. 25, 1977, that the rotational speed of the sun increased about 4 per cent at the start of the Maunder Minimum, a period from 1645 to 1715 when there were no spots on the sun and no evidence of an ongoing sunspot cycle. The researchers analyzed sunspot motions, as inferred from old records of the sun's appearance. Eddy had shown previously that the Maunder Minimum occurred at the same time as the so-called Little Ice Age, when the European climate was unusually severe.

New stars and nebula. New studies of stars revealed information about two very young objects. The Becklin-Neugebauer object in the constellation Orion may be as young as 2,000 years old and is driving off its surrounding dust cocoon by means of a powerful stellar wind. MWC349, a massive young star, was another subject of investigation. See THE BIRTH OF A STAR.

O. D. Dokuchaeva of Moscow University reported an object with an unusual emission-line spectrum and a histo-

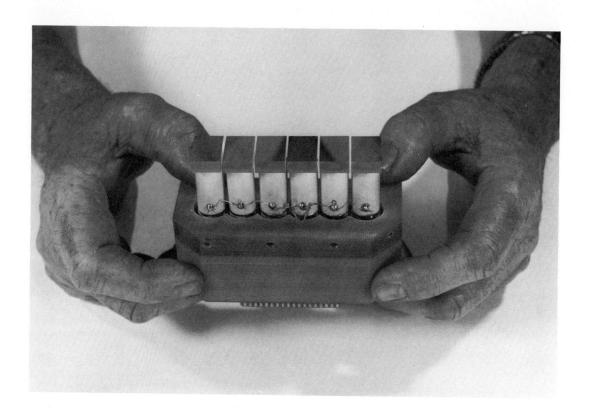

Astronomy
Continued

Six mirrors, each capable of vertical movement of a few wavelengths, actuate piezoelectric columns beneath them. The system is used with optical telescopes to correct the "twinkling" of stars caused by atmospheric interference.

ry of marked brightness changes in October 1976. In May 1977, Paul A. Feldman of the Herzberg Institute of Astrophysics in Ottawa, Canada, reported that the object, HM Sagittae, was a radio source, while Richard J. Stover and Svein Sivertsen of the University of Texas in Austin proposed that it was a planetary nebula.

Bernard W. Bopp of the University of Toledo in Ohio announced in August 1977 that HM Sagittae was a "possible embryonic planetary nebula," presumably ejected recently from its parent star. An October analysis by Feldman favored this conclusion. HM Sagittae was described by Kris Davidson and his colleagues at the University of Minnesota in Minneapolis in February 1978 as probably a symbiotic star, a very unusual binary system consisting of one hot and one cool star. However, studies at the Asiago Astrophysical Observatory in Italy, the University of Washington, and Goddard Space Flight Center supported Bopp's theory.

New facilities. The first major finding by the Very Large Array, the world's most powerful radio telescope, came while the system of 27 large telescopes was still under construction near Socorro, N. Mex. On Oct. 4, 1977, Robert M. Hjellming of the National Radio Astronomy Observatory at Charlottesville, Va., located the radio counterpart of an X-ray-emitting quasar that had been detected by the third Small Astronomy Satellite (SAS-3) on August 11.

Two new space observatories were launched to monitor cosmic radiation. The first High Energy Astrophysical Observatory (HEAO-1) went into orbit on August 12 and completed its initial scan of the sky on Feb. 12, 1978. Its major finding was that the diffuse X-ray background radiation is caused by an intergalactic plasma at a temperature of about 500,000°C. The International Ultraviolet Explorer, launched in earth-synchronous orbit on January 26, is in constant touch with a Goddard Space Flight Center ground control station and is operated for eight hours a day by controllers at a station in Madrid, Spain.   [Stephen P. Maran]

Astronomy

Continued

High-Energy Astronomy was able to post several significant developments in 1977 and 1978. The High Energy Astronomy Observatory (HEAO-1) completed the first systematic scan of the celestial sphere in X rays in the range of 150 to 100,000 electron volts (0.15 to 100 kev) and in low-energy gamma rays. Gamma rays and X rays are the shortest and most energetic wavelengths of radiation in the electromagnetic spectrum, which also includes, in ascending order, ultraviolet, visible light, infrared, and radio waves. Objects that emit X rays and gamma rays must be studied from space observatories because the waves cannot pass through the earth's atmosphere. The HEAO-1 results, reported in February, show great promise, but the data will take some time to analyze.

New common stars. Elihu Boldt of Goddard Space Flight Center in Greenbelt, Md., Gordon Garmire of the California Institute of Technology in Pasadena, and C. Stuart Boyer of the University of California, Berkeley, used the large X-ray detector on HEAO-1 to study about 20 new stars. They detected an increasingly large number of faint X-ray stars of much lower luminosity than classic X-ray binary stars, such as Hercules X-1, Cygnus X-1, and Centaurus X-3, which are among the strongest emitters of electromagnetic radiation in our Galaxy. A binary star consists of two stars that orbit each other. Classic binary stars emit mostly X rays, and astronomers discovered that they were binary stars through the variation in their X-ray pulsations. The newly detected stars are known mainly by their radio or optical characteristics; X-ray emissions form a smaller fraction of their total output.

Extragalactic objects. The number of detected objects in this class is rapidly increasing. Results on this subject were reported in July 1977 by British, Australian, and Italian astronomers. Using data obtained with the *Ariel-5* satellite, an X-ray receiver, they reported on quasars, Seyfert galaxies, and BL Lacertae objects. Quasars are intense emitters of radio waves; Seyfert galaxies have extremely bright nuclei and peculiar spectra; BL Lacertae objects are the central regions of giant elliptical galaxies. Harvey Tanan-

baum, Gerry Peters, William Forman, Riccardo Giacconi, and Christine Jones of the Center for Astrophysics in Cambridge, Mass., and Yoram Avni of the Weizmann Institute of Science in Israel in August 1977 examined data from the *Uhuru* orbiting X-ray observatory.

The *Ariel-5* and the *Uhuru* results, as well as results from the third Small Astronomy Satellite (SAS-3), provided the most exciting new discoveries — two new quasars and the brightest Seyfert galaxy in the Southern Hemisphere.

The intergalactic medium. Richard Mushotzky, Peter Serlemitsos, Barham W. Smith, Elihu Boldt, and Stephen Holt of the Goddard Space Flight Center used the OSO-8 satellite to study galactic clusters. They reported in March that lines indicating the presence of ionized iron commonly appear in the spectra of intergalactic gases.

The existence of intergalactic gases was unknown until 1972. The gases were discovered when the *Uhuru* satellite detected low-density, high-temperature clouds filling the space between galaxies forming a cluster. Ionized iron lines were discovered in the X-ray emission of clusters in 1976.

This finding proved that the radiation comes from a highly ionized gas filling the space between galaxies. Its temperature reaches millions of degrees, but its density is very low, corresponding only to 1,000 particles per cubic centimeter — considered a very good vacuum on earth. The distances between galaxies are so great, however, that the total mass of gas in the space between the galaxies equals the mass of all the stars in all the galaxies of the clusters. The importance of the discovery of intergalactic gas cannot be overemphasized. At one stroke, X-ray astronomers doubled the known amount of mass in the universe.

The Goddard study revealed that there exists probably as much iron throughout the galactic medium as there is in the region of the sun. According to present theories, this means that the gas probably played a role in the formation of an early generation of stars and was later expelled from them. See THE BIRTH OF A STAR.

Because it is reasonable to believe that these stars were formed in the galaxies we see, the gas must have come

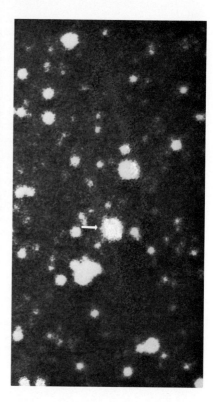

Area in the Milky Way near the constellation Ophiuchus, *right*, was reexamined optically on the basis of data from the HEAO-1 satellite and found to contain an X-ray nova, *far right*, now visible where none had been seen before.

Astronomy

Continued

from the galaxies themselves. Jeremiah Ostriker of Princeton University in New Jersey and Amos Yahil of State University of New York at Stony Brook proposed in 1973 that galactic winds must have spread the gases through space, and their theory seems to have been proved.

But larger questions remain. Some have to do with the dynamics of the gas we see. In order for gas at temperatures of millions of degrees to remain confined, we must invoke gravitational attraction from a large mass, 10 times greater than that found in visible galaxies or in the gas itself. This problem is not new, since it arises in the question of the confinement of the galaxies, as well as that of the gas. Several recent X-ray investigations deal with the relation of gas temperature and luminosity to the characteristics of clusters, such as the number and degree of concentration of the visible galaxies. Neta Bahcall of Princeton University Observatory reported on this problem in 1977.

Other researchers question whether even more gas may be present than has been detected. Jones, Giacconi, William Forman, and Stephen Murray of the Center for Astrophysics in May reported finding experimental evidence that a large halo of gas may surround the core region of the clusters containing most of the galaxies. This gas would be much less dense but would occupy an even larger volume of space than the gas that has been found.

The extended halo would have an extremely low X-ray surface brightness, and it could have escaped detection. The inferred mass would be almost 10 times greater than previously believed. This would mean that clusters are composed of similar amounts of gas and stars and galaxies. If confirmed, this would settle the problem of the nature of the total mass present in clusters of galaxies. For some time, astronomers have recognized that the total mass visible in galaxies is apparently only a fraction of the total mass there. Confirmation of the extended X-ray halos would provide direct evidence that this missing mass exists in galaxy clusters.   [Riccardo Giacconi]

Astronomy

Continued

Cosmology. One of the longest-standing challenges in observational cosmology has been to measure the earth's motion by detecting anisotropy, or different temperatures in different directions, in the radiation from the black-body background of the universe. George Smoot, Marc V. Gorenstein, and Richard A. Muller of the University of California, Berkeley, reported in October 1977 that they had detected the anisotropy by studying this radiation. It consists of emissions of microwaves from the most distant part of the universe. It was probably emitted as intense gamma rays over 15 billion years ago when the universe was forming, and the frequency has since been greatly red-shifted.

The experiment involved flying a twin-antenna radio telescope in a special U-2 reconnaissance plane 20 kilometers (12 miles) above the Western United States. In 11 flights, the Berkeley group surveyed over two-thirds of the celestial Northern Hemisphere. They used the dual antenna to compare the temperature difference in separate regions of the sky.

Because the plane flew above 90 per cent of the earth's atmosphere, its sensitive instruments could detect the radiation with a minimum of interference. The earth's motion relative to the background radiation causes a Doppler shift, which results in slightly warmer emissions in the direction in which the earth is moving, and slightly cooler emissions in the opposite direction.

The observers found that the Galaxy is moving toward the constellation Leo and away from Aquarius at about 600 kilometers (370 miles) per second. This high velocity had never been detected before because the earth, the sun, and the Milky Way Galaxy are all moving together. This is an important new discovery, because scientists had previously assumed that the velocity of our Galaxy was much smaller. The full implications of this result are not yet understood.

Is the universe closed? Jerome Kristian, Allen R. Sandage, and James Westphal of the Hale Observatories in Pasadena, Calif., in April obtained the first indication that Hubble's law deviates from a linear relation. The more distant a galaxy is from earth, the greater its red shift, the shift of its light toward the red end of the spectrum. This has provided the basis for Hubble's law: The farther from the earth a galaxy is, the faster it is moving. Hubble's law has provided the most important evidence for the expansion of the universe. The Hale team's new measurements of red shifts and magnitudes of distant galaxies seem to indicate that this expansion is noticeably decreasing in velocity, so the universe must be closed. More data are needed before their result can be considered final.

New quasar observation. The first direct observation of the ultraviolet spectrum of a quasar, or quasi-stellar object, was made in September 1977 by Arthur Davidsen, George Hartig, and William Fastie of Johns Hopkins University in Baltimore with a rocket-borne telescope. Astronomers study the ultraviolet region from space observatories because the earth's atmosphere screens out most ultraviolet light.

The 40.6-centimeter (16-inch) telescope was flown in a sounding rocket to a height of 200 kilometers (124 miles) and observed the quasar 3C 273 for four minutes at wavelengths that included that of neutral atomic hydrogen, the most abundant element in the universe.

The Johns Hopkins team found that the spectrum of 3C 273 is similar to that of quasars with a large red shift. But they saw no absorption lines, so they concluded that there can be very little hydrogen throughout the intergalactic medium, and very little absorbing material immediately around the quasar. If more remote quasars are like 3C 273, the absorption lines seen in their spectra must be caused by gas clouds in the line of sight between the quasars and the earth. This supports the idea that quasar red shifts are of cosmological origin, because the farther away a quasar is, the more likely it is that there will be gas clouds between it and the earth. And from the amount of hydrogen observed, there are many gas clouds.

Because quasars are so far away, they may be useful as cosmological measuring tools. Jack Baldwin of Lick Observatory on Mount Hamilton in California studied quasars with a large red shift and found evidence in June 1977 that the equivalent widths of certain emis-

245

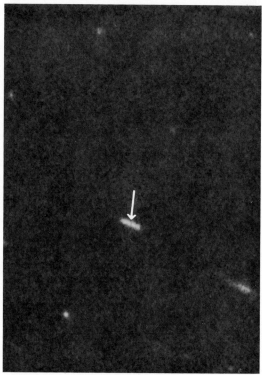

Astronomy

Continued

Charles T. Kowal sits at the blink microscope, *above*, that he used to examine photographic plates on which he discovered Chiron. The evidence, *above right*, may mean it is a comet, or an unusual asteroid.

sion lines in their spectra correlate well with quasar luminosity. Baldwin based his conclusion on the assumption that the red shifts are cosmological – caused by the great distance of quasars – so that once the spectra are measured, scientists can infer the intrinsic luminosity and absolute magnitude of a quasar. In this way, they can use quasars as "standard candles" – units of luminosity to which other celestial objects may be compared – and construct a red-shift magnitude diagram similar to that developed for bright cluster galaxies. The ultraviolet measurement of 3C 273 enables scientists to study quasars with both small and large red shifts – that is, at varying distances from the earth – and estimate whether the expansion of the universe has slowed down significantly. Baldwin says tentatively that it has.

The evolution of galaxies. Studies of two remote clusters of galaxies reported in January 1978 by Harvey Butcher of the Kitt Peak National Observatory near Tucson, Ariz., and Augustus Oemler of Yale University in New Ha-

ven, Conn., revealed evidence for much change in galactic colors over a long time. Using photometry in two colors at red shifts of 0.39 and 0.46, the researchers studied faint galaxies in two rich clusters containing many stars. Similar nearby clusters are made up of galaxies that contain no dust or gas.

Two types of gas-free galaxies appear uniform and regular – round, elliptical galaxies and flattened galaxies. All gas-free systems contain only old stars, and are relatively red. But Butcher and Oemler found that between one-third and one-half of the galaxies in the two remote clusters have the bluer colors of spiral galaxies, in which stars are still forming. This finding suggests that the galaxies in rich clusters have undergone strong evolution. Star formation ceases when a spiral galaxy is stripped clean of gas, and it eventually comes to resemble a flattened, gas-free galaxy (see THE BIRTH OF A STAR). Astronomers therefore infer that spiral galaxies have been systematically evolving into flattened, gas-free galaxies.   [Joseph Silk]

Biochemistry

Two teams of researchers reported in December 1977 that they had combined efforts to achieve one of the most-often-predicted applications of recombinant-DNA technology. Recombinant DNA refers to splicing some of the genetic material deoxyribonucleic acid (DNA) of a complex organism, such as a human being, into plasmids, small circular DNA molecules in bacteria. If the spliced DNA is a human gene that specifies the production of a useful but difficult-to-synthesize substance such as a hormone, the stage is set for the bacteria to become a valuable hormone factory. Plasmids normally exist in multiple copies of each bacterium, so if the bacteria express the human gene, they will provide high yields of the hormone.

Biochemists Arthur D. Riggs and his collaborators at City of Hope Medical Center in Duarte, Calif., and Herbert W. Boyer and his co-workers at the University of California, San Francisco, worked together to create such a factory to produce the hormone somatostatin in bacteria. Somatostatin is a small hormone, consisting of only 14 amino acids linked in a chain. It is found in many different tissues and in many animal species, including humans. It inhibits the secretion of other hormones such as insulin, glucagon, and somatotropin, or growth hormone.

The first step was to obtain the gene for somatostatin. A gene is a series of units called base pairs. Each group of three adjoining base pairs—called a triplet—corresponds to a single amino acid in the product, usually a protein, that the gene codes for, or is programmed to produce. Because the scientists knew the amino acid sequence for somatostatin, they could deduce the structure of the somatostatin gene and synthesize it. This required a sequence of 42 base pairs—very few compared to most genes—but the California researchers added several clever and crucial features to their sequence. At one end of the sequence, they added an additional three base pairs, which would add the amino acid methionine to the gene's final product. At the other end, they added six base pairs that do

A ring of bacterial genetic material called a plasmid was opened and a gene for the human hormone somatostatin was synthesized and added to it. Inserted in other bacteria, the combined genetic material produced its usual products and human somatostatin.

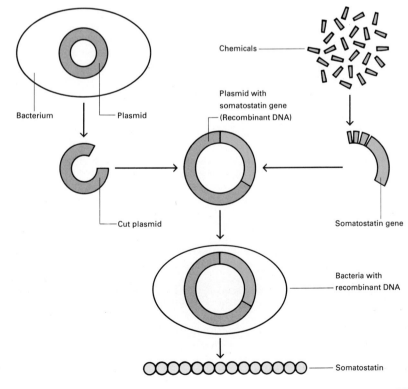

Bacterium — Plasmid

Cut plasmid

Chemicals

Plasmid with somatostatin gene (Recombinant DNA)

Somatostatin gene

Bacteria with recombinant DNA

Somatostatin

not have corresponding amino acids, but signal the bacteria to stop reading triplets and adding amino acids because product synthesis is complete.

The scientists were concerned about whether the small somatostatin protein could survive in a foreign environment. Like most organisms, bacteria possess protein-degrading enzymes that destroy foreign molecules. To protect against this, the scientists joined the gene sequence of the somatostatin to the gene sequence of a known bacterial protein, beta-galactosidase. Thus, the synthesized product would be beta-galactosidase proteins with a somatostatin tail. The use of the beta-galactosidase gene had another advantage: The expression of this particular gene can be regulated to produce many copies of its protein.

Somatostatin genes were spliced into plasmids in such a way that the base pairs that would cause the extra methionine to be added were the link between the somatostatin and the beta-galactosidase genes. Then the plasmids were introduced into the bacteria *Escherichia coli.* When the scientists later examined the bacteria's cell contents by various techniques, they detected somatostatin. However, the somatostatin molecules were still attached to the end of beta-galactosidase molecules by the expected methionine. The scientists added a substance called cyanogen bromide. This material specifically cleaves an amino-acid chain at any point that contains methionine. As a result, pure somatostatin was released.

This experiment shows that mammalian hormones can be synthesized in bacteria, in this case starting with a chemically synthesized gene. Parallel studies in which rat growth hormone was produced in bacteria, also reported in December 1977, emphasized the significance of the achievement. Rat growth hormone is a much larger, more complex substance than somatostatin and is closely related to somatotropin.

Biochemist Howard M. Goodman and his associates at the University of California in San Francisco did the growth-hormone work. Taken together, the somatostatin and growth-hormone experiments indicate that large-scale production of human hormones for the treatment of a variety of deficiency diseases may be possible within the next decade.

Gene expression. New studies of the expression of genes have disproved an apparently established fact of considerable importance. Scientists have long believed in the colinearity of the gene and its product. In other words, we believed that the amino-acid sequence of a given protein corresponds to a continuous series of triplets in DNA. Experiments carried out with bacteria seemed to establish this. However, the new studies were done on the genes of mammals. Surprisingly, they show the presence of chains of base pairs in the middle of gene sequences that do not code for any of the gene product's amino acids. Several examples of such gene inserts were discovered in 1977 and 1978, indicating that they may be quite common. See GENETICS.

Protein movements. Biochemists Günter Blobel and Robert Jackson of Rockefeller University in New York City reported in December 1977 on studies that should help us learn some of the mechanisms by which proteins move about within mammalian cells and are secreted from them.

The internal structure of mammalian cells is very complex. The cell contains many folds of membranes, forming channels through which a variety of different proteins are transported from one part of the cell to another or are excreted from the cell.

The proteins are synthesized by relatively complex cellular machinery. The final step in the synthesis is performed on the ribosomes, tiny cellular structures that are attached to the cell's membrane. An important question has been: How do the proteins that are secreted get across membranes during or after their synthesis, and what triggers the movement?

Scientists know that the proteins are synthesized as presecretory proteins — forms that are larger than the final proteins that are released. The presecretory proteins are usually 15 to 30 amino acids longer than the final released product.

In 1975, Blobel and B. Dobberstein of Rockefeller University proposed a theory to take these facts into account. They suggested that the 15 to 30 amino-acid extension in the presecre-

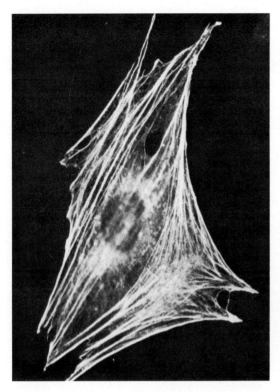

Biochemistry

Continued

The tubulin of a cell fluoresces, *above*, after treatment with special substances. Other substances make actin fluoresce in a similar cell, *above right*. Actin and tubulin are major proteins of cell structure, and viewing them separately allows scientists to study their distribution.

tory form combines somehow with the ribosome and the membrane. They proposed also that this combination makes specific changes, perhaps in the membrane's structure, that allow the protein to move across the cell's membrane. At the same time, they suggested, the 15-to-30 amino-acid extension was cut away.

This theory requires the presence in membranes of a specific enzyme to cut away the amino-acid extension converting the presecretory protein into the secreted form when it is transported across the membrane. Blobel and Jackson isolated such an enzyme from the membranous material of dog pancreas cells. The enzyme cleaved the amino-acid extension from several presecretory proteins in laboratory experiments. For example, preprolactin and pregrowth hormones were successfully converted to their active hormones by the enzyme. The stage is now set for a detailed study of the enzyme and many other aspects of protein secretion.

Decreasing allergy. Immunologist David H. Katz and his colleagues at the

Scripps Clinic and Research Foundation in San Diego have discovered a substance in the blood of mice that dampens, or reduces, their allergies. The key to the discovery was the scientists' observation that mice exposed to a low level of X rays become extremely allergic to pollen and other substances. This led the scientists to believe that the radiation had turned off some natural damping activity.

Further experiments established that the damping is caused by a substance in blood serum. The scientists showed that the damping material works by retarding the production of immunoglobulin E, or IgE, a substance known to play a major role in allergies.

Although the discovery does not promise any immediate new methods of treating human beings, a similar damping substance probably exists in human blood serum. Scientists hope that further research with the substance, once it is isolated, will help them to understand allergy better. This, in turn, may lead to improved treatment for allergy sufferers. [Julian Davies]

Books of Science

Here are 23 outstanding new science books suitable for general readers. They are selected from books published in 1977 and 1978.

Anthropology. *Food in Chinese Culture: Anthropological and Historical Perspectives,* edited by Kwang C. Chang, is a collection of essays on the complex interrelationship of social custom and the amount and type of food that is available. Each essay treats a particular period in Chinese history and explains the significance of food in the culture of the society. (Yale University Press, 1977. 429 pp. illus. $20)

Humankind by Peter Farb is a survey of distinguishing cultural traits of the human species. The book describes our primate heritage, adaptation, cultural characteristics, and the future development of humanity. (Houghton Mifflin, 1978. 544 pp. illus. $15.95)

Killing the Hidden Waters by Charles Bowden. Cities in the American Southwest use reserves of underground water that have taken centuries to accumulate. Early American Indians in that region, unable to use these hidden waters, lived under conditions of extreme hardship. Bowden tells how they survived and discusses the depletion of these nonrenewable resources and its probable consequences. (University of Texas Press, 1977. 207 pp. illus. $9.95)

Letters from the Field, 1925-1975 by Margaret Mead is a compilation of her letters describing "what it has meant to be a practicing anthropologist over the last 50 years." The letters brought the unknown world in which she worked to the friends she left behind in the United States. (Harper & Row, 1977. 343 pp. illus. $12.95)

Astronomy. *Guide to Mars* by Patrick Moore is a comprehensive summary of what is known about Mars as a result of surveys and spacecraft contact, as well as what was thought about the planet before that contact. The book discusses the Martian surface, soil, geology, and moons. There is also a discussion of the search for life there. (Norton, 1978. 214 pp. illus. ($9.95)

The Historical Supernovae by David Clark and F. Richard Stephenson is a scholarly study of Chinese and other historical records that describe the appearance of supernovae, known to the Chinese as "guest stars." The relation-

ship of many of these stars to the strong radio waves often discovered along with them is also probed. (Permagon, 1977. 233 pp. illus. $15)

Scientists Confront Velikovsky, edited by Donald Goldsmith with an introduction by Isaac Asimov. This book is a collection of five papers, four of which were presented at the 1974 meeting of the American Association for the Advancement of Science. They dispute psychiatrist Immanuel Velikovsky's theory that certain Biblical passages are accurate historical accounts of a close encounter of the Earth and Venus after Venus was formed out of a piece torn from Jupiter. (Cornell University Press, 1977. 183 pp. $8.95)

Atmospheric Sciences. *Earth's Aura* by Louise Young presents recent findings about the earth's atmosphere and its relationship to the world's overall weather. Young covers such topics as jet streams, the ozone layer, and solar wind, and also discusses the atmospheres of other planets in our solar system. (Knopf, 1977. 305 pp. illus. $12.95)

Biology. *The Life Science: Current Ideas of Biology* by Peter B. Medawar and Jean S. Medawar. This series of essays by the co-winner of the 1960 Nobel prize for physiology or medicine and his wife discusses such topics as demography, immunology, cancer, biological inheritance, and aging in the light of recent discoveries. (Harper & Row, 1977. 196 pp. $8.95)

The Spontaneous Generation Controversy from Descartes to Oparin by John Farley is a history of 400 years of debate about spontaneous generation, the theory that some simple life forms developed from nonliving material. (Johns Hopkins University Press, 1977. 226 pp. $13.50)

Brain Research. *The Dragons of Eden: Speculations on the Evolution of Human Intelligence* by Carl Sagan deals with the evolutionary development of the human brain and the implications this has for understanding human behavior, society, and intellectual functioning. The "dragons" are the darker depths of our minds. (Random House, 1977. 263 pp. illus. $8.95)

The Mechanics of the Mind by Colin Blakemore was drawn from a lecture series produced by the British Broad-

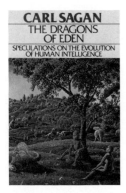

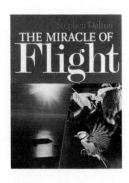

casting Corporation in 1976. Many colorful illustrations enhance discussions of sensation, sleep, memory, consciousness, and the evolution of thinking about the relationship of body and mind. (Cambridge University Press, 1977. 208 pp. illus. $6.95)

The Purposive Brain by Ragnar Granit is a collection of essays incorporating historical introductions and experimental results to explain how the human brain works. The book discusses stereoscopic vision, the mapping of functions by location within the brain, and the benefits of comparing brain processes with computer logic. (Massachusetts Institute of Technology Press, 1977. 244 pp. illus. $11.95)

Cosmology. *The First Three Minutes: A Modern View of the Origin of the Universe* by Steven Weinberg tells how the big bang theory of the origin of the universe came to be accepted as the standard model and how the first three minutes of its existence relates to the present structure and composition of the universe. Steps in the search for an "echo," or proof, of the big bang are part of the story. (Basic Books, 1977. 177 pp. illus. $8.95)

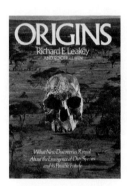

Ten Faces of the Universe by Fred Hoyle is a collection of 10 essays in which our world and the universe are described as a biologist, a physicist, a mathematician, and a geophysicist might see them. Hoyle emphasizes the nature of the changes described through the various viewpoints, and concludes with some predictions about future social changes. (W. H. Freeman, 1977. 207 pp. illus. $10.95)

Environment. *Architecture and Energy* by Richard Stein examines the need for new design and construction styles. Observing that buildings consume one-third of the energy used in the United States, the author points the way toward types of buildings that use less energy. (Anchor, 1977. 322 pp. illus. $12.95)

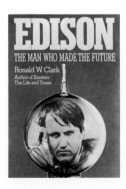

The Zapping of America: Microwaves, Their Deadly Risk & the Cover-Up by Paul Brodeur traces the history and increasing use of microwave technology in all sectors of society. The author argues that present standards of exposure to microwaves are too high and can result in harmful biological effects. (Norton, 1977. 343 pp. $11.95)

Flight. *The Miracle of Flight* by Stephen Dalton covers the fundamentals of flight: the first creatures to fly (insects); the feathered wing (birds); and the development of powered aircraft. There are vivid color photographs of all stages of flight. (McGraw-Hill, 1977. 168 pp. illus. $14.95)

Philosophy of Science. *A Sense of the Future* by Jacob Bronowski is a collection of 19 of the mathematician's articles, published between 1948 and 1974. Bronowski believed that Western civilization could draw on the understanding of nature achieved through science as a source of values and inspiration. (Massachusetts Institute of Technology Press, 1977. 286 pp. $12.50)

Prehistoric Man. *The Emergence of Society: A Prehistory of the Establishment* by John Pfeiffer. The author draws on archaeological evidence to support his theories about the rise of social man. He traces the development of society from the introduction of farming to the establishment of cities and other complex social forms. (McGraw-Hill, 1977. 512 pp. illus. $15)

Origins: What New Discoveries Reveal About the Emergence of Our Species and Its Possible Future by Richard E. Leakey and Roger Lewin. Building on the work of the late Louis S. B. Leakey and his wife, Mary, the authors describe recent fossil discoveries, the early humans that they represent, and their implications for understanding the roots of human aggression. (Dutton, 1977. 264 pp. illus. $17.95)

Technology. *Edison: The Man Who Made the Future* by Ronald Clark is a biography that describes the times in which the inventor worked, his major achievements, and his efforts to build an able staff of scientists and technicians. The book also traces the steps that led to the founding of the General Electric Company. (Putnam's, 1977. 256 pp. illus. $12.95)

Perpetual Motion: The History of an Obsession by Arthur Ord-Hume describes several centuries of ingenious and not-so-ingenious efforts to produce perpetual-motion machines, as well as some notable hoaxes. Electrical, nuclear, and atmospheric devices are included along with the purely mechanical ones. (St. Martin's, 1977. 235 pp. illus. $15)   [William G. Jones]

Botany

The chemical compound glyoxylate can be used to reduce photorespiration and thus increase photosynthesis in tobacco plants, biochemists David J. Oliver and Israel Zelitch reported in June 1977. The two scientists treated tobacco plant samples with glyoxylate at the Connecticut Agricultural Experiment Station in New Haven and found that it inhibited the production of glycolate. This chemical is involved in photorespiration, a process in which plants use oxygen and, at the same time, give off carbon dioxide.

At high light intensities, photorespiration increases, and it competes with photosynthesis, in which the plant takes in carbon dioxide to make "food" with which to grow. Only the excess of carbon dioxide fixed by photosynthesis over that given off by photorespiration goes into plant growth.

The researchers reported that reducing photorespiration doubled the amount of carbon dioxide fixed by photosynthesis. The work may be important to agriculture because temperate crop plants, such as wheat and soybeans, photorespire. Inhibiting this process could greatly increase yields by increasing photosynthesis.

Blue light and guard cells. At about the same time, other researchers reported new findings on how stomata function. These porelike openings in the leaf take in carbon dioxide during photosynthesis. Stanford University biologists E. Zieger and Peter K. Helper isolated guard cells, which control the opening and closing of stomata. These kidney-shaped cells swell in the morning when carbon dioxide levels within the leaf have been drastically reduced by photosynthesis. The swelling opens the stomata and allows more carbon dioxide to enter the plant.

The researchers found that light controls the mechanism for the swelling, but not just by reducing carbon dioxide levels through photosynthesis. It is only the blue wavelengths of sunlight that affect stomatal opening whereas both blue and red light are highly effective in photosynthesis. The blue light stimulates potassium to build up inside the cells, which causes the cells to absorb water, swell, and thus open the stomata.

Inhibiting flowers. Plants produce florigen, a hormonal substance that theoretically promotes flowering under certain daylength conditions that can vary from plant species to plant species. Plants also apparently contain other substances that inhibit flowering under unfavorable daylengths. Plant physiologists Anton Lang of Michigan State University and Mikhail Kh. Chailakhyan and I. A. Frolova of the K. A. Timiryazev Institute of Plant Physiology in Moscow reported in June 1977 that they experimented on three varieties of tobacco plants—a short-day plant that flowers when daylength is less than a particular maximum, a neutral-day plant whose flowering is not affected by daylength, and a long-day plant that flowers only after a minimum daylength is reached. The researchers grafted short-day and long-day plants onto neutral-day plants and then grew them under various light conditions.

The results clearly demonstrated the existence of florigen, first proposed by Chailakhyan in the 1930s. When exposed to short days, the short-day grafts caused the neutral-day plants to flower earlier; under long daylengths, long-day grafts produced the same results.

However, the experiment also suggested that other substances in day-sensitive plants retard flowering. In case of a long daylength, for instance, the short-day grafts retarded flowering in the neutral-day species. Perhaps more significantly, the long-day tobacco prevented flowering of the neutral-day plant when exposed to short daylengths. Both florigen and its inhibiting counterpart apparently move across the plant grafts to affect the host species. But neither substance has been extracted from the plants, purified, and chemically analyzed.

Plants and the numbers game. Biologists Roman Maksymowych of Villanova University and Ralph O. Erickson of the University of Pennsylvania demonstrated in June 1977 that treatment with a plant hormone, gibberellic acid, greatly affects phyllotaxis, or leaf arrangement, in cocklebur shoots. It also almost doubled leaf-production rate. It probably affects the plant's leaf initiation and spacing mechanism.

Botanists have known for many years that the arrangement of many plant organs, such as leaves on a stem, florets

A spruce tree, one of hundreds buried nearly 10,000 years ago during the last advance of the Wisconsin ice sheet, is uncovered during work near Marquette, Mich.

Almost As Dead As the Dodo

On the island of Mauritius in the Indian Ocean stood 13 trees of the species *Calvaria major* in 1973. They were the only such trees in the world. They were tall—as high as 30 meters (98 feet)—and old; none was younger than 300 years. Some were dying and some may have since been lost in the great cyclone of 1975. Each year they dropped seeds encased in wrinkled plumlike fruit. But the seeds did not germinate; there were no new trees. Even when horticulturists planted the seeds in nurseries, they failed to germinate. The trees seemed doomed to extinction. Why?

As a wildlife ecologist, I was studying endangered species of birds on Mauritius at that time, but the problem of the *Calvaria* tree fascinated me, and I took it up as a side interest. In 1977, I reported that I had found a solution to the problem.

As it turned out, my main research on birds and my interest in *Calvaria* were linked. A fundamental law of ecology states that many of the organisms in a natural community interact with and depend on one another. This predicts that the extinction of a species can have far-reaching and unforeseen consequences for other organisms, even for those whose relationships with the lost species may be obscure.

Many examples show how the loss of certain types of vegetation can have a disastrous impact on animal populations that depend on those plants for food or shelter. However, there are very few examples of the reverse, in which a plant species suffers as a result of the elimination of an animal. This is what happened to *Calvaria*.

The *Calvaria* seed, about the size of a walnut, has an incredibly thick and tough seed coat. When tested with a hydraulic press, *Calvaria* seeds have withstood more than 590 kilograms (1,300 pounds) of pressure before fracturing. In contrast, a hickory nut fractures under less than 50 kilograms (100 pounds) of pressure. Apparently, the *Calvaria* seed's tough shell prevents the seed from breaking out.

Some scientists speculated that genetic problems were to blame and that the tree was doomed to extinction because it could not reproduce. But if the plant was doomed, it was not because of a genetic problem. I believe the *Calvaria* tree was becoming extinct for the lack of the dodo.

The dodo, a large, flightless bird that has become the symbol of extinction, died out in Mauritius in 1681, the victim of human slaughter and introduced predators such as dogs and pigs. We know very little about the ecology of the dodo, but we do know that it was a seedeater, and we know it was about as big as a large turkey, big enough that it could ingest large fruits and seeds. The *Calvaria* fruits must have been a steady part of the dodo's diet; the seeds have been discovered among the remains of dodos found in marshes on Mauritius. I believe that the *Calvaria* tree evolved specially thickened seeds that could withstand the grinding action of the dodo's gizzard and pass through the bird's gut intact.

As a result, an interesting mutual relationship may have developed between the *Calvaria* tree and the dodo. The thick-walled seeds not only could withstand ingestion by dodos, but they actually needed to be worn thin in the dodo's powerful gizzard before they could germinate. When the dodo died out, there was no other creature to take its place. The *Calvaria* tree was unable to reproduce and, as a result, it almost followed the dodo to extinction.

I tested this hypothesis by feeding *Calvaria* seeds to substitute dodos—domestic turkeys. I fed 17 seeds to the turkeys; 10 of the seeds were either regurgitated or passed through the turkey's gut after being worn down in the gizzard. The other seven were crushed in the gizzard. When I planted these 10 seeds, three of them germinated, perhaps the first *Calvaria* seeds to germinate in 300 years. Foresters on Mauritius are now germinating seeds that they have worn down artificially and the future of the *Calvaria* tree, prized for its fine wood, seems assured.

Relationships like that between the *Calvaria* and the dodo show how delicate the balance in ecological communities can be. Many other intricate and often obscure relationships exist between plants and animals. And it is likely that other such accidental near-extinctions have occurred and will occur in the future. Not all organisms are as lucky as the *Calvaria*. The dodo certainly was not. [Stanley A. Temple]

The Dodo greets Alice in Wonderland.

A plantlet produced from the leaf tissue of a Douglas fir seedling developed in a nutrient medium, *above*. Such plantlets placed in test tubes containing other nutrients develop root systems, *right*. The new method should allow scientists to breed identical genetically superior trees in great numbers and prove valuable in forestry programs.

Botany

Continued

in a sunflower, or scales on a pine cone, can be expressed as fractions related to the Fibonacci series. In this mathematical construction, each member of the series is the sum of the two preceding members. One such series would be: 1, 1, 2, 3, 5, 8, 13, 21, 34. . . . For example, a stem may produce five new leaves spiraling around three times before one leaf is directly above another. This forms the Fibonacci fraction $3/5$.

G. J. Mitchison of the Laboratory of Molecular Biology in Cambridge, England, suggested in 1977 that Fibonacci leaf arrangement results from an expanding and growing stem and an as-yet-unknown mechanism for spacing new leaves on the stem. Mitchison believes that the spacing mechanism may be a growth-inhibiting substance that prevents new leaves from forming too close together.

Wonder tree. Scientists are looking for unused plants that might help solve energy and food shortages. *Leucaena,* a plant native to Mexico and related to the mimosa, is one possibility, according to a National Research Council panel headed by horticulturist James L. Brewbaker of the University of Hawaii. In September 1977, the panel reported that some *Leucaena* varieties grow rapidly and may produce more wood in a growing season than any other plant yet studied. This could prove a valuable energy asset. In addition, the plant can be used for cattle forage and has produced striking livestock weight gains on marginal rangelands. It is also a source of paper products.

Oldest plants yet. Paleobotanist Elso S. Barghoorn of Harvard University in Cambridge, Mass., has found what he believes to be the oldest fossil algae yet reported. Algae are simple plants. In October, he described algae preserved in the Figtree Group, a geologic formation in South Africa. He believes the fossils are blue-green algae because many seem to have been fossilized while reproducing in typical blue-green algal fashion – binary-cell division in which one cell forms two that "pinch off" from each other. The Figtree rocks have been dated at 3.5 billion years old. [Frank B. Salisbury]

Chemical Technology

New automobile lubrication systems, advances in the technology for using hydrogen as an energy source, potential new sources of gasoline, and the development of dry-cleanable leather were among advances that chemical technologists produced in 1977 and 1978.

Foiling friction in automobile engines saves wear and increases gasoline mileage. Several oil companies in 1977 introduced motor oils containing special additives to reduce friction.

Atlantic Richfield Company of Los Angeles blended graphite particles about 0.5-micron in diameter with other additives to produce a black oil that the company claims will reduce gasoline consumption by 4.8 per cent in the average U.S. car. Exxon Corporation of New York City announced in August 1977 a mineral oil for automobiles containing an additive supposed to increase gasoline mileage 4.5 per cent. The additive is dissolved in the oil, making it different from others, which are suspended solids.

Hydrogen as a fuel. Westinghouse Electric Corporation of Pittsburgh an-

nounced in mid-1977 that its researchers are developing a new method of producing hydrogen from sulfurous acid. Until now, the two major techniques for obtaining hydrogen were water electrolysis – passing an electrical current through water to break it down to its elements of hydrogen and oxygen – and reacting steam with natural gas. Both are expensive, so alternative techniques are under development. In the Westinghouse method, sulfurous acid is electrolyzed at temperatures up to 452°C (845°F.) and pressures of 21 kilograms per square centimeter, or 300 pounds per square inch (psi).

General Atomic Company of San Diego announced in September that it is developing a scheme that involves reacting water, sulfur dioxide, and iodine to form sulfuric acid and hydrogen iodide. At increasingly higher temperatures, the reaction causes the hydrogen iodide to break down into iodine and hydrogen and the acid decomposes to form water and sulfur dioxide. The hydrogen is collected, and the other chemicals and water can be recycled.

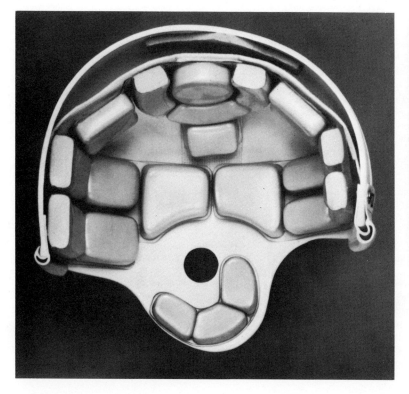

A new material consisting of tiny, sealed, air-filled cells cushions the 35-meter (115-foot) fall of an egg, *above,* and serves as a helmet shock absorber, *left.*

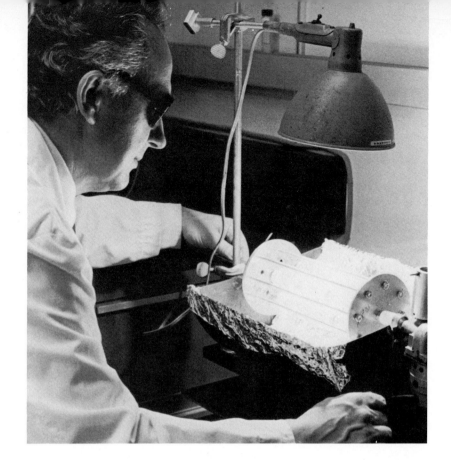

Using an artificial light source, chemist Gerhard N. Schrauzer of the University of California tests the method he developed to produce ammonia at room temperature. In Schrauzer's process, nitrogen gas is reacted with water in the presence of sunlight and a metal-treated titanium oxide catalyst.

Chemical Technology

Continued

Sandia Laboratories of Albuquerque, N. Mex., in November 1977 proposed that water containing about 10 per cent natural organic materials—particularly the cellulose from wood—be injected into the hot magma in the earth's crust to release hydrogen. Hydrogen would be produced in direct proportion to the amount of a form of iron called ferrous iron in the magma, according to Sandia scientists. The chemical reaction that occurs when ferrous iron is oxidized releases hydrogen from organic compounds. With the magma at a temperature of 1300°C (2372°F.), the injected water would produce steam and gases containing 10 per cent hydrogen, 4 per cent carbon dioxide, and lesser amounts of carbon monoxide and methane. The hydrogen could be collected by conventional methods, such as cryogenic separation, which cools the gases to the various temperatures at which they liquefy.

The greatest problem would be drilling down to the magma. But magma chambers thought to lie 2 to 3 kilometers (1.2 to 1.9 miles) below the ocean floor may be within reach. Casings set in the drilled holes would prevent seawater from rushing in.

The Lurgi Company of Frankfurt, West Germany, announced in June 1977 that it had developed a more efficient apparatus for producing hydrogen through water electrolysis. Existing equipment operates at atmospheric pressure, but the Lurgi apparatus produces hydrogen at a higher pressure, 30 kilograms per square centimeter (430 psi). This eliminates the need to compress the gas for storage in a second step.

The Institute of Gas Technology in Chicago announced in August 1977 that it is developing hydrogen "sponges" in small canisters as one method of igniting gas ranges that have no pilot lights. When the burner is turned on, a chemical reaction ignites the hydrogen, which in turn ignites the gas.

Hydrogen "sponges"—metals that absorb hydrogen under pressure for later release—can store up to twice the weight of hydrogen gas as a container with an identical liquid volume. These

Chemical Technology

Continued

sponges are mainly nickel-alloys with a crystal structure that form hydrides by taking up large amounts of hydrogen. Some researchers envisage wide usage for this hydrogen-storage system when hydrogen is used as the main fuel in such areas as home heating and cooling and in motor vehicles.

Alternative gasoline. Two new processes announced during the year promise future supplies of gasoline, but at higher prices. Heavy U.S. dependence on imported crude oil for refining into gasoline has sparked extensive research into alternative sources.

Mobil Oil Corporation announced in January 1978 that it had produced high-octane gasoline from methanol, methyl alcohol, at a pilot plant in Paulsboro, N.J. Mobile researchers combined methanol vapor and a synthetic zeolite catalyst in a reactor to give off hydrocarbon vapors, which when compressed to liquid form yield 64 per cent high-octane gasoline. The spent catalyst is regenerated and used again. The gasoline produced would sell for 40 cents to 50 cents per gallon more than petroleum gasoline, so the system is not yet practical. But experts believe the Mobil process will blaze a simplified trail to producing motor fuels from coal, which can be converted to methanol.

Synthetic natural gas (SNG) is an intermediate product in the process. The Mobil technique could be added to an SNG plant, thus producing two products at the same time.

Workers completed construction in March 1978 of a new coal liquefaction plant near Pittsburgh. It was scheduled to begin processing coal into high-octane gasoline in just one step in late 1978. Conoco Coal Development Company, Shell Development Company, and the U.S. Department of Energy are participating in the project.

In the process, equal quantities of zinc chloride catalyst and coal are fed along with hydrogen into a molten-salt reactor. The reaction that takes place at temperatures of 343° to 441°C (650° to 825°F.) and pressures of 105.5 to 316.4 kilograms per square centimeter (1,500-4,500 psi), produces hydrogen and hydrocarbons. The hydrocarbons are then used to make fuel gas, gasoline, and oil.

Developers claim that gasoline made from coal by this process is economically competitive with gasoline refined from petroleum. But formidable technical problems involving corrosion in the reaction containers must be overcome before the process can operate as efficiently as a petroleum refinery.

Dry-cleanable leather. The U.S. Department of Agriculture's Eastern Regional Research Center (ERRC) in Philadelphia in July 1977 announced the development of a technique for turning out tanned hides that are more uniform in structure and also more easily subjected to other types of finishing. The new treatment, called PolyRetanning, may help leather manufacturers compete with synthetic products.

PolyRetanning combines several finishing steps into one, essentially bonding a plastic mixture to the leather fibers. Larger amounts of the plastics tend to penetrate into less dense areas of leather fiber, giving the finished leather a more uniform thickness and increasing the amount of the original hide that can be used commercially. Also, varying the ingredients in the plastic mixture gives the leather specific qualities, such as toughness or stretchability.

Suede made this way can be conventionally dry-cleaned, eliminating a costly problem for owners of high-priced suede garments.

Tire recovery. Researchers have found ingenious ways to recycle the mountains of castoff tires that accumulate in industrialized countries. Gould Incorporated of Rolling Meadows, Ill., in December 1977 opened a pilot plant in Cleveland that shreds old tires into 0.64-centimeter (¹/₄-inch) waste-rubber particles. Then special grinding equipment Gould developed converts the particles into tiny 20-micron bits at high speed without degrading the rubber's physical properties. New tires may contain up to 30 per cent of this recycled rubber, compared with only 5 per cent of the rubber recovered by techniques using heat and pressure, which degrade the quality of the rubber.

Batchelor Robinson Metals and Chemicals Limited of Birmingham, England, is testing a different approach to making use of old tires. Its technique produces, among other products,

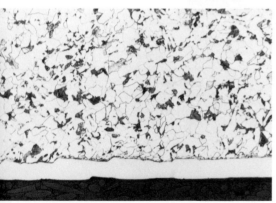

Powdered metallic glass, *top*, which cannot
be effectively fused by heat, is spooned into
a tube and surrounded with explosive. The
explosion forms it into a superstrong rod,
right. Bonded to steel, the alloy appears
as a white band, magnified 300 times, *above*.

high-grade industrial fuel oil instead of recycled rubber. Tires shredded into coarse fragments are fed into a reactor that contains little oxygen and operates at relatively low temperatures for treating waste rubber, 300° to 700°C (572° to 1292°F.). The heat breaks down the molecules in the rubber to simpler liquid substances, such as fuel oil. The firm plans to have a commercial plant operating by 1979.

Cold coal. The extreme cold that gripped the Midwestern and Northeastern United States during the winters of 1976-1977 and 1977-1978 triggered some hasty research into ways of unloading frozen coal from hopper cars at industrial plants.

Dow Chemical Company's Dowell Division in Tulsa, Okla., and Apollo Chemical in Whipanny, N.J., both came up with chemicals called freeze-conditioning agents. When sprayed on coal before it is loaded into bins or hopper cars, these agents allow it to flow almost as freely in cold weather as in warm. The sprays weaken ice crystals that form on the treated coal so they will easily crumple under slight pressure. The chemical compositions of the sprays consist of polymers, or giant molecules, combined with penetrating and dispersing agents.

Flame-resistant fiber. In October 1977, American Hoechst Corporation of Somerville, N.J., introduced Trevira 271, a flame-resistant polyester fiber. U.S. government agencies have declared a number of flame-retardant products unsafe because they may cause cancer. American Hoechst claimed Trevira 271 is safe even for children's sleepwear, the part of the garment business hit hardest by the safety bans.

American Hoechst incorporated a phosphorus-based modifier in the chemical structure of the polyester fiber. The company emphasized that the modifier, the fiber, and water extracts from the fiber all passed tests that predict the potential of a substance for causing cancer. American Hoechst claims that its Trevira 271 is self-extinguishing; if subjected to a flame, it melts and shrinks. [Frederick C. Price]

Chemistry

In November 1977, chemists used an analytical technique called nuclear magnetic resonance (NMR) to provide the first chemical image of a living human being.

Raymond Damadian, Lawrence Minkhoff, Michael Goldsmith, Michael Stanford, and their co-workers at the Biophysical Laboratory, State University of New York Downstate Medical Center in Brooklyn, obtained an image of a cross section of a person's chest. By focusing the NMR signal, a technique Damadian calls focused NMR, or FONAR, the radiation can be directed inside the body without apparent harm. The output signals are processed to give a color-coded television image of the person's anatomy.

NMR is based on magnetic moments present in the nuclei of most chemical elements and their isotopes. Water, for example, is placed in a magnetic field and radio waves of the proper frequency are beamed at it. Some of the hydrogen nuclei absorb the radio frequency (RF) radiation and are excited into an upper energy state. These excited nuclei resonate like a tuning fork when it vibrates at its natural frequency.

The RF field is usually scanned across the sample or pulsed directly at it. When the RF radiation ceases, the resonating nuclei return to the lower state, giving off the energy that they had absorbed. However, the frequency of this emitted radiation varies, depending upon what other types of atoms are in the molecule. In water, of course, this would be oxygen.

The NMR equipment usually converts the emitted energy to a graph that shows the signals as peaks. Each peak is characteristic of a particular type of nucleus and provides information about the molecule's structure. For example, in a large complex molecule, specific atoms attached to different positions give NMR peaks at different frequencies. These peaks indicate the type as well as the amount of the atom in the molecule.

In 1971, Damadian found that he could distinguish normal human tissue, which contains about 65 per cent water, from cancerous, or malignant tissue,

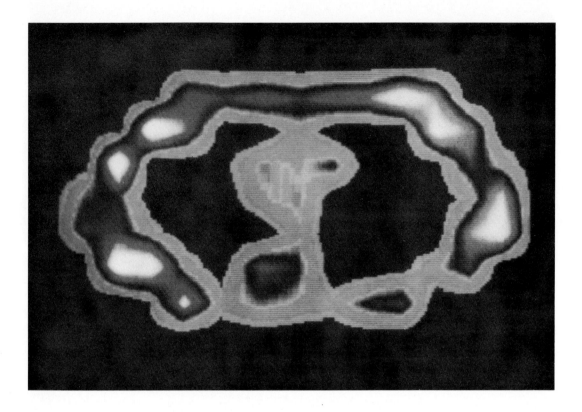

Chemistry

Continued

An image of a cross section of a human chest was made by magnetic resonance signals from the nuclei of water molecules in tissues. This technique avoids the X rays and computer processing of other imaging methods.

which contains about 90 per cent water, by measuring the NMR signals given off by the hydrogen in the water molecules. Thus it appeared that NMR might be a useful nonsurgical technique for detecting tumors.

The FONAR technique could provide information similar to that obtained by computerized axial tomography (CAT). A widely used brain- and body-scanning technique, CAT has a disadvantage in that it exposes the patient to X rays and requires elaborate computer equipment.

Damadian's team built a FONAR instrument with a superconducting magnet and an RF transmitting coil large enough to hold a human body. The instrument is hooked up to a TV screen to give a color readout of the scan. The FONAR data is taken as a cross section, similar to taking a slice of bread out of a loaf of bread and looking at one side. Darker areas are regions of low signal amplitude, indicating that little water is present, such as in the air-filled lungs. Stronger signals, indicating more water, appear lighter.

The next step in this research will be to use the new FONAR apparatus on a patient with a known tumor to determine how well the tumor can be seen. Damadian estimates that it will be two to five years before his method is ready.

Researchers are using increasingly stronger RF fields and magnets to increase the sensitivity of NMR for analysis. Typical NMR instruments use radio frequencies around 100 megahertz (MHz). A few instruments can operate at 300 MHz. In April 1978, researchers successfully operated a 600-MHz NMR instrument with nearly twice the resolving power of previous instruments. The achievement was announced by Carnegie-Mellon University in Pittsburgh, Pa., and Intermagnetics General Corporation, Guilderland, N.Y., which built the NMR's superconducting magnet. The instrument will be housed at Carnegie-Mellon and will become part of the National Institutes of Health's National NMR Facility for Biomedical Studies. It will allow investigations of biological molecules that would have been impossible before.

Chemistry

Continued

Small-ring molecule in smog. While investigating the chemical reactions responsible for photochemical smog, a team of researchers at the National Bureau of Standards (NBS) in Gaithersburg, Md., discovered the simplest member of a new class of organic small-ring compounds. Called dioxirane, the unusual molecule consists of a ring of two oxygen atoms and a carbon atom. Two hydrogens are attached to the carbon's other two bonds.

Smog results from the action of sunlight and oxygen on polluting compounds spewed into the air, mainly from automobile exhausts. The oxygen is converted to ozone, a highly reactive three-atom form of oxygen. Ozone reacts further with other chemicals to produce a variety of substances that contribute to the unhealthy and corrosive nature of polluted air.

By studying how the ethylene in automobile exhausts reacts with ozone, NBS chemists John T. Herron and Robert E. Huie determined that 90 per cent of the reaction products were neutral molecules, rather than free radicals—molecular fragments with a single unpaired or free electron. This finding conflicts with accepted atmospheric models that postulate many more free radicals.

NBS physicists Richard D. Suenran and Frank J. Lovas then reacted ethylene and ozone in a microwave spectrometer at −196°C, a temperature low enough to stabilize highly reactive species. They detected the extremely short-lived dioxirane molecule. Herron, Huie, and Richard I. Martinez confirmed the existence of the dioxirane by mass spectrometry, a technique that measures the ratio of mass-to-charge in molecules and fragments of molecules. The 3-membered ring dioxirane has never been found at normal temperatures because it is extremely reactive, and it collapses almost immediately to its more stable open-chain form.

Metal-metal bonds. "We are in a state of astonishment, not of understanding," said chemist F. Albert Cotton of Texas A & M University, College Station, in September 1977 when he reported some new compounds containing chromium and molybdenum.

Studying the compounds by X-ray diffraction, Cotton and co-workers Ste-

phen Koch and Michelle Millar discovered that the bond between the two chromium atoms in the center of the molecule $Cr_2(2,6\text{-dimethoxyphenyl})_4$ is only 1.847 angstroms (A) long. The shortest such bonds previously measured were from 1.96 to 1.98A. The short distance between the two metal atoms indicates that extremely strong electronic forces hold them together. The bond between chromium atoms was found to be a quadruple, or four-link bond—a type found in other metal-metal bonds.

Cotton calculated the "formal shortness" of the bonds. Formal shortness is the ratio between the observed metal-metal bond lengths and twice the atomic size for different atoms. He found that his chromium-chromium bond established a new formal-shortness record of 0.778A.

Analysis of large molecules. A new technique called plasma desorption mass spectrometry can be used to vaporize and ionize large biological molecules such as chlorophyll without breaking them into fragments. Developed by chemist Ronald D. MacFarlane of Texas A & M, reported in March 1978, the technique involves bombarding a surface with nuclear fragments of californium-252, a man-made radioactive isotope that undergoes fission spontaneously. The heavy ionized fission fragments have energies greater than 100-million electron volts.

When they strike a surface, the californium fragments transfer their energy to it in one-trillionth of a second, causing the surface molecules to vaporize instantly to a plasma, an ionized superheated gas. The ionized molecules are then accelerated in the mass spectrometer and their mass-to-charge ratio is used to determine the kinds of species—molecules and molecule fragments—formed. Ions vaporized in this process reach temperatures near 10,000°C. But a notable feature of the technique is that the surface molecules—either singly or else in groups—remain intact when vaporized in spite of the high energies of the bombarding particles.

MacFarlane used his technique to obtain the first direct experimental confirmation of how chlorophyll molecules transfer solar energy from the surface

Chromium atoms (large clear balls in center) in a model of tetra dichromium are linked by a quadruple bond only 1.85 angstroms long. This is the shortest, and thus the strongest, chemical bond yet measured.

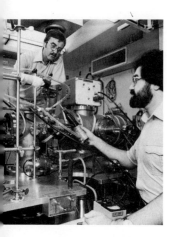

National Bureau of Standards chemists studying a reaction between ozone and ethylene discovered the intermediate chemical dioxirane. The new compound may play a role in the formation of smog.

of a leaf into its interior. Indirect evidence indicated that a stack of chlorophyll molecules acted as an antenna and the solar energy traveled through the stack by progressively forming short-lived positive and negative chlorophyll ions.

MacFarlane found that a sample of plant chlorophyll absorbed the nuclear radiation pulses from the californium-252 as if they were bursts of sunlight. Analysis of the products confirmed the presence of positive and negative chlorophyll ions. Pieces of the chlorophyll "antenna," containing up to four chlorophyll molecules, were also produced.

An unusual organic molecule was synthesized by Ohio State University chemists in March 1978. Many chemists would like to synthesize pentagonal dodecahedrane, a 12-sided molecule composed of five-membered cyclopentane rings.

Leo A. Paquette, Robert A. Snow, Jean L. Muthard, and Tadeusz Cynkowski reported that they had synthesized a related compound, C_{16}-hexaquinacene. The molecule is shaped like an igloo with three doors and is so nearly spherical that Paquette believes he can add suitable metal atoms to the double bonds at the bottom of the molecule to form a cavity that is almost spherical.

Hydrogen storage. In October 1977, chemists Dan Fraenkel and Joseph Shabtai of the Weizmann Institute of Science in Rehovot, Israel, reported that hydrogen can be stored in and recovered from molecular sieve zeolites. Zeolites are aluminosilicate minerals with a three-dimensional framework of channels and interconnecting cavities, or pores, that can trap various compounds, depending on their molecular size. A zeolite used as a highly selective method of separating molecules by excluding those larger than its pore size is called a molecular sieve.

Hydrogen is attracting considerable interest in the search for alternative energy sources. The term "hydrogen economy" has been coined to describe the use of hydrogen as a multipurpose fuel for heating and cooking, power generation, and transportation. A reliable storage system for the gas is crucial to the widespread use of hydrogen. Because hydrogen boils at a very low

temperature, storing it as a liquid is too expensive to be economically feasible.

Hydrogen, the smallest diatomic molecule, is not easily trapped in zeolite pores. But the Israeli chemists forced hydrogen into a special zeolite called "cesium-A type." They used high temperatures and pressures – typically 200° to 400°C and from 25 to 914 kilograms per square centimeter (350 to 13,000 pounds per square inch). When cooled to room temperature, the zeolite stored more than 90 per cent of the hydrogen for about five days.

The trapped hydrogen can be released by slowly heating the zeolite to the trapping temperature. When stored under pressure, the zeolite retains about 0.6 per cent of hydrogen by weight, an amount comparable to storing hydrogen in the form of metal hydrides, another experimental method.

According to University of Hawaii chemists, two factors seem to help stabilize the new compounds: the bonding of hydrogen to the zeolite and the formation of a metal complex with silver ions. In addition, the geometry of the new molecule ion was surprisingly similar to that of the hydrocarbon cyclopropane with cobalt ion.

New twist to old reaction. The classical Kolbe reaction, discovered by German chemist Adolph W. H. Kolbe in 1849, took a new and surprising twist in March 1978. In this reaction, an aqueous solution of a carboxylic acid such as acetic acid (CH_3COOH) is converted electrochemically to ethane (C_2H_6) and carbon dioxide (CO_2). Chemists Bernard Kraeutler and Allen J. Bard of the University of Texas, Austin, used an electrode made of semiconducting titanium dioxide and a high intensity light to convert the CH_3COOH almost exclusively to methane (CH_4) and CO_2.

According to Kraeutler and Bard, the titanium dioxide electrode disperses in a powder throughout the reaction mixture. This seems to serve two purposes. It causes the acetic acid to photooxidize. It also reduces the free methyl radicals to methane as soon as they are formed so that they do not have a chance to combine to form C_2H_6. The technique is interesting because it produces CH_4 – the chief compound of natural gas. [Lawrence Verbit]

Communications

Progress in communications in 1977 and 1978 primarily involved expanding the capacity of existing systems to handle the ever-increasing communications traffic. This was done by wider use of computers in telephone systems, by new satellite-communications concepts, and by technological advances in electronic-equipment design.

Satellite communications. Bell Telephone Laboratories in Murray Hill, N.J., announced in December a new concept, the scanning/spot-beam, that could triple the capacity of communications satellites scheduled for launch in the 1980s. The new system would have a dozen microwave spot beams permanently focused on major cities and a scanning beam to serve less densely populated areas. The scanning beam would sweep across the United States 80 times per second, sending and receiving bursts of information at up to 600 million binary digits (bits) per second. Bits — sequences of 0s and 1s — are used to code messages.

Most communications satellites now in use have one microwave beam wide enough to cover the United States. The scanning beam would be about the width of Maine. With it, each satellite could handle 50,000 telephone conversations at a time, compared with the 15,000 they now handle.

This increased capacity would be possible, in part, because the narrower beams could reuse transmission frequencies. Each satellite is allocated a specific bandwidth, or range of frequencies, for transmitting and receiving messages to and from earth receiving stations. If stations are not far enough apart, those sharing a frequency can garble each other's messages. Because the separate beams in the scanning/spot-beam system are hundreds rather than thousands of miles wide, stations only a few hundred miles apart may share a frequency without interference. Also, the narrow beam would transmit to antennas on earth as little as 3.7 meters (12 feet) in diameter, compared with the 30.5-meter (100-foot) diameter now required.

High-frequency tests. In February, Satellite Business Systems of McLean,

New Bell Labs precision research antenna is used to test the effects that rainfall has on high-frequency signals.

Coding for Privacy

Until now, secret coded messages have been in the province of mystery, espionage, and intrigue. But they may soon be as common in everyday life as a postage stamp. Computers are used increasingly to process, store, and transmit a great deal of information about the workings of businesses and the lives of individuals. Since this information is transmitted over public communications channels, such as telephone wires, a crucial problem of ensuring privacy arises. And the solution seems to lie in developing unbreakable codes.

Many businesses rely on networks in which computers communicate with other computers. For example, banks use such networks to transfer large sums of money. Now computer networks can even be used to deliver electronic mail. In a town near Tokyo, 3,000 households are experimenting with sending and receiving mail over closed-circuit television. A person types a message into a computer, which transmits it to the recipient's TV screen.

It is easy to tap into a computer transmission line and intercept messages. But one way to keep such information as bank transactions and electronic mail private is to cast it in codes. Computer messages are transmitted as strings of numbers. A good code scrambles these numbers so it is impossible to read the message without a key that unscrambles the code.

Special computers create complex codes for secret government messages. But first, the key to decoding them must be sent to the recipient.

Sending a decoding key takes time. It may be completely impractical to use these conventional keys in a large computer network, such as one for electronic mail. If you wanted to send a private message to someone, you would first have to send them the key to decode your message by courier or traditional mail, because computer lines can be tapped. Thus any time gained by using a computer would be lost by the disadvantage of sending the key.

Fortunately, mathematicians and computer scientists have recently devised a new way to code that seems to avoid many drawbacks of traditional systems. The new coding schemes — public key cryptosystems — eliminate the need to send secret keys by making encoding procedures public while keeping decoding procedures secret.

The new systems were proposed by electrical engineer Martin E. Hellman of Stanford University and graduate student Whitfield Diffie. They use special mathematical functions that make encoding easy but decoding impossible without some additional information. The coding functions, called trapdoor one-way functions, are like a puzzle made up of two pieces — both are necessary to make sense of a message encoded with one piece.

To use one of the new coding systems, you would place your encoding function in a public file, but keep your decoding function secret. Anyone could send you a coded message merely by looking up your encoding function. But only you could decode the message.

Hellman and another Stanford graduate student, Ralph C. Merkle, based one of these coding systems on the fact that it is easy to select a small group of numbers at random from a larger group and add them up; but it is very difficult to reverse this procedure — to try determining which numbers in a large group add up to that total.

In the Hellman-Merkle system, the public code would be a large group of numbers, chosen in a special way. The method of choosing them is being kept secret while the inventors await a patent. A person sending you a message would use numbers from your public key and transmit the encoded message with the sum of the numbers.

Since the way in which you chose the large group of numbers holds the secret to decoding the message, you can determine which numbers add up to the sum and unscramble the code. But an eavesdropper would have to try out all possible ways to add various numbers in the large group to find which total that particular sum. The more numbers in the group, the more difficult it would be to break the code. However, experts still disagree on how many numbers are necessary for a completely secure key.

Government security agencies as well as private businesses are interested in these new codes. Some experts believe that cryptography stands on the brink of a revolution, with new coding systems helping solve the problems of computer privacy. [Gina Bari Kolata]

Va., began testing digital-pulsed and high-frequency microwave transmissions using an experimental Canadian-U.S. satellite. Stations in Chicago and Catonsville, Md., transmitted and received satellite-relayed signals of 11 and 14 gigahertz (a gigahertz is 1 billion cycles per second).

Conventional domestic satellites use signals of 4 and 6 gigahertz. The high-frequency 11- and 14-gigahertz signals are considered more difficult to use than low-frequency signals because rainstorms affect them more. However, General Telephone and Electronics Corporation and Bell Laboratories have been experimenting since April 1976 with specialized antennas to determine how rain and ice crystals affect the reliability of high-frequency signals for satellite communications. For example, the tests revealed that much of the interference can be overcome by diverting signals to an earth station far from a storm, then relaying the signals to their proper destination by wires or low-frequency microwaves.

Mobile telephones. Illinois Bell Telephone Company prepared in 1977 for July 1978 field trials in Chicago of a new mobile telephone system that theoretically permits unlimited reuse of frequencies on car-telephone channels. Most mobile telephone networks now use one 12-channel transmitter-receiver system to cover a 20,331-square-kilometer (7,850-square-mile) area. With 30 to 40 subscribers on each channel, the present system can handle a maximum of 480 subscribers. Only 12 conversations — one on each channel — are possible at one time.

The new mobile-telephone system breaks up a large area formerly handled by a single transmitter-receiver into a honeycomb of smaller coverage "cells," each with its own transmitter-receiver. In Chicago, ten 26-kilometer (16-mile)-wide coverage cells will blanket a 5,439-square-kilometer (2,100-square-mile) area.

American Radio Telephone Service plans a similar system for the Washington, D.C.-Baltimore area. The region will be subdivided into five cells, each 35 kilometers (22 miles) wide. Nippon Telephone & Telegraph has scheduled a similar system to begin commercial service in Tokyo in July 1979.

In all three systems, a microcomputer built into the trunk of a car equipped with a mobile phone handles signals with the transmitter-receivers. At least one central computer linked to the transmitter-receivers constantly monitors the location of each mobile unit making a call. The computer compares signal strength from several cells in the unit's area and directs the most powerful signal to serve that mobile unit. This permits mobile units to pass from one cell to another without disrupting a phone call. In addition, hills, underpasses, and tall buildings, which sometimes weaken a signal, are no longer a problem, because another nearby transmitter-receiver will take over the mobile unit signal automatically.

One of the most important features of the cellular concept is that it can meet increasing customer demand by simply being subdivided into more and smaller cells. As the cells shrink in size, limited frequencies allotted to the mobile telephone network can be reused at increasingly smaller distances, allowing for a greater number of simultaneous calls within a cellular network. For example, frequencies in Chicago can be reused between two cells as little as 60 kilometers (37 miles) apart. At present, units sharing a frequency must be at least 161 kilometers (100 miles) apart.

Tiny TV. The Sony Corporation of Japan in March announced the development of a practical color camera for home television about the same size and weight as an 8-millimeter movie camera. This development caps more than 10 years' work in attempting to apply solid-state electronics principles to small, sharp-picture TV cameras.

Instead of the vacuum tube that ordinarily takes video pictures, the Sony has three silicon chips, called charged coupled devices (CCD). Researchers at Bell Telephone Laboratories invented the CCD in 1966 as a way of storing electrical charge in tiny areas on a semiconductor.

Each CCD in the Sony camera has 111,192 of these tiny areas to measure variations in the light of an image. The light focused on the CCD creates a pattern of electrical charges that vary with light intensity. These variations are transmitted to TV receivers to form an image.   [Darlene R. Stille]

265

Drugs

The Food and Drug Administration (FDA) approved the anticonvulsant drug valproic acid, sold under the trade name of Depakene, on Feb. 28, 1978. This compound is used to treat absence seizures, especially the petit mal epileptic type. An absence seizure is a very brief clouding or loss of consciousness, usually lasting from two to 15 seconds.

Petit mal is most prevalent in children and young adults and often seriously retards the learning process, even making learning impossible in some victims. The Epilepsy Foundation of America championed the licensing of valproic acid and estimates that the drug may benefit more than 560,000 epileptics who suffer more than one seizure each year.

Scientists do not know how the drug works. Some have suggested that it may increase brain levels of gamma-aminobutyric acid, a substance that is present in the central nervous system.

Studies by neuroscientist Buna J. Wilder of the University of Florida and others showed that this agent is effective even in patients whose seizures could not be controlled with previously available medicines.

Valproic acid may cause brief nausea, vomiting, and indigestion, and it can also cause drowsiness if taken with alcohol or barbiturates. Those who take the new drug will need periodic liver tests, because cases of liver failure have been reported among users.

Pneumonia vaccine. The FDA in November 1977 also approved for marketing the first vaccine against pneumococcal pneumonia, the most common form of the disease. Known as Pneumovax, the vaccine provides immunity against 14 of the 86 types of *Streptococcus pneumoniae* bacteria that have been identified. About 80 per cent of all pneumonia infections are caused by these 14 strains. Vaccination produces antibodies in the blood that attack the polysaccharide (a kind of carbohydrate) capsule that covers the bacteria. These antibodies destroy the *S. pneumoniae* germs before they can cause a serious pneumococcal infection.

If a person who has not been vaccinated contracts pneumonia or if the

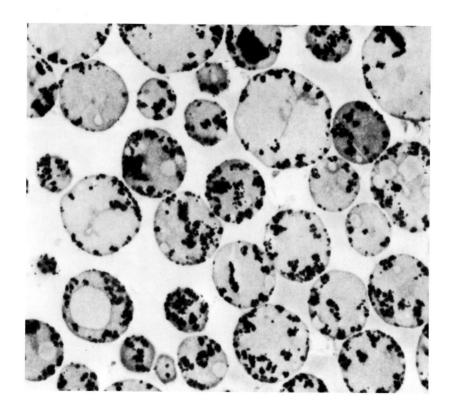

Tiny microspheres, magnified 50,000 times, are being used experimentally to deliver drugs to treatment sites. The dark dots are magnetic particles that allow doctors to guide the spheres with a magnet from outside the body.

Drugs

Continued

infection is caused by a strain not affected by the vaccine, an antibiotic, usually penicillin, must be used to prevent the multiplication of the bacteria. This treatment is usually very effective, but a pneumonia-producing bacterium that is resistant to penicillin was reported in South Africa in September. If such antibiotic-resistant strains of bacteria become more common, vaccination may become the only protection against this form of pneumonia.

The new vaccine has been recommended initially for people who run a high risk of serious pneumococcal infections – those who have had the spleen removed, those with sickle-cell anemia, and children with the nephrotic syndrome, a kidney disease, for example. Vaccination is also important for those with heart, lung, or liver disease and severe diabetes. The protective effect lasts for at least five years but may persist for much longer. See MEDICINE (Internal Medicine).

Magnetic drug delivery. Tiny magnetic spheres are being tested as drug-delivery vehicles. Immunologist and surgeon David F. Ranney and his associates at Northwestern University Cancer Center in Chicago reported in April 1978 that they used the microspheres to carry drugs through the bloodstream to the treatment site.

The microspheres consist mainly of the protein albumin along with the drug to be used, but they also have particles of a magnetic material. After injection, doctors use a magnetic field outside the body to guide the spheres to and hold them at the treatment site. In an experiment on rats, the researchers concentrated 100 times more of the drug at the treatment site than they could with standard procedures. The new system may prove important in treating surgically inaccessible cancers, abscesses, and lung clots.

Antiviral drug. Although dozens of antibiotics treat bacterial infections effectively, few are effective and safe in combating diseases produced by viruses. One such drug, idoxuridine, is used against a herpes virus that produces an inflammation of the cornea of the eye, and another, amantadine hydrochloride, is active against influenza A viruses. Now a third antiviral agent, adenine arabinoside, or Ara-A, is available.

Virologists Charles A. Alford and Richard Whitley of the University of Alabama Medical Center headed a nation-wide team of investigators who evaluated Ara-A in patients with herpes virus encephalitis, which is a life-threatening brain inflammation for which there previously was no effective therapy. The scientists found that the 70 per cent death rate in untreated cases fell to 28 per cent when Ara-A was administered. The death rate dropped to 10 per cent when the drug was administered before the victim lost consciousness. This is the first instance of effective drug therapy against a viral disease with a high mortality rate.

Saccharin-ban delay. In response to intense public pressure, Congress delayed the FDA ban on the artificial sweetener saccharin for 18 months in October 1977. The delay was granted to allow time to study evidence that saccharin can cause bladder cancer in humans and to conduct new tests on the toxicity of the widely consumed food and beverage additive. In the meantime, all products containing saccharin must bear a label stating, "Use of this product may be hazardous to your health." The National Cancer Institute and the FDA started a study in March 1978 in five states and four metropolitan areas in an attempt to determine precisely what role, if any, saccharin has to play in producing bladder tumors in humans.

New drugs introduced in the United States in 1978 included:
- Norpace (disopyramide), a compound to control the irregular heartbeat that may occur after a heart attack and in chronic heart disease. Its chief side effects are dry mouth, difficulty in urinating, occasional vomiting, and a drop in blood pressure.
- Tagamet (cimetidine), a substance that inhibits the secretion of acid in the stomach, is useful in treating peptic ulcers and preventing hemorrhaging caused by acid erosion of the stomach lining. Headache, fatigue, and diarrhea occur, but are usually mild.
- Zaditen (ketotifen), a new oral agent for the treatment of bronchial asthma. It is effective enough to allow many patients to reduce or discontinue the use of bronchodilators and adrenal corticosteroids.   [Arthur H. Hayes, Jr.]

Ecology

Ecologists and other scientists were concerned during 1977 and 1978 about the increasing concentration of carbon dioxide (CO_2) in the atmosphere, most of it added through the burning of fossil fuels. One important question is what effect increased atmospheric CO_2 will have on the photosynthesis rates of the earth's vegetation. In the late spring of 1977, ecologists Kathleen Green and Robert D. Wright of the University of Redlands in Redlands, Calif., reported on their field studies of photosynthesis of ponderosa pine (*Pinus ponderosa*) that they exposed to increased levels of CO_2.

They chose four trees in California's San Bernardino Mountains and enclosed the ends of branches, where the tree's new growth appears, in three clear plastic chambers, about 6 liters (0.2 cubic feet) in volume. The chambers were equipped with hoses to supply various air mixtures. They used fans, radiators, and thermostats to keep the temperature inside the same as that outside. The chambers were also connected to an infrared gas analyzer.

The ecologists monitored each tree for two days a month in June, July, and August, the peak period for new growth, measuring the tree's rate of CO_2 exchange every 30 minutes.

During the first day, the ecologists supplied the chambers with natural air – in which the CO_2 content ranged between 300 and 350 parts per million (ppm). On the second day, they added CO_2 to the air supply, raising the CO_2 content to a range of 450 to 500 ppm.

When the ecologists analyzed gases in the chamber, they found that net photosynthesis increased 84 per cent with the added CO_2. The more CO_2 present, the more the leaves took it up and the more oxygen they gave off. Green and Wright also tested trees whose leaves showed smog damage and found that increased CO_2 levels stimulated photosynthesis, but to a lesser degree than in healthy trees.

These results seem to indicate that photosynthesis in ponderosa pine forests may increase in proportion to increases in atmospheric CO_2 expected during the next several decades. Carbon diox-

An ecologist adjusts the chemical mixture in water sprayed from a rain machine designed to test the effects of acid rain on plants. Sulfur and nitrogen oxides given off by coal-burning industrial plants cause acid rain.

ide levels in the 450- to 550-ppm range may nearly double current photosynthesis rates. How much this increased photosynthesis will stimulate plant growth, and which species will be favored, are among the many questions ecologists will be trying to answer.

The role of fire in the ecology of certain plants is of continuing interest, especially since some areas have fires fairly regularly. Ecologist Donald T. Wicklow of the University of Pittsburgh reported in late 1977 on seed germination of the chaparral herb *Emmenanthe penduliflora*, which is found throughout the coastal ranges of California. This herb appears regularly in chaparral one year after the area has burned. In years when there have been no fires, the herb decreases markedly, indicating that fire may somehow cause the seeds to germinate.

Previous studies in which the seeds were exposed to fire showed that fire alone does not cause the seeds to germinate. Some factor in addition to fire seemed to be involved. Analysis of the leaves of other chaparral plants showed that they produce toxic organic compounds that inhibit germination. Since fire destroys these leaves, scientists thought this could account for the prevalence of *E. penduliflora* on burned sites. However, they found that the herb's seeds still would not germinate in soil free of these inhibitors.

Wicklow suspected that the burned remains of chaparral shrubs, such as *Adenostoma fasiculatum* might somehow stimulate germination. So he designed laboratory and field experiments to test this theory.

In the laboratory, Wicklow placed seeds in Petri dishes containing a double layer of filter paper or layers of either soil, sand, perlite, vermiculite, or peat. Then he added burned or charred stem segments of *A. fasiculatum*, or its ashes. He kept two sets of control seeds in dishes containing unburned stems or no stem materials. Wicklow incubated the dishes for 30 days at 10°C (50°F.) to simulate winter conditions, and then set them out at room temperature to simulate spring conditions when the seeds usually germinate.

Wicklow found that the seeds germinated only in the dishes containing soil and burned pieces of stem. The seeds would not germinate in the control dishes or in any other medium.

Wicklow carried out field studies on five plots in southeast San Benito County, California, using four ways to test the chaparral stands:
■ Cutting all brush on one plot to ground level and removing it.
■ Cutting the brush on another plot and burning it on the site.
■ Burning cut brush on a large piece of asbestos cloth and scattering the ashes in rows on the cleared plot.
■ Scattering the ashes of burned shrubs on a plot containing uncut shrubs.

A plot of undisturbed chaparral served as a control.

E. penduliflora seeds germinated on the two cleared plots containing burned plant materials, whether the brush was burned on the site or the ashes scattered there later. It did not grow on any plot containing unburned shrubs, even when ashes had been scattered there. The evidence from both laboratory and field showed that fire seems to trigger germination in this chaparral herb by eliminating aboveground foliage that may contain biochemical inhibitors to germination and by providing a germination cue in the form of burned plant remains. This unusual phenomenon illustrates once again how ecological systems have evolved extremely complex mechanisms for survival.

Metamorphosis and survival. Ecologists have extensively studied the relationships between predators and animals with a simple life cycle in which the animal retains the same form and merely grows as it gets older. But little attention has been given to the role of predators in complex life cycles, such as those of frogs and toads, which undergo metamorphosis and assume radically different forms. In the summer of 1977, ecologists Richard J. Wassersug and David G. Sperry of the University of Chicago reported on their studies of how susceptible the chorus frog (*Pseudacris triseriata*) at various stages of its development is to predation by the garter snake (*Thamnophis sirtalis*).

When the tadpoles hatch from eggs, they have long tails and no exposed limbs. They move about by swimming. During metamorphosis, their hind limbs, then forelimbs appear, and their tail disappears. Metamorphosis is completed when the tail is absorbed and the tadpole is fully transformed into a frog.

The scientists collected several hundred chorus frog tadpoles from a pond in Cook County, Illinois, and kept them in aquariums at a temperature of 20° to 21°C(68° to 70°F.).

Wassersug and Sperry conducted three predation experiments – in a simulated natural water-land foraging area, on land, and in water. For the first type of experiment, they constructed a foraging area in a glass-front cage and set it next to a water-filled aquarium. The cage was raised so that its floor was flush with the top of the aquarium. A ledge surrounded the outside rim of the aquarium. The scientists set branches over and into the water to provide perches and climbing ramps. Then they placed tadpoles, tadpoles changing into frogs, and new frogs in the aquarium or the cage. To prevent drying of the frogs not in the water, they repeatedly moistened the inside of the cage with an atomizer.

The scientists added five garter snakes and observed them periodically as they foraged for 10 hours. The scientists then removed the snakes, forced them to regurgitate their stomach contents, and counted the tadpoles and frogs they had eaten. The snakes preyed the most heavily on the animals undergoing metamorphosis.

Wassersug and Sperry conducted the land experiment with one snake set among 15 transforming and 15 newly metamorphosed frogs in a glass aquarium without water. The scientists covered the bottom of the aquarium with wet paper towels and kept the walls moist with sprayed water. They ran the experiment four times with four different sets of animals.

During the first two trials they allowed each snake to forage for 30 minutes, then removed them and counted how many frogs of each type they had consumed. In the second two trials, the scientists observed the snakes continuously throughout the 30-minute periods.

In this land experiment, the snakes captured significantly more transforming tadpoles than young frogs, although the snakes struck about the same number of times at each type. They simply failed to capture as many young frogs. So the ecologists suspected that the snakes had no innate preference for tadpoles changing into frogs.

In the water experiment, the ecologists placed 15 tadpoles and 15 frogs undergoing metamorphosis in a plastic tray 20 by 30 by 10 centimeters (8 by 12 by 4 inches) that was nearly filled with water. They set this tray in the water-filled aquarium used for the foraging area experiment in such a way that the water level in the tray was the same as that in the aquarium. The tray prevented the tadpoles from diving too deeply. The scientists then placed one snake in the foraging area. It was free to roam in the glass cage next to the aquarium, perch on branches above the water, or swim in the aquarium or plastic tray. Wassersug and Sperry observed the snake for an hour, recording the number of strikes the snake made and the number of tadpoles and metamorphosing animals it captured.

They found the snake struck at significantly more tadpoles, but captured significantly more tadpoles undergoing metamorphosis. The ecologists concluded that more tadpoles changing into frogs were captured by snakes in both the land and water experiments not because snakes prefer them but because the metamorphosing tadpoles cannot escape as easily as tadpoles or young frogs.

In water, the metamorphosing animals did not appear as efficient at diving as tadpoles. Their degenerating tails and protruding forelimbs seemed to hinder smooth movement. Most metamorphosing animals that left the water for land remained close to the water and seemed less able to escape from the snakes than the fully transformed frogs. Because the tadpoles undergoing metamorphosis retained part of their tail, they could not hop as far as frogs that had completed metamorphosis.

The finding that transforming tadpoles are more vulnerable to predators is important to understanding the life cycle of frogs and toads. Frogs change most drastically between the time their forelimbs appear and the time the tail is completely absorbed. But this is the briefest of their life stages. The fact that this takes a relatively short time may represent an adaptation to high mortality risks from predation during metamorphosis.　　[Stanley I. Auerbach]

Electronics

In the latest advance in computers, logic and memory circuits of unprecedented speed and extremely high density were announced by research scientists at the International Business Machines (IBM) Corporation in February 1978. The experimental circuits are based on the Josephson junction — a device that was proposed by Brian Josephson of Cambridge University in England in 1962.

The theory, for which Josephson shared the Nobel prize in physics in 1973, predicted that in a junction of superconductors — materials, such as columbium bismuth that lose all electrical resistance at or near absolute zero, $-273°C$ $(-459°F.)$ — electrons could "tunnel," or pass through, extremely thin insulators separating the junction without a drop in voltage. This contrasts with normal tunneling, which is accompanied by a voltage drop. The ability to switch between normal tunneling with a voltage drop and Josephson tunneling without a drop is the basis of the Josephson logic and memory circuits.

Tunneling is a phenomenon of electrons that permits them to penetrate electrical barriers because they behave like waves. Josephson tunneling is affected by the density of current carriers and the presence of a magnetic field. When either the density or the field exceeds a critical value, the insulating layer reverts to the normal voltage drop. A small current passing above each Josephson junction generates sufficient magnetic field to switch it into a voltage-drop state.

IBM scientists in Zurich, Switzerland, and Yorktown Heights, N.Y., used these characteristics to make experimental memory and logic circuits, respectively. The memory contains nearly 4,500 Josephson junctions in an array designed to test the feasibility of using them in a 16,000-bit memory chip. Because the memory cells are superconducting, no power is required to hold the data in storage. The memory has an access time of 15 nanoseconds (billionths of a second) and consumes only 10 microwatts (millionths of a watt). This is several hundred times

Drawing by Stevenson; © 1977 The New Yorker Magazine Inc.

"As of September 1st, I'm sorry to say, you will all be replaced by a tiny chip of silicon."

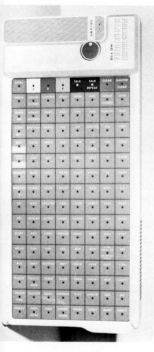

A student with a speech handicap learns to use a speech synthesizer that can generate almost all the words in the English language and can produce sentences.

faster than silicon memory chips, at several-hundredths of the power.

The logic circuits developed at IBM in Yorktown Heights include all the functions necessary to perform computer logic operations. These circuits can switch from function to function in 50 to 100 picoseconds (trillionths of a second), about 1,000 times faster than the fastest silicon circuits available. Moreover, because so little heat is generated, many Josephson junctions can be packed very close together. For example, the IBM researchers in Zurich conceive of memory densities of up to 125,000 bits per square centimeter (800,000 bits per square inch). This means that computers can be made much smaller and can operate much faster than ever before.

Consumer electronics innovations also appeared in late 1977. In September, the Japanese firms Mitsubishi Electric Corporation, Sony Corporation, and Hitachi Limited demonstrated a digital stereophonograph of ultra-high fidelity. The system uses plastic disks similar to those used in ordinary sound recording. But instead of the continuous audio signal of conventional recordings, it uses pulse code modulation. In this system, the audio signal being recorded is sampled at a high rate and converted to a series of coded pulses before being recorded on the disk. The recording is in the form of tracks whose opacity varies according to the presence or absence of pulses.

For playback, the disks spin at 1,800 revolutions per minute. A laser beam shining on the disk is the "pickup." Its reflected waves are detected and converted to electrical signals, which in turn are converted to the original sound. The system has a virtually perfect frequency response from direct current to 20 kilohertz.

In photography, automatic electronic focusing became the newest improvement in cameras. The Visitronic system, developed by Honeywell Incorporated of Minneapolis, Minn., is being incorporated into a completely automatic camera made by Konishiroku Photo Industry Ltd. of Tokyo, Japan. It works like a conventional split-image focusing system, which relies on superimposing two images of the scene being photographed.

The heart of the Visitronic system is an integrated circuit that contains two arrays of photodiode sensors. Each array receives the image reflected by separate mirrors. One is a fixed reference and the other is movable and linked mechanically by a solenoid to the camera lens. The electronic circuitry is arranged so that the signals produced by the two arrays will match when the image is in focus.

The Polaroid Corporation of Cambridge, Mass., takes a different approach in its SX-70 automatic camera – ultrasonic echo ranging. The camera carries a transducer that transmits and receives four ultrasonic frequencies. These are emitted for 1 millisecond when the photographer presses the push button. Using four frequencies, between 50 and 60 kilohertz, eliminates interference that could be caused by reflections from targets with different absorption characteristics. The camera's electronics system calculates the range by timing the signals returning from the subject to the transducer. Then it activates a motor to focus the lens. The entire process requires only a few thousandths of a second.

Automotive progress. Fuel management, pollution control, and safety continue to be United States government mandates to automobile manufacturers. More and more, automakers are turning to the microcomputer – a semiconductor device that incorporates powerful computer functions in tiny chips of silicon – to solve these vexing, and often conflicting, problems.

Chrysler Corporation has been a leader in using electronic technology to help conserve fuel. The lean-burn system introduced in its 1977 cars has been upgraded from a relatively unsophisticated analogue type to a microcomputer-based design in the 1978 models. The lean-burn system has sensors that monitor throttle position, manifold vacuum, and water and inlet-air temperature. Signals from these sensors control ignition timing for maximum engine efficiency. The latest version also meters the fuel.

General Motors Corporation has an electronic spark-advance system called Misar – for *mi*croprocessed *s*ensing and *a*utomatic *r*egulation. It works from a "map" of spark-advance set-

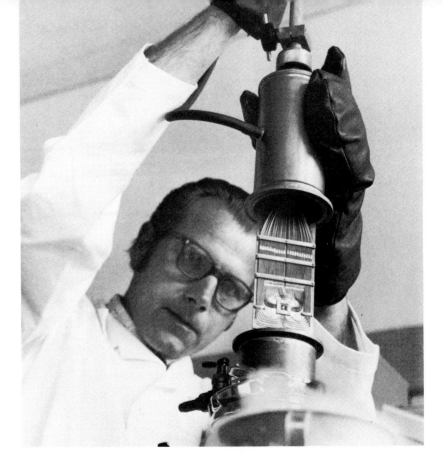

Experimental Josephson memory circuit is lowered into a liquid helium bath for testing. When operated at very low temperatures, these new devices provide unusually large data-storage capacity.

Electronics

Continued

A portable digital thermometer weighing less than 370 grams has a range of 0° to 550° C. Light-emitting diodes provide the numbers for the temperature display.

tings stored in the computer memory. A microcomputer designed by Rockwell International Corporation of Pittsburgh, Pa., examines input data on crankshaft position, manifold vacuum, coolant temperature, and timing. The microcomputer then "looks up" in the memory the appropriate spark advance required to match the best driving conditions at that instant and transmits the data to the distributor.

Ford Motor Company announced that it is pursuing three distinct engine-control systems in 1978 – two aimed at emission control and the third at fuel economy. The first uses a microprocessor to regulate exhaust-gas emissions. This system takes information from seven engine-condition sensors and uses it to control two "actuators." One governs the ignition system that produces the high-voltage pulses fed to the spark plugs. The other actuator controls the exhaust gas recirculation valve to divert unburned fuel from the exhaust back into the intake manifold.

A second Ford innovation is a feedback carburetor system designed to work with the three-way catalytic converter now found in most U.S. cars. The catalyst chemically converts harmful pollutants such as hydrocarbons, carbon monoxide, and oxides of nitrogen into harmless wastes. But the converter operates effectively over a very small range of combinations of fuel and air that most carburetors cannot adequately maintain.

The third system explored by Ford is the most unusual. It is based on the idea that engines are designed to meet peak demand, but are seldom operated at that point and thus are basically inefficient. Ford's first system, the dual displacement engine, (DDE) system was designed to recognize when full engine power is not required. It would then turn off three of its six cylinders.

Tests indicated, however, that improved fuel efficiency was lost to the gearing system requirements. Ford is now developing a variable displacement engine (VDE) in which controls can shut down from one to eight cylinders according to electronically sensed conditions.   [Samuel Weber]

Energy

Energy research during 1977 and 1978 focused on alternate energy sources for the future. There were major accomplishments in fusion research, magnetohydrodynamic (MHD) generators, and in techniques for reprocessing nuclear reactor fuel to prevent the manufacture of plutonium, an essential ingredient of atomic bombs. In addition, the first federally sponsored wind turbine to generate power for a commercial utility in the United States began operating.

The largest U.S. test facility for converting coal into low-energy gas opened in October in Windsor, Conn. Built by Combustion Engineering, Incorporated, the facility will consume 4.5 metric tons (5 short tons) of pulverized coal per hour to produce about 271,272 cubic meters (890,000 cubic feet) of gas per hour.

Nuclear fuel reprocessing. The Electric Power Research Institute of Palo Alto, Calif., and the United Kingdom Atomic Energy Authority on Feb. 27, 1978, announced a major new technique, called the Civex process, for reprocessing nuclear fuel in such a way that weapons-grade plutonium would not be produced. Major international debates about plutonium-producing breeder reactors arose following President Carter's April 1977 recommendations that construction of the U.S. Clinch River breeder reactor in Tennessee be canceled and that all countries renounce plutonium as a nuclear fuel because it could be used to produce atomic weapons.

Breeder reactors produce more fuel, in the form of plutonium, than they consume. If the plutonium is not reprocessed into more nuclear fuel, it would pose a serious nuclear-waste-disposal problem. Current reprocessing techniques separate spent reactor fuel into pure uranium and pure plutonium.

In the Civex process, machinery shielded behind several meters of concrete would automatically take radioactive spent fuel from reactors and fabricate new fuel elements consisting of uranium that did not undergo fission in the reactor, plutonium, and various radioactive waste products.

Such automation was proved possible in the mid-1960s at the Fuel Cycle Facility near Idaho Falls, Ida., which automatically took in spent nuclear fuel from an experimental breeder reactor through a concrete hatchway, refabricated it into new fuel, and sent it back to the reactor. The facility operated off and on for five years, and no human entered the process area during this period. The main feature of the Civex process is the concentration of plutonium it would maintain during the reprocessing cycle—never more than 20 per cent. A 60 per cent plutonium concentration is required to produce weapons. Since the Civex equipment would be highly radioactive, the plant would have to be shut down for many weeks before anyone could go near it to alter it to produce weapons-grade plutonium. Such a shut-down would be noticed by international monitors.

Fusion and electricity. Scientists at Sandia Laboratories in Albuquerque, N. Mex., in June 1977 produced the first thermonuclear neutrons in the United States by compressing deuterium-filled fuel pellets the size of BBs with electron beams. This was an important preliminary step toward the eventual production of electrical energy by electron beams. Russian scientists conducted similar experiments in early 1976 using different fuel-pellet designs.

The Sandia researchers aimed high-powered bursts, or pulses, of electron beams at hollow spheres containing the deuterium, an isotope of hydrogen found in seawater. The electrons caused the spheres to implode, or burst inward, and generate enough heat and pressure to fuse two deuterium nuclei together, creating an atom of helium.

This reaction emits a spare neutron that does not fit into helium's atomic structure. Enormous numbers of these spare neutrons produce vast amounts of heat that can be used to produce steam to generate electricity. Each electron pulse produced about a million neutrons from the deuterium-filled fuel pellets. A commercial-size electron-beam fusion reactor would release trillions of neutrons per pulse, but scientists expect that such a system is many years away.

MHD generator. The world's first high-magnetic-field MHD generator operated for 10 hours at a test facility near Moscow in December 1977. This marked a major milestone in the U.S.-Russian program to develop MHD

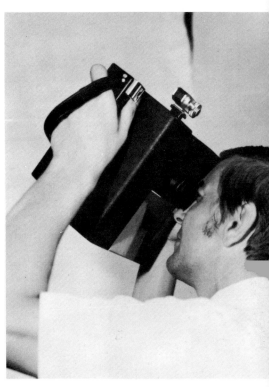

A newly developed, hand-held camera, *right*, which is
sensitive to infrared radiation given off by heat,
takes a photograph of a house and superimposes lines
that show heat loss around windows and chimney, *above*.

Aerial thermograph pictures taken in a program
sponsored by the Minnesota Energy Agency show
roof heat leaks as bright spots, *left*. An agency
worker interprets pictures for owners, *above*.

Energy

Continued

generators, which began in 1973. The generator is scheduled to operate at full power in mid-1978.

The MHD generator does not have the steam turbine of a conventional electrical generator, but uses ionized (positively or negatively charged) combustion gases directly from fossil fuels to generate electricity. The gases pass through a duct surrounded by a powerful magnetic field. The joint U.S.-Russian project uses a 36.3-metric-ton (40-short-ton) superconducting magnet built by the Argonne National Laboratory near Chicago. The magnetic field creates an electrical current in the gases, which is drawn off by electrodes in the duct wall.

MHD electricity generation promises to be more efficient than conventional methods. Conventional power plants convert only 35 per cent of the fuels' energy potential to electricity; with an MHD generator, this would increase to an estimated 50 or 60 per cent.

Solar satellite. The idea of placing a solar-power satellite in orbit around the earth to collect solar energy gained interest and stirred controversy during the year, particularly with the first successful flight tests of the space shuttle in August. Design studies center on a solar satellite that would produce 5,000 megawatts of power. Its overall dimensions would be 13.1 by 4.9 kilometers (8.1 by 3.1 miles), and it would weigh about 18 million kilograms (40 million pounds). Because of its size and weight, it would have to be assembled in space. The parts would be carried up by a space shuttle and assembled by remote-controlled robots or by a work crew operating from a space station. See SPACE GOES COMMERCIAL.

The solar-satellite proposal has generated a great deal of debate, because many experts believe it is impractical. Its main advantage is that the solar energy outside the earth's atmosphere is from four to 11 times greater than it is on earth even in areas where there is abundant sunshine. In addition, it would not be affected by day and night cycles. The electrical power produced would be sent by a microwave beam about 9.6 kilometers (6 miles) in diame-

A powerful electron beam sprays molten metal as it strikes an aluminum target in a test to determine if such beams can be used for fusion power.

ter to a receiving antenna on earth, then reconverted to electricity.

Wind energy. The first federally sponsored wind turbine-generator, or windmill, feeding into the power grid of a municipal utility began operating on Jan. 28, 1978, in Clayton, N. Mex. The wind generator produces 200 kilowatts—enough power for about 60 homes—and provides approximately 15 per cent of the electrical power requirements for Clayton's population of 3,000 persons. Natural gas-power turbines generate the remaining 85 per cent.

The windmill blades are 38 meters (125 feet) in diameter. They rotate at a constant speed of 40 revolutions per minute (rpm) in wind velocities between 13 and 55 kilometers (8 and 34 miles) per hour. This is done with a constant-speed rotor system that produces a stable electrical output. It is less expensive to operate than regulating the electrical power after it is generated. In wind velocities above or below 13 to 55 kilometers, the rotor blades are feathered, or turned, to increase or decrease wind resistance, and maintain

the 40 rpm speed. Similar wind-generator systems are scheduled to be installed on Culebra island, Puerto Rico, and on Block Island, off Rhode Island, in 1978.

Light-bulb efficiency. New developments announced in January 1978 by the General Electric Company and Massachusetts Institute of Technology (M.I.T.) will result in more efficient light bulbs to conserve energy. General Electric developed a new fluorescent lamp phosphor that produces 10 per cent more light than the conventional type and thus could reduce wattage needed to light various areas.

M.I.T. developed a chemical film that can be applied to the inside of an incandescent light bulb to reduce heat loss from the bulb. As a result, the electrical energy required to maintain the filament of the bulb at its normal operating temperature is reduced 60 per cent. A 40-watt light bulb coated with the film will give off as much light as a 100-watt standard bulb. The bulbs will help conserve energy without lighting reductions.   [Marian Visich, Jr.]

Environment

The United States Congress revised two federal acts principally responsible for controlling environmental quality in 1977. In each case, the legislators compromised between the environmental and industrial positions.

Amendments to the Clean Air Act of 1970, signed by President James E. Carter, Jr., on Aug. 8, 1977, delayed stiffer clean-air controls on automobile emissions for two years, until the 1980-model year, and set back until 1987 the date for those metropolitan areas that have severe carbon-monoxide and other automobile-emission problems to comply with federal standards. The revised Clean Air Act also allows new pollution sources to be built in areas where the air quality does not meet federal standards, if plans are made to avoid a net pollution increase by reducing pollution from other sources.

The Clean Air Act appears to be having a substantial effect. The Environmental Protection Agency (EPA) reported that sulfur dioxide levels have dropped 27 per cent, particulates have decreased 12 per cent, and carbon

monoxide is down 20 per cent since that act was passed.

Amendments to the Water Pollution Control Act of 1972, signed by Carter on Dec. 28, 1977, also extended deadlines for compliance, but did not significantly weaken the act. The legislation now allows case-by-case extensions for industrial-waste dischargers who, despite a "good faith" effort, could not meet the July 1, 1977, deadline for installing the best practicable technology to control discharges into water. About 85 per cent of industrial firms met the 1977 deadline. EPA also may extend the deadline for compliance by municipal sewage-treatment plants up to six years.

EPA has begun to implement the provisions of another major piece of environmental legislation, the Safe Drinking Water Act of 1974. It has been known for some time that the chlorine treatment used to control bacteria in drinking water to prevent such diseases as cholera and typhoid produces chloroform and other related compounds through reactions with or-

Frozen Fresh Water

The dream of using icebergs to provide water for arid lands took on new life at an October 1977 conference on iceberg towing held in Ames, Iowa.

More than three-fourths of the world's fresh water is locked in Arctic and Antarctic glaciers. From time to time, huge icebergs break from these glaciers and drift toward the equator, where they melt in the warm seas. Scientists believe that it may be feasible to tow some of these icebergs to dry regions, such as Australia, Saudi Arabia, and southern California, anchor them near the coast, and pipe off the melting water.

The most promising source of funds for such towing investigations is Saudi Arabia, a nation that is rich in oil but desperately short of water. In 1977, Prince Muhammad al-Faisal al-Saud resigned as governor of that nation's Saline Water Conversion Corporation and started a private company, Iceberg Transport International, Limited, with $1 million of his own money. The company is devoted to developing icebergs as sources of fresh water. Prince Muhammad's wealth and influence attracted glaciologists, engineers, and oceanographers to two major conferences on iceberg towing in 1977— one in Paris in June and the Ames meeting in October.

Experts agree that the rectangular, smooth-surfaced, very large icebergs from the seas around Antarctica would be more suitable for towing than the smaller, craggy Arctic icebergs. The U.S. *LandSat-2* satellite photographed one Antarctic iceberg in April 1977 that was as large as the state of Rhode Island. It was estimated to contain enough fresh water to supply all of California for 1,100 years. That one was too large to tow, but there are plenty of towable size—bergs about 1.6 kilometers (1 mile) long, 3,000 meters (1,000 feet) wide, and 2,700 meters (900 feet) deep.

There are obvious technological problems in moving an iceberg, such as keeping it from melting too quickly en route, and getting the fresh water from the iceberg to the shore. But several schemes have been proposed to overcome some of these problems. For example, in 1972, physicists John Hult and Neil Ostrander of the RAND Corporation suggested using atomic-powered tugboats to tow the icebergs.

Crews, helped by auxiliary personnel aboard launches and helicopters, would lasso the icebergs with steel cables and tow groups of as many as 20 in trains up to 80 kilometers (50 miles) long. They would travel at about 1.6 kilometers per hour, taking several months to reach their destination. To minimize the loss of fresh water by melting en route, Hult and Ostrander proposed covering the icebergs with plastic sheeting. At their destinations, the icebergs could be broken into pieces small enough to flow through flexible underwater pipes leading to shore.

The French engineering company CICERO, in 1977, proposed sinking huge spikes into the icebergs to hold tow ropes. Then, with torpedoes and electrically heated wires, they would cut a rough prow in each iceberg to reduce drag as it moved through the ocean. The crew would also insulate the bottom and sides with plastic sheeting and sailcloth and attach a collar of thick strips of polyurethane foam around the top to create a pond of melted water. This would help insulate the ice from the heat of the sun's rays.

However, glaciologists say that anchoring spikes on the bergs would be difficult, because the top layers consist of soft snow rather than ice. And the electrically heated iceberg slicers would consume huge amounts of energy.

A plan, proposed in November by oceanographer Warren Denner of the U.S. Naval Postgraduate School in Monterey, Calif., requires no tugboats. Instead, six huge underwater pontoons would be mounted on the sides of each iceberg. The pontoons would contain liquid ammonia that should vaporize in the relatively warm water at the ocean surface. The gas vapor in each pontoon would run a turbine that would turn a propeller to move the iceberg. The gas would then flow through pipes to the top of the iceberg where the cold ice would convert it back into liquid ammonia, and it could be used again.

Plainly, no satisfactory towing method has yet been perfected. But even cautious glaciologists believe they can eventually transport Antarctic ice water at least as far as the arid areas south of the equator.   [Peter Gwynne]

Environment

Continued

Radioactive debris from a Russian satellite was scattered over the wastes of Canada's Northwest Territories after the craft fell from space in January.

A barge moves through inland waters in France, pumping oxygen into stretches of water that have been depleted of oxygen by pollutants.

ganic materials in the water supplies. Some of these chemicals are suspected, based on animal tests, to be carcinogens, cancer-causing agents, and their presence in drinking water is of particular concern because of the resulting long-term exposure.

EPA has proposed a standard of less than 0.1 milligram of these materials per liter (0.26 gallon) of water – less than 100 parts per billion. The EPA will also require municipal water systems that serve 75,000 persons or more to install activated carbon filters to remove these compounds within the next two years, if they cannot comply with that standard.

Dumping wastes. Ironically, the successes in cleaning up the air and water have made another environmental problem more obvious. Waste chemicals from industrial and manufacturing processes may no longer legally be dumped into sewers or oceans or burned in open pits or incinerators.

EPA estimates that of the 29 million metric tons of toxic chemicals generated last year, less than 10 per cent was

adequately disposed of by proper incineration, safe landfills, or waste recovery. The remainder was discarded illegally in a wide variety of ways. For example, drums containing explosive waste guncotton (cellulose nitrate) were simply dumped beneath the Pulaski Skyway in Newark, N.J.; warehouses have been rented, filled with barrels of various kinds of wastes, such as industrial solvents, and then abandoned; barges containing hazardous wastes have been taken out to sea and blown up; and barrels of toxic materials are being discarded in rural areas.

A chemical company in New Jersey dumped toxic chemical wastes in a Rhode Island rural area during the summer of 1977, contaminating streams that feed a drinking-water reservoir. There were reports of nosebleeds and nausea from area residents and the Conservation Law Foundation of Rhode Island brought legal action to stop the dumping.

Increasing chemical hazards. The list of chemical compounds suspected to be carcinogenic or otherwise toxic con-

French workers use a floating rubber barrier to contain the oil slick, *above*, after the supertanker *Amoco Cadiz* ran aground and broke up off the coast of Brittany, *right*.

Environment

Continued

tinues to grow at an alarming rate. The Environmental Defense Fund claims that 4-methoxy-*m*-phenylenediamine, a compound commonly used in permanent hair dyes, causes tumors in rats and poses a potential risk to humans by absorption through the scalp. Two common industrial solvents, benzene and acrylonitrile, are suspected to be carcinogens and the Occupational Safety and Health Administration sharply lowered human exposure limits for them.

Under the Toxic Substances Control Act of 1976, EPA must protect the public from such chemical hazards. But U.S. industry currently produces 70,000 chemicals and about half of these are pesticides that present a higher risk because they must be toxic to some living organisms to be effective.

EPA reports that it lacks the personnel needed to test these compounds adequately and that industry does not always make its test data public. For example, Velsicol Chemical Corporation was indicted for withholding toxicological data on pesticides and has

been criticized in House Commerce Subcommittee hearings for continuing to sell Tris, a flame retardant used in children's sleepwear, after the firm knew that the compound was a suspected carcinogen.

Spilling oil. The supertanker *Amoco Cadiz* went aground on March 17, 1978, north of Brest, France, off the Brittany coast, and eventually lost all of its 220,000 metric tons of oil in the largest oil spill ever recorded. Unlike the lucky New England coast, which never was hit by the *Argo Merchant* spill off Nantucket Island in late 1976, the Brittany coast was coated with large quantities of the oil. Because of high seas, salvage and antipollution equipment were ineffective and the oil had to be removed with shovels and rakes.

It was too soon, by the summer of 1978, to assess the damage from the *Amoco Cadiz* spill, but data from an intensive study of the *Argo Merchant* spill was encouraging. Oil spills apparently disperse more rapidly than might have been expected, at least in open ocean. Six months after the *Argo Mer-*

chant spill, only one of the numerous bottom-sediment samples taken near the wreck site contained even a trace of oil. Other studies have shown that maritime animal and plant life recovers rapidly after the weathering and dispersal of spilled oil.

Much less is known about the biological effects of slow oil leakage into bodies of water near oil wells, tanker ports, and municipal sewage plants. Much of the oil from the last source appears to be used crankcase oil – a disturbing discovery because recent tests have shown that used lubricating oil can cause genetic changes and thus may be carcinogenic.

The concern about the effects of oil-drilling operations on the outer continental shelf off the northeast coast of the United States has led to determined opposition by environmental groups to drilling. The Supreme Court of the United States in February 1978 declined to review a lower court ruling allowing exploratory drilling to begin in the Baltimore Canyon area off the New Jersey coast in April. Legal action

brought by Suffolk County, New York, and by the Natural Resources Defense Council under the National Environmental Policy Act had delayed the start of drilling.

Destroying species. During 1977 and 1978, Congress considered providing some relief from the absolute prohibition placed on federal projects that might destroy a critical habitat of an endangered species, as required by the Endangered Species Act of 1973. Attorney General Griffin B. Bell appeared before the Supreme Court in April to argue that the threat to the tiny snail darter – a 7.6 – centimeter (3-inch) fish – should not be allowed to block the completion of the Tellico Dam on the Little Tennessee River. On June 15, the court decided for the fish.

In the same way, a small blind salamander has halted a plan to replenish an underground reservoir that is the only source of drinking water in San Antonio, Tex. Proposed amendments would allow a federal decision to go ahead with some projects that would eliminate a species. [Harold R. Ward]

Genetics

Genes in adenovirus 2 are split, or separated into two parts, by other genetic material and spliced together during gene expression, or function. This was reported by virologists Susan M. Berget, Claire Moore, and Phillip A. Sharp of the Massachusetts Institute of Technology in Cambridge in August 1977. Adenovirus 2 infects human cells, and finding split genes in this virus is important because the virus must use human enzymes to splice the split gene. Because human cells have the enzymes needed to splice these viral genes, it is possible split genes may also be a part of the normal gene structure in humans and other higher organisms. Molecular biologist Daniel F. Klessig of Cold Spring Harbor Laboratory in New York confirmed the adenovirus 2 findings and measured the section of genetic material that separates the two parts of the gene.

Except for a few viruses, all organisms studied so far have genes composed of deoxyribonucleic acid (DNA). DNA is a long, threadlike molecule made up of two intertwined strands

that carry chemical groups called bases. Four bases are found in DNA: adenine (A), guanine (G), thymine (T), and cytosine (C). Each base juts off the DNA strand and pairs up with a base jutting off the other DNA strand at the corresponding position – A pairs with T and G pairs with C. The length of a DNA molecule is measured by the number of base pairs it contains.

The sequence of base pairs along a DNA molecule determines the genetic information in a gene. This sequence codes, or specifies, the substance that the cell is to manufacture, usually a particular protein molecule. In bacteria and the viruses that infect them, the gene information is uninterrupted – that is, the information for making a protein is read by the cell's machinery from one end of the gene to the other. Although scientists had generally assumed that genes of higher organisms would be decoded in the same manner, the adenovirus 2 findings and other recent research imply that many, perhaps most, genes of higher organisms are interrupted by at least one seg-

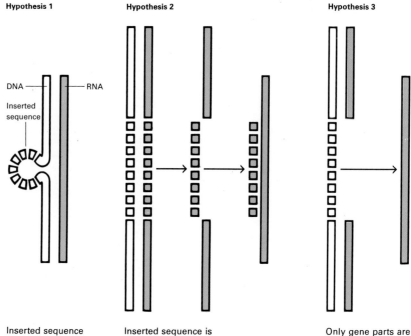

Inserted sequence forms a loop and is by-passed during gene transcription.

Inserted sequence is transcribed, but is eliminated from RNA.

Only gene parts are transcribed. These are then fused.

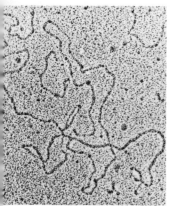

A Split Gene
Fragment of adenovirus 2 DNA, *above*, contains loops of inserted genetic material that separate parts of functioning genes. Three hypotheses, *right*, suggest possible ways such a split gene could be expressed.

Genetics

Continued

ment – and maybe several – of DNA that does not code for protein.

The first evidence for a split gene structure was provided earlier in 1977 by biochemists David M. Glover, Raymond L. White, and David S. Hogness of Stanford University School of Medicine in California, and Peter K. Wellauer and Igor B. Dawid of the Carnegie Institution of Washington's Department of Embryology in Baltimore. These researchers studied a gene in the fruit fly *Drosophila melanogaster* that is responsible for the production of a type of ribonucleic acid (RNA) called 28S ribosomal RNA.

Glover, White, and Hogness reported that the 28S ribosomal RNA gene was split into two parts separated by a DNA sequence of 5,400 base pairs of unknown function. Each *Drosophila* cell contains about 500 copies of the 28S ribosomal RNA gene and Wellauer and Dawid showed that about one-third of the genes are not split. The inserted DNA sequences in the split genes range in size from 500 to 6,000 base pairs. Because *Drosophila* cells

contain so many copies of this gene, only the unsplit genes may function.

Conclusive evidence for a split gene structure in a normal functioning gene was reported in November 1977 by geneticists R. Breathnach, J. L. Mandel, and P. Chambon of the Institute of Biological Chemistry in Strasbourg, France. Their studies of the gene in chickens that codes for ovalbumin, a major protein component in egg white, showed the gene is split by a 2,500 base-pair insertion of DNA.

In the same month, immunologist Susumu Tonegawa of the Institute for Immunology in Basel, Switzerland, found a 93 base-pair insertion in a mouse gene that codes for an antibody. This is a type of protein used in the body's immune defense against organisms and other foreign materials.

Then, in December, enzymologists A. J. Jeffreys and R. A. Flavell of the University of Amsterdam in the Netherlands found a 600 base-pair insertion in the gene for rabbit beta-globin. This gene codes for a major component of hemoglobin, the oxygen-carrying protein in blood. Since this gene is generally believed to be a typical gene, its split nature suggests that many other genes in higher organisms may be split.

Unknown function. The inserted DNA segment's task is unknown. Indeed, it is not clear how the coding segments of a gene are spliced together. In transcription, the first stage of gene expression, the two strands of a DNA molecule separate from each other. One of the strands then serves as a pattern, or template, for the synthesis of an RNA molecule. RNA is chemically similar to DNA and also contains four bases that pair as do the DNA bases.

In processing, the second stage of gene expression, the RNA molecule undergoes a type of chemical alteration. Certain bases are added to one end of the molecule, different bases are added to the other end, and additional chemical changes may also occur. The fully processed RNA is known as messenger RNA. The third and final stage of gene expression, translation, occurs on ribosomes, tiny particles in the cell. Here, a protein molecule is manufactured according to the messenger RNA's base sequence.

Three possibilities. Geneticists have at least three hypotheses to explain how the coding segments of a split gene could be spliced when the gene is to be expressed. During transcription, the inserted segment of DNA could form a loop that is by-passed as the RNA molecule is produced. The insertion could also be transcribed into RNA and then be cut out during processing. Or the two coding halves of the split gene could be transcribed separately and then joined together during processing. RNA transcript produced by adenovirus 2 is nearly the same size as its parent DNA. This supports the second theory, but the evidence is not yet conclusive.

No matter how the splicing occurs, split genes in higher organisms are a completely unexpected development. Many geneticists believe that the inserted sequences may help control when and in what cells a gene becomes active – triggers certain genes to function in blood cells, for instance, and not in bone cells.   [Daniel L. Hartl]

Geoscience

Geochemistry. Geochemists made great advances in 1977 and 1978 in understanding the chemical properties and chemical evolution of objects that enter the earth's atmosphere from outer space. Improvements in the sensitivity of instruments used to analyze rock and mineral samples made this progress possible. With these instruments, scientists can now chemically analyze material weighing only trillionths of a gram and at the same time examine the sample microscopically with magnifications as great as 100,000 times. In addition, techniques for obtaining and analyzing samples in a noncontaminated environment have improved.

The work culminates a decade of studying rocks and minerals brought from the moon by the U.S. and Russian programs. Comparison of this material with earth rocks has provided a framework in which the earth's chemical processes can be viewed in relation to the more general chemical processes in the solar system.

Brownlee particles. Geochemist Sundar Rajan of the Carnegie Institution's Department of Terrestrial Magnetism in Washington, D.C., and his co-workers elsewhere used the new techniques in 1977 to show that tiny dust particles collected in 1976 by Donald Brownlee of the University of Washington in Seattle definitely came from outside the earth's atmosphere. Brownlee's particles were collected by U-2 aircraft flying in the stratosphere.

Geochemists have been trying to collect and analyze interplanetary dust for decades. We know that it continually strikes the earth as fainter meteors or "shooting stars," and that most of it comes from comets.

Previous attempts to collect interplanetary dust have ended in disappointment. Particles collected by balloons, rockets, and spacecraft usually turned out to be industrial contaminants or other earth materials, such as dust from volcanic explosions.

About half of Brownlee's particles were shown to be aluminum oxide left in the stratosphere by the engines of earlier solid-fuel rockets. But the other half were unlike any known contami-

Geoscience

Continued

nants. The discovery that these tiny particles contain helium from the sun that must have been implanted by the solar wind confirmed their extraterrestrial nature. Each particle has only about 10^{-14} grams of helium. However, considering the small size of the particles, that is a significant amount. Proportionally, it compares to the concentration of oxygen in the earth's air.

Scientists understand the solar-wind implantation phenomenon from studies of lunar-surface dust. However, the earth's magnetic field repels such electrically charged solar-wind particles, so the presence of solar-wind helium demonstrates their extraterrestrial origin.

Chemical analyses. Using high-voltage electron microscopy and high-voltage electron spectroscopy, Rajan and others mapped the distribution of the various chemical elements within the delicate structures of these dust grains on a scale of dimensions less than the wavelengths of visible light. Their measurements confirmed the primitive composition of this material and opened the door to understanding the processes by which these microscopic objects were formed.

Most of the dust grains are fragments from comets. But some of them may come from beyond the solar system. Thus, we may now have samples of the interstellar medium from which new stars and their planets form.

During the year, Brownlee and his co-workers also identified the presence of extraterrestrial matter in muddy sediments from the ocean floor. Contamination from earth rock fragments is minimized at locations far from islands and continents. Brownlee showed that extraterrestrial dust-grain surfaces are oxidized to form magnetite, a magnetic iron oxide, during their passage through the earth's atmosphere. Because of this, a magnet can separate these grains from the rest of the material relatively easily.

For many years, scientists have found iron-nickel particles in oceanic sediments that were probably formed as droplets when larger meteors entered the atmosphere. Researchers have also found silicate particles that may have a

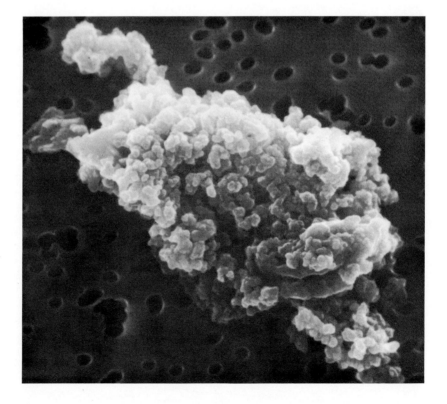

Brownlee particle is one of many collected in the stratosphere by U-2 planes. Analysis showed the particles contain solar helium, indicating they are of interplanetary origin.

Shooting
Stars
On Ice

Although meteors — shooting stars — are a common enough sight on a clear night, meteorites — meteors that strike the earth — are rarely recovered. Until recently, the entire world collection of meteorites numbered scarcely 2,000. But recent finds in Antarctica have dramatically increased that number.

During the Antarctic summers of 1969 through 1975, Japanese field parties found 992 meteorites on the surface of the windswept blue icecap in eastern Antarctica, in an area of less than 300 square kilometers (116 square miles).

This amazing concentration prompted a joint United States-Japan team to search the blue icecap region of Victoria Land, about 3,200 kilometers (1,990 miles) to the west. This team recovered 320 meteorites in this region during 1976, 1977, and 1978. The number of meteorites that fall in Antarctica is no greater than elsewhere, but the meteorites are not subject to varying weather that would erode and eventually destroy them. The cold and dry Antarctic climate provides excellent protection against weathering; the meteorites are never exposed to water or to temperatures above freezing. The ice sheet creeping slowly toward the edge of the continent carries meteorites that have fallen and been buried over millions of years. Strong dry winds evaporate some of the ice and leave meteorites on the windswept ice surface.

Such meteorites help us learn about the formation and composition of the solar system and even hold clues to the origin of life. An Antarctic meteorite recovered in January 1978 is the second one ever found that contains amino acids — the precursors of proteins and of life itself. Resembling compacted clay, the meteorite would have been eroded by only a few rainstorms. There are certainly many more like it waiting on the ice.   [Edward J. Olsen]

Geoscience

Continued

similar origin. However, the new work is by far the most clear-cut identification of extraterrestrial silicates in oceanic sediments. Some of these particles are probably fragments from types of stone meteorites with which we are familiar. But some are more akin to the Brownlee particles.

Allende meteorite. The new analytical procedures have also led to important advances in the geochemical study of meteorites. Most attention was directed toward more detailed studies of the structure of the Allende stone meteorite that fell in northern Mexico in 1969. Work on the Allende meteorite in 1976 had shown that it contains a chemically heterogeneous mixture of primitive material.

Particularly noteworthy were the centimeter-sized calcium-aluminum inclusions, or fragments, that researchers found in the meteorite. The unusual mineralogy of these inclusions led many geochemists to suggest that they were relics of crystals that condensed from a high temperature "solar nebula" during the earliest stages of solar-system history. They subsequently found that not only the chemical composition of the inclusions but also the isotopic composition, or atomic-weight differences in the same element, pointed back to the formation of elements in stars prior to the formation of the sun. Most surprisingly, these isotope irregularities were found on a microscopic scale and indicated that chemical mixing in the early solar system was incomplete.

Eighteen elements in samples of the Allende meteorite demonstrate such isotopic anomalies, or peculiarities. These include the elements that were studied and measured in determining the age of the meteorite and the time scale for events in the solar system during its formation. It is quite likely that the new findings will require some revision of these time scales.

In 1977, geochemists Ahmed El Goresy and his colleagues at the Max Planck Institute in Heidelberg, West Germany, and David Wark and John Lovering of Australian National University in Canberra reported that they had discovered microscopic nuggets containing rare metals, such as platinum and iridium, in these inclusions. The most remarkable of the nuggets contain extremely small particles of nearly pure platinum, rhenium, iridium, and other metals. At the high temperatures at which the calcium-aluminum inclusions were believed to have formed, such chemically similar metals should quickly blend with one another, forming homogeneous alloys. On the other hand, if they formed in low temperatures and at the low densities of space in the early solar system, it is hard to understand how the individual atoms of these metals found one another to form pure particles. In such conditions, it is more likely that the atoms would simply condense onto the surface of some other material.

Origin of meteorite particles. One interpretation of the origin of these strange Allende meteorite particles and their isotopic anomalies came from astrophysicist Donald D. Clayton of Rice University in Houston. Clayton suggested that the particles were not formed in the solar system, but in the atmospheres of older stars, and later were incorporated into the Allende material when it was formed about 4.5-billion years ago. Such grains could be created during the last stages of a star's life while it is a red giant, or even later during its final explosion as a supernova. During these stages, one might expect unusual material to form.

The temperatures in more typical stars, such as the sun, are not high enough for any but the most simple nuclear-fusion reactions in their interiors. However, in red giants and supernovae, temperatures are 100 times hotter, and all atomic nuclei participate in these reactions, generating material with differing isotopic compositions.

Clayton's ideas are quite speculative. But they fit in well with a 1977 discovery by geochemists William Herbst and George Assousa of the Carnegie Institution's Department of Terrestrial Magnetism. They observed that stars in the process of formation can be found in the remains of old supernovae. So there is a chain of events linking the death of old stars to the birth of new ones, at least in some cases. The strange Allende particles may be a link in this chain. [George W. Wetherill]

Geology. Much research in 1977 and 1978 focused on studies of plate tectonics and ancient plate motions. Through these studies, geologists have developed a more precise picture of the geologic history of western Nevada and western Canada, as well as the Mid-Atlantic Ridge.

Plate tectonics is the study of the about 20 huge, slowly moving, lithospheric plates, each 70 to 155 kilometers (45 to 95 miles) thick, which form the earth's shell. Mid-ocean ridges and deep gulfs, such as the Red Sea and the Gulf of California, form where the plates pull apart. Volcanic island arcs, such as the Marianas and the Lesser Antilles, form in the ocean where one plate slides beneath another. And mountain systems, such as the Andes, form on land where one plate slides beneath another that is supporting a continent.

The more geologists learn about past plate motions, the more complex the known history of the earth becomes. Robert Speed of Northwestern University in Evanston, Ill., studied the geology of western Nevada, which was formed by the slow-motion collision of an island arc with a continent during the Triassic Period, about 200 million years ago. Speed hoped to determine the source and history of three different groupings of rocks in western Nevada that are all 200 million to 300 million years old but that were formed in completely different environments.

A chaotic, jumbled mixture of sedimentary and igneous rocks from the bottom of the ocean was pushed eastward onto the continental shelf during the Triassic Period. The shelf, now underneath these deep-ocean rocks, was composed of shallow-water sedimentary rock. A chain of extinct volcanic islands with rock material like that of the volcanoes of modern island arcs, lay to the west of the continental shelf. Speed concluded after studying fossils in the sedimentary rocks and other geologic relationships that the plate containing the island arc had pushed the deep-ocean rocks onto the continental shelf.

Speed believes that the ocean floor between the island arc and the continent gradually slid beneath the plate containing the arc, and that sediments

Geoscience

Continued

on the ocean floor were scraped up in front of the advancing arc. The arc then piled up on the edge of the continent, pushing the scrapings onto the continental shelf. This ponderous collision occurred at a velocity of perhaps 5 centimeters (2 inches) per year.

Western Canada. These plate movements marked the start of a different geologic history for western North America. There was little volcanic activity, and few mountains formed, during most of the preceding period. But the Pacific side of North America has undergone intense geologic activity since the lithospheric plates collided.

Government geologists published research papers regarding the movement of the plates as they are recorded in the rocks of western Canada and southern Alaska. The geologists gave a detailed history of the rocks in this area. One large mass of rock is part of another former island arc of the same age as the one that lodged in Nevada. But long after the Nevada arc became part of North America, the other arc was in the southwest Pacific. Its north end, now in

southern Alaska, then lay in the tropics on the far side of the Pacific. Its south end, now part of Canada's Vancouver Island, lay in the Southern Hemisphere near New Zealand. The floor of an ocean larger than the present Pacific disappeared beneath the island arc and the plate containing North America before the island arc finally lodged against the continent.

The geologists determined the island arc's former location from the magnetic orientation of its volcanic rocks and the character of marine fossils in the sedimentary rocks that were once part of the reefs around the islands. When volcanic rock crystallizes from lava, its grains of magnetic minerals retain a magnetic orientation, the study of which is called paleomagnetism.

The rocks recorded both the horizontal direction and vertical inclination of the earth's magnetic field at the time and the place where the lava cooled. Scientists can determine the amount of rotation and latitude change in a volcanic island that has been moved by comparing the paleomagnetism in the

A total of 686 holes at 451 sites (white dots) on the ocean floor were completed by drilling ship *Glomar Challenger* on March 15, 1978. Cores from the holes have revealed much about the geology of ocean beds.

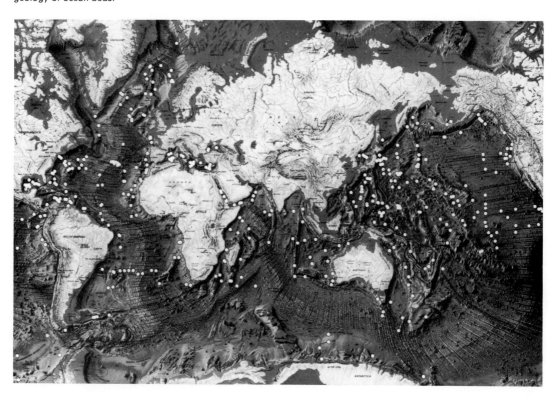

rocks with the magnetic field at the present site.

The fossil marine invertebrates in the sedimentary rocks that are now part of Vancouver Island are like those that once lived in the Southern Hemisphere. As the floor of that vanished Pacific Ocean slid beneath North America and an island arc, volcanic islands and seamounts were scraped off against the island arc and the continent's edge.

Several large tracts of ancient ocean floor and seamounts are preserved, relatively intact, in British Columbia. The volcanic islands were fringed by reefs. The fossils of a tropical Asian type preserved in these reefs are unlike any organisms that then lived in North America. Types of fusulines found in the reefs are a particularly important example. Fusulines are an extinct kind of foraminifera – single-celled animals that grew small spiral shells. They lived in shallow water in tropical seas and grazed on algae.

Mid-ocean study. Marine geologists also reported important plate-tectonic developments during 1977. Follow-up studies of the French-American Mid-Ocean Undersea Study (FAMOUS), conducted during 1973 and 1974 by French and American geologists, revealed new information. Using deep-ocean submarines, designed exclusively for sea-floor research, the FAMOUS team made detailed observations of the actively spreading belt of the Mid-Atlantic Ridge in an area southwest of the Azores.

Robert Ballard of Woods Hole Oceanographic Institution in Massachusetts and Tjeerd van Andel of Stanford University in California reported in 1977 that tension fractures had been found in the inner rift valley at the crest of the Mid-Atlantic Ridge. Their report also analyzed the faults, fissures, and other structures seen during 15 FAMOUS dives into the rift valley.

Surveys in limited regions of the Mid-Atlantic Ridge at the time of the FAMOUS studies demonstrated that it is forming because of the east-west separation of North America, with the western Atlantic floor attached to it, from Europe and the eastern Atlantic floor. Ballard and Van Andel discovered that the tension fractures within the segment of the rift they studied

indicated extension in a direction 20 degrees north of west, oblique to the direction of the major motion.

Ken Macdonald of the Scripps Institution of Oceanography in San Diego produced a surprise in a report on his analysis of the magnetic polarity in the rocks of the Mid-Atlantic Ridge. Oceanic crust, crystallized from magma rising at the center of the Mid-Atlantic Ridge, holds a record of the orientation of the earth's magnetic field at the time the magma cools.

The crust formed by this cooling adheres to the separating plates and moves outward from the rift where the magma is rising. The earth's magnetic field changes in irregular cycles of reversing magnetic polarity every 50,000 years or so, and the polarity of the earth's field is frozen into the magnetic minerals of magma when it crystallizes.

When a magnetometer, which measures the strength of the total earth's magnetic field at any point, is towed over strips of magma crystallized with alternate magnetic polarities, it records alternately high and low magnetic field strengths. In most of the FAMOUS studies, the magnetometer was towed on the sea surface, 2,000 to 6,000 meters (6,600 to 19,800 feet) above the sea floor. The results thus provided only an average reading of the magnetic intensity of the rocks beneath.

However, Macdonald also towed a recording magnetometer close to the sea floor in the FAMOUS survey area. His analysis showed that the magma does not adhere equally to the edges of both plates as the sea floor spreads.

Geologists had always thought the process was symmetrical, that half of each new increment of upwelling magma adhered to each separating plate. They assumed that the crust added to each plate in a given length of time – in a given period of magnetic polarity – would be equal. But Macdonald's study showed that the process is quite irregular. In some places, twice as much lava adheres to one plate as to the other while spreading continues for a million years or so. Then the relationship reverses, and twice as much lava adheres to the other plate. These switches are irregular, but they average out to agree with the sea-floor spreading predictions. [Warren Hamilton]

Geoscience

Continued

Geophysics. U.S. and Japanese geophysicists continued to focus much of their attention on the possibility of finding a way to predict the onset of earthquakes by foreshocks, ground strains, and other unusual events. They failed, however, to predict the June 12, 1978, quake that rocked central and northern Japan, killing at least 21 people and injuring 340. The undersea quake registered 7.5 on the Richter scale. An earthquake of magnitude 7 or more can cause great damage and kill many people if the shocks are centered in a populated area.

Examination and re-examination of the records of earthquakes in China in 1975 and 1976 and one that occurred in January 1978 in Japan, all of magnitude 7 or more on the Richter scale, gave hope that accurate predictions may someday be possible. Each had been monitored with arrays of tiltmeters, strain meters, and equipment that recorded variations in the local magnetic field and electrical resistivity. There was also continuous observation of the variation in radon gas emissions, indicating strained rock in the lower crust of the earth.

The reports of R. D. Adams of Victoria University in Wellington, New Zealand, and the 10-member U.S. Haicheng Earthquake Study Delegation were of special interest. They described the successful prediction of a magnitude-7.3 earthquake in Liaoning Province in China on Feb. 4, 1975. This earthquake cracked or destroyed 90 per cent of the buildings in Haicheng, a city with a population of 90,000. But there was little loss of life because the quake was accurately predicted and people were evacuated.

The U.S. delegation reported that China issues four stages of earthquake predictions. They vary from long-term warnings based on the preserved records of ancient quakes to imminent warnings based on an increasing number of foreshocks and such factors as variations in the water table and the unusual behavior of geese, deer, rats, dogs, and cats.

The imminent warning issued the day the Haicheng earthquake occurred

"I wouldn't worry. With continental drift, Africa or South America should come by eventually."

225 million years ago

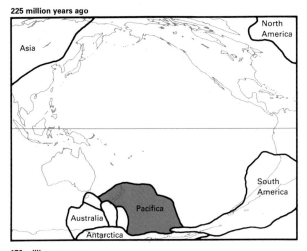

170 million years ago

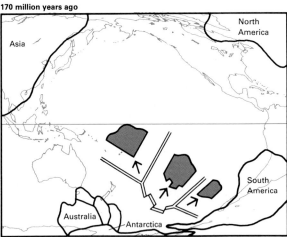

100 million years ago

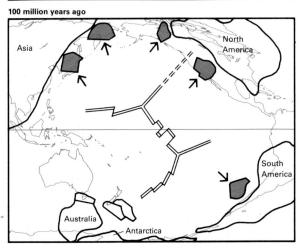

A geophysical study of sea-floor spreading and mountain ranges indicates that an eighth continent, Pacifica, once existed near Antarctica, but broke up and crashed into other continents.

was based mainly on the increasing number of foreshocks immediately after changes in well-water levels, changes in the local magnetic field, and reports of strange animal behavior. The foreshocks decreased some six hours before the main shock.

However, China's observers failed to predict one of the most destructive earthquakes of modern times, the 7.8-magnitude Tangshan quake on July 28, 1976. Geologists Cinna and Larissa Lomnitz of the National University of Mexico and Chi Wang of the University of California, Berkeley, who visited China in 1977, reported that 650,000 persons were killed in the Tangshan quake. They said that the Chinese had issued a second-stage warning for the area based on variations in the tilt of the land and magnetic-field intensities, but that there were none of the foreshocks that appeared so vital in forecasting the Haicheng earthquake. Local water-level changes and unusual animal behavior had also been reported, and there were changes in electrical resistivity in the earth's crust and radon gas emission, but these were so scattered geographically that the Chinese could not predict the quake.

The Japanese Meteorological Agency and geophysicist Hiroshi Wakita of the University of Tokyo reported on the events surrounding a magnitude-7 earthquake on Jan. 14, 1978, on Japan's Izu Peninsula. No warning was issued before the quake, which killed nine people and caused considerable property damage. The quake had been expected for a long time and scientific instruments had been installed there.

A month before the earthquake, the Izu water table dropped, then rose. Three weeks before, tiltmeters and strain meters recorded a contraction of the earth. And two days before, radon emissions declined, then increased, and the number of foreshocks and other seismic activity increased.

Foreshocks as predictors. One problem in earthquake prediction is how to distinguish foreshocks from other small earthquakes. Geophysicists Lucile Jones and Peter Molnar of the Massachusetts Institute of Technology in Cambridge reported in December 1977 that 55 per cent of the earth's major earthquakes have foreshocks as-

Geoscience

sociated with them. Geophysicists Mizuho Ishida and Hiroo Kanamori of the California Institute of Technology in Pasadena published records in August 1977 that showed many small quakes preceded the destructive February 1971 San Fernando earthquake, which was of magnitude 6.6. These small quakes increased from 1961 to 1965, then decreased, and increased again from 1969 until the big quake occurred in 1971.

Double seismic zones. Researchers reported in October on studies of the physical mechanism of earthquakes that take place deep in the earth where the earth's lithospheric plates, the giant plates that form the earth's outer shell, sink into the mantle, the thick layer of molten rock beneath the plates. A team led by A. Hasegawa of Tohoku University in Sendai, Japan, and E. Robert Engdahl of the National Oceanic and Atmospheric Administration in Boulder, Colo., and Christopher H. Scholz of the Lamont-Doherty Geological Observatory of Columbia University in Palisades, N.Y., described a series of earthquakes occurring in two parallel lines, one pair in a zone beneath northern Japan and the other pair in a zone beneath the Aleutian Islands. In each case, the parallel lines are about 30 kilometers (18 miles) apart.

Crustal break. The Consortium for Continental Reflection Profiling, a research group that includes geophysicist Scott B. Smithson of the University of Wyoming in Laramie and his colleagues at Cornell University in Ithaca, N.Y., reported in April 1978 that they had charted the extent of a major fault in the earth's crust that extends beneath Wyoming. The researchers used mechanically induced seismic waves reflected back from underground rocks. The northwest-to-southeast fault forms the Wind River Range in Wyoming.

The scientists traced the fault northeastward for a distance of 55 kilometers (33 miles) from its surface break, 30 kilometers (18 miles) south of Lander, Wyo., and found it went to a depth of about 35 kilometers (21 miles), the deepest that a major crustal feature has been followed from the surface. The results of the Wyoming study demonstrate that such faults can extend down to the mantle.   [Thomas J. Ahrens]

Paleontology. Princeton University geologists Alfred G. Fischer and Michael A. Arthur published the results of an extensive study of fossil organisms and deep-sea sediments in November 1977. They concluded that the world's oceans have oscillated between two phases – warm, slow-mixing waters containing a large number of different animal species, and cool, rapidly mixing waters with fewer species. Fischer and Arthur called the phases polytaxic – having many different kinds of organisms – and oligotaxic – having few kinds of organisms.

Most of their evidence for the ocean cycles came from examination of sediment cores taken from the ocean floor during the Deep Sea Drilling Project beginning in 1968. These cores provided detailed information on the history of the oceans and on variations in species diversity, shown by the number of shells of tiny single-celled animals known as planktonic foraminifera. These animals live near the surface of the ocean, and when they die their shells sink to the ocean floor and are preserved in the sediment there.

Number of species. Fischer and Arthur said that the complete cycle of a polytaxic and an oligotaxic phase lasts about 32 million years. The cycles can be traced back to the time between the Paleozoic and Mesozoic eras, about 225 million years ago. Mass extinctions of animals occurred then and the ocean phase was oligotaxic.

Since that time, almost exactly seven of these cycles have occurred, and the oceans are again oligotaxic. The maximum extent of this phase is not due for another 2 million years, but the oceans are already cool, their waters rapidly mixing, and the diversity of some groups of ocean plants and animals has decreased.

Fifteen million years ago, during the polytaxic late Miocene Epoch, oceans were warmer and contained more animal species. Also, the ocean floor eroded less because currents were weaker during the slow-mixing period.

There also were some large predators in the oceans. The shark *Carcharodon megalodon*, a close relative of today's great white shark, probably grew nearly 15 meters (50 feet) long and had teeth 20 centimeters (8 inches) long.

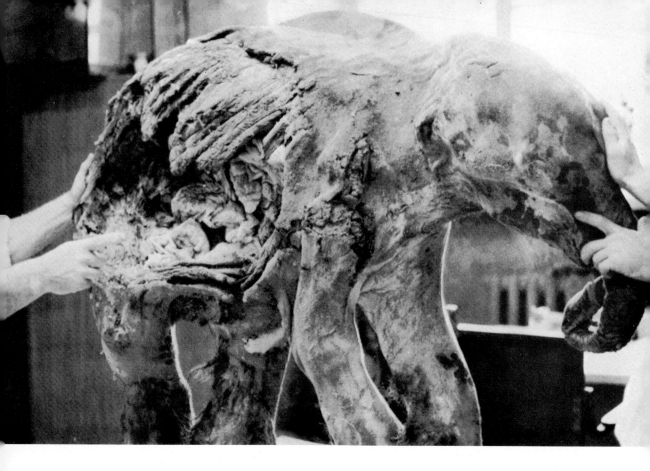

Geoscience

Continued

A baby mammoth, frozen in the mud of a bog where it died 10,000 years ago, was found in Siberia on June 23, 1977. Skin samples have been sent to U.S. paleontologists for study and the animal will be stuffed later for exhibition at a Russian museum.

Other superpredators lived in earlier polytaxic times. During the Eocene Epoch, about 47 million years ago, a whale called *Basilosaurus* predominated. It, too, measured about 15 meters long. Eighty million years ago, toward the end of the Cretaceous Period, the superpredators were marine reptiles called mosasaurs.

The two previous polytaxic phases – the early Cretaceous and the late Jurassic periods – were marked by another group of enormous reptiles, the pliosaurs. These creatures were probably only about 12 meters (40 feet) long at most, but they made up in bulk what they lacked in length. A third group of marine reptiles, the ichthyosaurs, were the superpredators in the two even earlier polytaxic phases, the early Jurassic and middle Triassic periods. Ichthyosaurs looked much like huge porpoises, reaching lengths of 12 to 15 meters (40 to 50 feet).

Fischer and Arthur found less than 10 species of planktonic foraminifera in the sediments that accumulated during the Oligocene Epoch, about 30 million

years ago, which was an oligotaxic phase. There was less diversity in other groups as well, such as fish, sharks, and whales. At the same time, sediment cores indicate that a great deal of land and sea-floor erosion took place. Chemical studies of the shells of the foraminifera indicate that the surface waters were about 5°C (9°F.) cooler during the Oligocene Epoch than during the later Miocene Epoch, a polytaxic phase with about 30 foraminiferal species.

The best record of these 32-million-year cycles was left in ocean sediments, but paleontologists have also found the effects on land. During two of the oligotaxic phases – the end of the Paleozoic Era and the end of the Mesozoic Era, 225 and 65 million years ago, respectively – there were mass extinctions among land animals as well as among marine animals.

The fossil record of the Paleozoic Era shows extinctions of many families of terrestrial reptiles and amphibians. Dinosaurs were the most prominent casualty at the end of the Mesozoic Era. In addition, fossil land plants indicate cli-

Geoscience

Continued

mate changes that parallel the changes in ocean temperature.

Plate movement a cause? High sea levels with flooding of the continents is associated with polytaxic times. Low sea levels occur in oligotaxic times. Fischer and Arthur speculate that high sea levels might moderate climate, reduce ocean circulation, and in general produce a more stable environment for the evolution of many types of animals.

But what causes these changes in sea levels? Fischer and Arthur suggest that the cycles may be related to plate tectonics, the movements of some 20 giant lithospheric plates that form the earth's outer shell.

Fischer and Arthur speculate that the oligotaxic phases are caused by slow plate movement. When the motion slows, less molten rock oozes up at the mid-ocean ridges where plates are moving apart, and the ridges cool and shrink. The slower movement enlarges the ocean basins and lowers the sea level relative to the continents.

At the same time, the two scientists think there may have been greater vol-

canic activity during such times, with most dust ejected into the atmosphere. The dusty atmosphere would reduce the amount of sunlight reaching the surface of the earth, cooling the climate and the seas. When plate movement speeds up, the mid-ocean ridges would rise and the continents would be flooded. This reduces volcanic activity and results in warmer climates.

Oregon leaves. Paleobotanist Karl J. Niklas of the New York City Botanical Garden reported that 30-million-year-old leaves remarkably well preserved were found in a volcanic ashfall in Oregon. The dry, sterile environment preserved the shapes and veins of the leaves, their cellular structure and, within the cells, such chemicals as carotenes, flavonoids, and chlorophyll.

The leaves were discovered by an amateur paleontologist, Bake Young. Only one other discovery of such ancient and well-preserved leaves has been reported. These leaves were found in West Germany in 1966 and have not yet been studied in such detail as have the Oregon finds.   [Ida Thompson]

A mastodon rib 12,000 years old was found at Sequim, Wash. A broken spearpoint protruding from it is the first direct evidence that mastodons were hunted by men so long ago.

Immunology

Experiments reported in March 1978 by immunologist Rolph M. Zinkernagel and his associates at the Scripps Clinic and Research Foundation in San Diego and the University of Texas Southwestern Medical School in Dallas provided important insights into how a major arm of the immune system works. In the past few years, many scientists have focused their efforts on finding out exactly how lymphocytes—the white blood cells that are active in the immune system— recognize and are triggered to react against antigens, foreign materials such as bacteria, viruses, and toxins.

Immunologists have discovered that thymus-dependent lymphocytes, called T cells because they must pass through the thymus to mature, will recognize and act against an antigen only if they also recognize a self-component. This self-component is related to a group of genes known as the major histocompatibility complex. T cells from a strain of mice of histocompatibility type A will kill virus-infected cells from an A-type mouse but not virus-infected cells from a strain of mice, such as B type, with a different histocompatibility complex.

Zinkernagel and his associates discovered exactly where T cells develop their self-structure-recognizing capacity. They exposed mice of type A to radiation that destroyed all the animals' lymphocytes and also the thymus, with the exception of its outer layer of cells—the thymic epithelium. Then the researchers injected these animals with bone-marrow cells from hybrids of type-A and type-B mice. Bone-marrow cells produce lymphocytes, so this step reconstituted the A-type animals' immune capacity, but with hybrid (AxB) lymphocytes.

Next, the scientists injected the mice with virus. The mice responded by producing T cells that could attack and kill only virus-infected A-type cells. These results were totally unexpected because T cells from AxB hybrid animals themselves can kill viral-infected A, B, or AxB cells.

The experiment suggested strongly that the T cells develop their self-structure-recognizing capacity in the

Clad in a germfree "space suit" that protects him against infection, 6-year-old David helps water the lawn. Victim of a rare disease that leaves his body with no defense against infections, David was confined to sterile rooms until receiving the suit.

thymic epithelium. Zinkernagel and his colleagues then demonstrated that this was the case. They removed the entire thymus of AxB mice and irradiated the animals to eliminate all their lymphocytes. Then they injected bone marrow into the mice from AxB mice. Next, they grafted thymic epithelium from A-type mice into the experimental animals. In other words, they artificially constructed AxB mice in which lymphocytes would become mature T cells within the epithelium of an A-type thymus gland. Then, they infected the animals with virus. The T cells produced killed only virus-infected A cells.

As a further test, the researchers repeated the experiment providing thymic epithelium from B-type mice. In these experiments, the T cells of the recipient mice could kill only the virus-infected B cells.

Evidence emphasizing that T lymphocytes can only recognize antigens when certain self-components are also present may be of practical importance in certain immune-deficiency diseases in humans that are treated by transplanting thymus tissue into the patient. When the thymus tissue and the patient's bone marrow do not match, T lymphocytes that are generated may not work against infectious agents because the "self" they learned to recognize in the thymus differs from that of the cells of the thymus recipient's tissue.

Subpopulations of human T cells. In July 1977, a team of immunologists from the University of Alabama in Birmingham reported that it was possible to separate human T cells with differing functions by virtue of their capacity to bind different classes of antibodies. Antibodies are proteins that immobilize certain antigens, either eliminating them directly or getting them ready for lymphocytes to eliminate. Types of T cells with differing functions are called subpopulations. One subpopulation may help produce antibodies, another may suppress antibody production, still another may attack antigens directly, and so on. Scientists have found such subpopulations in animals by means of identifying unique cell-surface components.

Immunologists Lorenzo Moretta, Susan R. Webb, Carlo E. Grossi, Pehr M. Lydyard, and Max D. Cooper performed the experiments. They mixed T cells obtained from human blood with ox red blood cells that had been coated with a type of antibody classified as IgM. Seventy per cent of the T cells attached themselves to the coated red blood cells, forming figures called rosettes in which several of the red blood cells surrounded a central T cell. When the scientists separated these T cells and tested them for their function, the cells proved to be the subpopulation that helps form antibodies. In contrast, when human T cells were mixed with ox red blood cells that had been coated with IgG antibody, about 20 per cent of the T cells formed rosettes with the red blood cells. When the scientists separated and tested these T cells, they turned out to be the subpopulation that inhibits the formation of antibodies.

Stuart Schlossman and his colleagues at Harvard Medical School in Boston took another approach to human T-lymphocyte classification. They injected rabbits with human T lymphocytes and observed that a specially prepared reagent reacted with only 50 to 60 per cent of the T cells once they were in the rabbits' blood. Further experiments indicated that these T cells are the subpopulation that helps produce antibodies. In April 1978, Schlossman and Robert L. Evans, Herbert Lazarus, and Ann C. Penta reported using the same technique to find the subpopulation of T cells that directly attacks and eliminates antigens.

In a separate study in April, Schlossman, Anthony Strelhauskas, Victoria Schauf, Barry Wilson, and Leonard Chess showed that human blood serum taken from victims of juvenile rheumatoid arthritis contained antibodies that could classify T cells into two unique subpopulations. Those T cells that clumped together with these antibodies were members of the subpopulation that suppresses antibody formation.

These findings may provide a method of evaluating levels of subpopulations of T cells in victims of various diseases. The last experiment hints that the overproduction of antibodies usually seen in juvenile arthritis patients could be linked to the presence of other antibodies that have depleted the T cells that normally suppress antibody formation.   [Jacques M. Chiller]

Medicine

Dentistry. Researchers discovered new evidence in 1977 and 1978 that periodontal, or gum, disease is caused by the products of the bacteria that form plaque on the teeth, not by the bacteria themselves. This had long been suspected because the bacteria are rarely found in gum tissue. Researchers do not know if periodontal disease is caused by the toxic effect of the bacterial products or by the body's immune response to them.

Richard R. Ranney, a dental researcher at Virginia Commonwealth University in Richmond, collected plaque from the teeth of persons suffering from chronic periodontal disease. He then tested samples of the patients' gum tissue and reported in March 1978 that white blood cells in the gum tissue showed a strong immunological response to the plaque.

Researchers Nicklaus P. Lang and Frederica N. Smith of the University of Michigan and the Veterans Administration Hospital in Ann Arbor reported in July 1977 that the immunological response to plaque bacteria varies with the state of the individual's gums. They tested four groups of patients, ranging from those with healthy gums to those with advanced periodontal disease. They found little evidence of white blood cell stimulation in healthy gums, but the immune response increased as they tested patients with mild or moderate gingivitis, or gum inflammation. The response was greatest in those with advanced periodontal disease. Lang and Smith also found that the bacteria *Bacteroides melaninogenicus* was most often associated with the advanced disease. *Actinomyces viscosus* was more frequently found with the less serious gingivitis disease.

However, Max A. Listgarten and associates at the University of Pennsylvania in Philadelphia and Forsyth Dental Center in Boston found no such relationship in another experiment. They infected germfree rats with bacteria from human periodontal lesions but reported in March 1978 that they could find no correlation between immune response and the severity of periodontal disease.   [Paul Goldhaber]

The teeth of a monkey vaccinated against *Streptococcus mutans*, the bacteria that cause dental decay, show no sign of tooth decay, *below and bottom right*. But the teeth of a nonimmunized monkey fed on the same diet show extensive tooth decay, *below and bottom*.

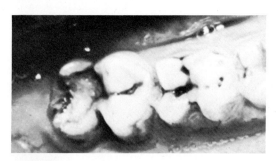

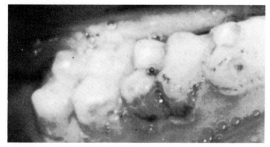

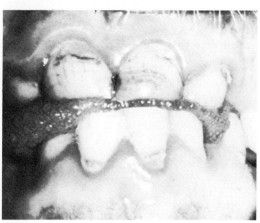

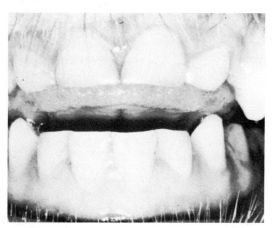

Medicine

Continued

Internal Medicine. A new vaccine against pneumococcal pneumonia was licensed by the Food and Drug Administration (FDA) in November 1977. Pneumonia is still a common cause of death. Although a variety of bacteria and viruses can cause these lower respiratory tract infections, the bacterium *Streptococcus pneumoniae* produces pneumococcal pneumonia, a particularly severe and often dangerous form of the disease.

Despite the long-standing availability of effective antibiotics, particularly penicillin, pneumococcal disease continues to take a heavy death toll, particularly among people suffering from other chronic diseases. As a result, scientists have tried to prevent pneumonia rather than merely provide effective treatment for the disease.

Studies carried out among military recruits in 1945 revealed that vaccines made from the polysaccharide capsule (a kind of carbohydrate) that surrounds the bacteria could stimulate the production of antibodies that would attack the disease organism. Medical researcher Robert Austrian and his associates at the University of Pennsylvania in Philadelphia further showed that protection could be provided only by vaccination against each specific strain of *S. pneumoniae*. However, the research also showed that most cases of clinical disease are caused by only a handful of the 86 known strains of the bacterium. Austrian demonstrated that simultaneous vaccination against a number of pneumococcal strains produced a satisfactory immunization against all of them.

Because pneumococcal pneumonia is particularly common among newly employed gold miners in South Africa, clinical evaluation of the vaccine's efficacy became an international collaborative effort involving the Merck Institute for Therapeutic Research Division of Virus and Cell Biology Research in West Point, Pa., South African gold-mining companies, and the South African Institute for Medical Research in Johannesburg. More than 1,500 persons were vaccinated in the early 1970s with either 6-strain or 12-strain vaccines. The number of pneumonia cases dropped 37 per cent among those vaccinated with the 6-strain vaccine and 32 per cent among the 12-strain group. The vaccines had no serious side effects, although there was some local swelling and low-grade fever. The vaccine licensed by the FDA gives protection against the 14 strains of *S. pneumoniae* that cause approximately 80 per cent of all pneumonia infections. Field trials of this vaccine began in 1973. More than 30,000 persons were vaccinated during these tests.

The new vaccine should not only lower the death rate — 13,000 to 66,000 adult Americans die each year from pneumococcal pneumonia — but may also have substantial value against two other infections — otitis media, an inflammation of the middle ear, and meningitis. These are frequently caused by *S. pneumoniae* among preschoolers. See DRUGS.

Cancer of the prostate. A new approach to the detection of cancer of the prostate was reported by biochemist Andras G. Foti and his associates at Kaiser Foundation Hospital and the University of California, Los Angeles, School of Medicine in December 1977. The prostate gland surrounds the male urethra where it emerges from the urinary bladder. It frequently enlarges as men age. Although the enlargement is often a benign process, it can be the result of cancer. This form of cancer is among the most common malignancies in men over 50 years old.

Early detection and prompt treatment can cure prostate cancer, particularly if the disease has not yet spread from the gland. For many years it has been known that an increase of acid phosphatase, an enzyme, in the bloodstream is associated with the growth of cancer in the prostate. Normally present in small amounts in blood serum, this enzyme increases substantially as the tumor begins to expand. Heretofore, doctors have found this marker by measuring its enzymatic activity. Unfortunately, this method has limited reliability because enzymes with identical biological properties are produced in other tissues, and the prostatic variety cannot be isolated from them. The enzyme's biological properties are also highly unstable.

Foti's new technique to measure prostatic acid phosphatase overcomes these limitations. He measures the en-

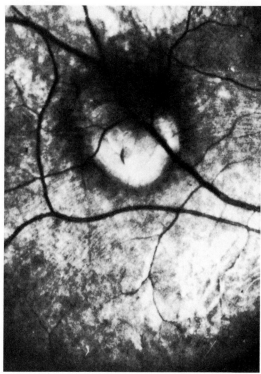

Medicine

Continued

A tiny nematode, a parasitic worm, coiled like a pretzel in a patient's eye, *above*, was destroyed without damage to the eye by an intense pinpoint laser beam, *above right*.

zyme's immunological characteristics with radioactive isotopes. Unlike the biological properties, the immunological characteristics are stable, specific to the prostate, and can be reliably related to prostatic activity.

Since serum enzyme levels are normally stable from puberty to old age, increases at any age ought to imply a malignant change within the prostate. Studies of untreated prostatic-cancer patients, healthy individuals, and patients with nonprostatic cancer and other diseases revealed that the immunological technique is considerably more sensitive in detecting this type of cancer, particularly in its early stage.

Home care for heart attack. Two recent studies, one in the United States and the other in Great Britain, have raised questions about current methods of taking care of a patient after an acute heart attack.

A Duke University Medical Center group headed by heart specialist J. Frederick McNeer presented data in February 1978 suggesting that the period of hospitalization after a heart at-

tack might safely be reduced in uncomplicated cases. At the end of one week's hospitalization, 67 patients who had no serious complications were discharged or assigned to further hospital care randomly. The discharged patients were treated at home and checked regularly by specially trained nurses. There were no deaths in either group. Those who remained in the hospital averaged $800 more in costs than did the home-care group, although both groups had the same rates of recovery.

The British report in April 1978 compared home and hospital treatment among patients whose general practitioners suspected they had suffered a heart attack. Heart researcher J. D. Hill and his associates at Nottingham General Hospital sent a hospital team in response to calls from general practitioners. A number of patients were excluded from the study either because their condition was severe enough to require hospital attention or because they lacked suitable resources for home care. The researchers randomly assigned the others suspected of having had heart attacks to either home or hospital care.

During the four years of the study, 500 patients were examined by the hospital team. Of these, 349 were diagnosed as having had a heart attack and 264 met the criteria for the test and were randomly divided into home-care and hospital-care groups.

The study's results indicate that doctors can select a group of patients for whom home care would pose no medical hazard. Of the 132 patients on home care, only 26 had to be hospitalized later. Death rates after six weeks were identical for both groups. Thus, it appears that patients can be identified for whom home care is as safe as hospital care. If this observation can be further confirmed, then the need for costly hospital care may be considerably reduced in many cases.

Insulin and exercise. The location of the injection site may be important in maintaining proper blood sugar levels in insulin-dependent diabetics who exercise, according to two Yale Medical School researchers. In a March 1978 report, Veikko A. Koivisto and Philip Felig described their experiments. They gave 11 young insulin-dependent diabetics injections of radioactively labeled insulin in the leg, arm, or abdomen. The diabetics then exercised the leg. The researchers reported that leg exercise accelerated the dispersal of insulin in leg injections, retarded it in abdominal injections, and had no effect on arm injections.

Although normal exercise has no significant effect on blood sugar levels in healthy individuals, it can sometimes result in hypoglycemia—disastrous blood sugar reduction—in diabetics. Because insulin also lowers blood sugar levels, the choice of injection site may be important to patients prone to exercise-induced hypoglycemia. Joggers, for example, might prefer to inject themselves in the arm to slow dispersal of insulin during exercise and thus lessen the danger of hypoglycemia.

Sniffing and swallowing. New evidence that contradicts popular beliefs about the use of cocaine was reported by C. Van Dyke and his associates at

A Brighter Life for the Color-Blind

People can normally discern 150 shades of color with three groups of cones in the retina. One group is sensitive to red, one to green, and one to blue. When we look at an object, specific cones are stimulated, according to the color of the object. People who are color-blind—8 per cent of men and 0.5 per cent of women—have a defect or absence of pigment in one or more groups of cones, generally in the red or green receptors. Usually, their blue-sensitive cones function normally. The X-Chrom lens, a special red hard-plastic contact lens, was developed to help people with this defect. It followed an idea I had to improve vision for scuba divers. I found that we could reduce the natural loss of color vision underwater by placing filters over divers' face masks. The filters make objects stand out as lighter or darker than their background, according to their colors.

Because, in humans, each eye functions independently, a color-blind person can assimilate unequal visual information without loss of perception. The dominant eye is uncorrected and gives the brain a true reading of some colors. In common color blindness, these are usually blues and yellows. The lens worn on the nondominant eye filters the colors that are confused—reds, greens, browns, and grays—into clearly separate shades or values that may not exactly match the colors that we see under normal circumstances. However, among other things, the X-Chrom lens can make a color-blind person see a cherry as red, and enable him to distinguish it from a green olive.

The X-Chrom lens makes it possible for color-blind schoolchildren to learn from color-coded books; for color-blind hunters to avoid mistaking a red cap for a deer's brown rump; and for color-blind drivers to identify highway signs. Moreover, millions whose view of life was once dull can look forward to a brighter future.　　[Harry I. Zeltzer]

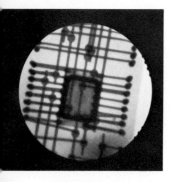

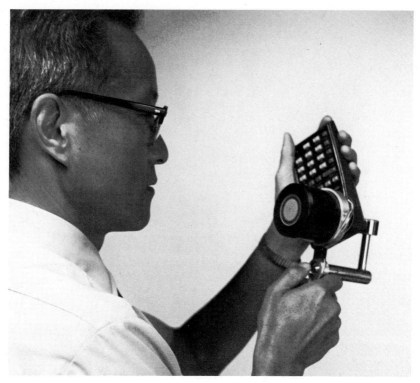

Astrophysicist Lo I. Yin scans a pocket calculator with his handheld X-ray imager, *right*, to get the X-ray image of an integrated circuit, *above*. The instrument has many possible medical uses, including on-field examinations of injured athletes for possible fractures.

Medicine

Continued

the Yale University School of Medicine in New Haven, Conn. Because of the intense euphoria that follows sniffing cocaine, the drug has become increasingly popular among drug abusers in the United States.

Andean Indians in Peru and Bolivia have chewed coca leaves, the source of cocaine, since ancient times to relieve hunger and to improve physical endurance. However, most observers in the United States believed that the drug had little or no effect when taken orally because intestinal enzymes destroyed its effectiveness. Consequently, many users thought that absorption through nasal mucous membranes was the only effective way to use cocaine.

To make up for the lack of scientific evidence regarding the effects of orally administered cocaine, the Yale investigators made a chemical evaluation of the drug when given by mouth. Four volunteers took part in the study, which was approved by the Yale Committee on Human Rights in Medical Experimentation and the National Institute of Drug Abuse.

Similar amounts of cocaine were given. The volunteers first applied the drug to the surface of their nasal membranes then later swallowed it in gelatin capsules. The researchers measured blood serum cocaine levels and recorded similar total absorption for both methods, although peak levels were recorded sooner after nasal use.

Although the two methods showed identical maximum blood levels and the same sense of euphoria, the euphoria tended to occur more rapidly with nasal administration, as might be expected with the more rapid absorption from that site.

These results serve as reminders that traditional beliefs arrived at without benefit of modern scientific technology may not always be accurate. They suggest that much of the mystique surrounding cocaine may be irrelevant to its effect and contribute to its appeal. Finally, the tests should serve as a caution to potential users that swallowing this hazardous drug carries the same risk as does the more common method of sniffing.   [Michael H. Alderman]

Medicine

Continued

Surgery. A "laser blade," consisting of a crystal scalpel and a laser beam passing through it, was developed in 1977 by surgeon James L. Doty and his associates at the University of Washington in Seattle. The new surgical tool should be especially useful in treating burn patients because it allows surgeons to quickly prepare the burned area for skin grafts without the severe blood loss that accompanies more conventional surgical treatment.

Infection continues to be the leading cause of death in patients with major burns. Antibiotics are only partially effective in treating third-degree burns, which injure the full thickness of the skin. This is because bacteria growing in the injured skin cannot be readily reached by antibiotics.

Surgeons have tried to treat severe burns by cutting away the dead burned skin, but the physical shock caused by this procedure and the profuse blood loss that follows it have limited such excisions to small areas of the body. This treatment is useful for burns that cover less than 20 per cent of the body,

but burns that cover larger areas cause the greatest number of deaths.

Doty's team beams light from an argon laser through a flexible optical fiber and a wedge-shaped piece of transparent crystal that serves as the scalpel blade. After the quartz blade cuts away the burned skin, laser radiation seals the blood vessels along the edge of the incision.

The device is so effective in reducing blood loss that Doty believes it may enable surgeons to remove all of the burned skin regardless of the extent of the burns. If all the burned skin can be removed immediately after the patient enters the hospital, skin grafting could be done before bacteria can grow.

Microscopic examination of the healthy tissue around the burned area shows only slight damage after the dead tissue is removed. This is important because extensive injury would prevent the healing of grafted skin used to cover burned areas. If it becomes widely available, this new technology will be of great help in treating severely burned patients.

A doctor checks a patient's pulsating air-pressure boots, which stimulate blood circulation and help prevent clots both during and after surgery.

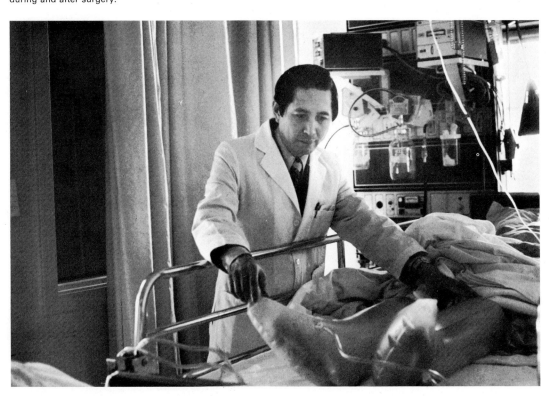

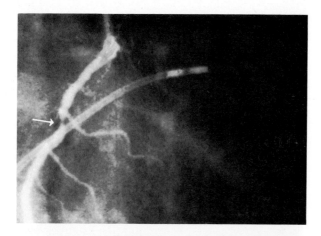

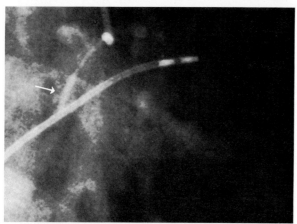

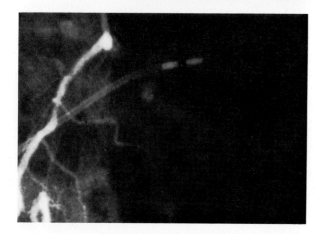

A coronary artery is almost completely blocked, *top*, by fat deposits (arrow). A catheter inserted into the artery is pushed to the block, *middle*, where a cylindrical balloon (arrow) is inflated to force the deposits back against the arterial walls, and open the artery, *bottom*. A line from a heart pacemaker runs diagonally across the X rays.

Recurring cancer. A New York City surgeon reported in October 1977 on a promising method to identify the recurrence of thyroid cancer that often occurs after a cancerous thyroid gland has been removed. Paul LoGerfo of Columbia University found that the presence of serum thyroglobulin, the protein in the body that picks up iodine, in the blood is a sure indication of thyroid cancer cells in patients whose thyroid gland has been removed.

Since the normal thyroid makes thyroglobulin, the level of this protein cannot be used to identify new cases of thyroid cancer. However, after a cancerous thyroid has been removed, the blood loses all its thyroglobulin. Thus, if thyroglobulin reappears, the thyroid cancer has spread to other organs and areas of the body.

LoGerfo used a radioimmunoassay test to detect thyroglobulin in patients' blood. He injected his patients with radioactively labeled thyroglobulin antibodies and their reaction indicated whether there was thyroglobulin in the blood. About half of 24 persons with recurrent thyroid cancer had tumors that were not detected until the new blood test drew attention to the problem. The test enabled doctors to start treatment in these patients while the cancer was still at an early stage.

Catching clots. A dramatic new way to deal with blood clots that have migrated to the lung was reported by surgeon Lazar J. Greenfield of the Medical College of Virginia. In the new technique, clots are removed through a catheter inserted into the pulmonary circulation system.

A common cause of blood clots is phlebitis, an inflammation of the veins. The migration of these blood clots to the lung is fortunately a rare event. Clots usually form in veins of the lower limbs or the pelvis. But, if a large clot breaks loose, it will travel to the right side of the heart and be pumped into the pulmonary circulation. Such a clot, a pulmonary embolus, can cause sudden death because it obstructs blood circulation through the lungs.

It has been estimated that as many as 140,000 Americans die each year from pulmonary embolism despite a variety of measures designed to prevent the formation and migration of clots. Sur-

Medicine

Continued

gery has been used since 1908, but the death rate is 50 to 60 per cent.

Greenfield's device is inserted into a large vein in the leg and passed up to the heart. The surgeon views the catheter through a fluoroscope as he guides it through the heart to the clot.

The catheter has a stainless-steel suction cup attached to its tip. By applying suction with a syringe, Greenfield can pull the clot into the cup and then remove the catheter. The procedure requires only local anesthesia in the groin, and the death rate from this operation is less than 25 per cent.

However, clots can recur. When Greenfield lost two patients to recurrent clots after the successful use of his new technique, he developed a filter to protect his surviving patients. He places the cone-shaped filter in the abdominal portion of the vena cava, the main vein coming up to the heart from the lower part of the body. The filter is passed through the leg vein to the vena cava. Once it is in position, a series of tiny hooks hold it in place. The filter is made of stainless steel and is designed to stop

clots from going into the lungs, without obstructing blood flow.

Stomach glue. A new way to control massive bleeding in the upper gastrointestinal tract — from ulcers or cancer, for instance — was reported by gastroenterologists Stephen E. Silvis and Thomas R. Martin of Minneapolis Veterans Administration Hospital in September 1977. The researchers used an adhesive made of cyanoacrylate to treat severe bleeding in patients considered too sick to undergo conventional surgery for the removal of all or part of the stomach. The adhesive is applied through a catheter, using an aerosol propellant. A flexible fiber optic endoscope is used to view the bleeding lesion and then the glue is applied to the surface to stop the bleeding.

The surgeons used the technique successfully in six of nine patients, although a second application was needed in some cases. In three cases, the bleeding was so massive and the stomach was so full of blood that the doctors could not precisely locate the bleeding point and could not apply the adhesive.

A monitor attached to the heart after open-heart surgery allows surgeons to check heart functions for the first two or three days after an operation. Then the device is removed through a small opening that had been left in the wall of the chest.

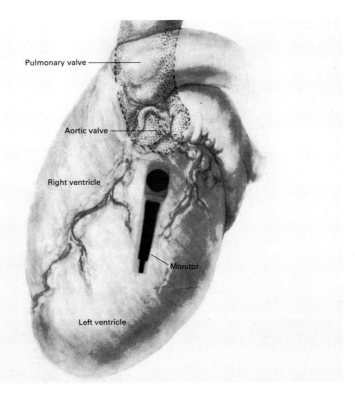

Pulmonary valve

Aortic valve

Right ventricle

Monitor

Left ventricle

Medicine

The adhesive sticks firmly to abnormal tissue to form a flexible seal and healing takes place beneath it. Later, the substance gradually erodes away. The doctors believe it passes out through the intestinal tract. However, in animal studies, researchers have found traces of the glue a year after treatment and this may limit widespread application of the substance in humans. The Food and Drug Administration banned the material in 1972 because of concern that it might cause cancer. However, Silvis obtained permission in 1976 because its use on the stomach surface means that most, if not all, of it will eventually be passed out in solid wastes. This should greatly increase the safety of the technique.

Coronary by-pass operations may be no more effective in prolonging life than treatment with heart drugs, according to a September 1977 report by the Veterans Administration (VA). The operation, developed only 10 years ago, is now performed on about 70,000 Americans a year. Surgeons by-pass a coronary artery clogged by cholesterol deposits by grafting a section of vein taken from the leg to the aorta to take the place of the clogged artery. The vein graft is then sutured to the artery beyond the obstruction to by-pass the blockage.

The VA study followed 686 heart patients who were treated either surgically or with drugs from 1972 to 1974. They found that 88 per cent of those who had by-pass operations were still alive after three years, but that an almost equal percentage — 87 per cent — had survived on drugs alone.

An exception, however, was the group with left-main-coronary disease, in which the lower left chamber of the heart is involved. In these cases, by-pass surgery had a clear edge over drug treatment, with a survival rate of 92 per cent compared with 70 per cent for drug-treated patients.

Since the cost of a by-pass operation averages $12,500 and the annual national cost runs to nearly $1 billion, the results of the VA study may prompt many to reconsider the benefits of the by-pass operation.   [Frank E. Gump]

Meteorology

Atmospheric scientists focused their efforts in 1977 and 1978 on observations, theories, and speculations about climate change. The reason has as much to do with agriculture as with meteorology. As the limits of the world's food production in feeding the increasing population become more apparent, any change in our present agriculture-supporting climate becomes alarming.

The second consecutive severe winter in the Eastern half of the United States added to uneasiness about the weather. Of course, two unusual seasons do not necessarily signal a change in climate, but they have reminded us that food supply is surprisingly vulnerable to extreme weather conditions.

Ecologist George M. Woodwell and his colleagues at the Marine Biological Laboratory in Woods Hole, Mass., reported in January 1978 that cutting down forests to enlarge farming and grazing areas, particularly tropical rain forests, can have far-reaching meteorological effects. One of the factors associated with this activity that may be changing the climate is the increasing carbon dioxide (CO_2) content of the atmosphere. Carbon dioxide is a very small — about 0.035 per cent — but vital part of the atmosphere. It helps to maintain the earth's temperature by allowing sunlight to pass through the atmosphere and warm the surface. At the same time, it absorbs the heat from the earth and reflects part of it back to the surface. This is known as the greenhouse effect. If such a small amount of CO_2 plays such an important role in the earth's climate, it follows that changes in the CO_2 level may bring about changes in climate.

According to Woodwell, the decay of humus and vegetable matter associated with clearing forests probably adds about 8×10^{15} grams of CO_2 per year to the earth's atmosphere. This increase exceeds that added by the burning of fossil fuels — coal, oil, and gas — about 5×10^{15} grams per year.

Before Woodwell published his report, most scientists assumed that the continuing increase in CO_2 was caused by the burning of fossil fuels, which release carbon that has been locked up

in the form of CO_2 for several million years. Significant increases in the atmosphere's CO_2 content have been occurring annually since at least 1958, when Charles D. Keeling of the Scripps Institution of Oceanography in San Diego began to measure CO_2 continuously on a shoulder of the volcano Mauna Loa in Hawaii.

Mauna Loa was chosen as a measuring site because it is remote from people and their industry and traffic, and the CO_2 level measured there is representative of the global average. The annual average of the CO_2 content between 1958 and 1978 on Mauna Loa rose by an average of 5 per cent, and the rate of increase is accelerating.

The changes that could result from the added CO_2 are hard to foresee. There is the alarming but unlikely prospect of a "runaway greenhouse effect," ultimately producing a climate on earth similar to that on Venus. The surface of Venus, with an atmosphere consisting of 95 per cent CO_2, stays at a temperature of 500°C (930°F.) because of the greenhouse effect. Less spectacular theories predict that other factors controlling climate will either overcome the CO_2 effect or offset much of it. For example, a slight average increase in air temperature would allow more water vapor to stay in the atmosphere, which would promote increased cloudiness and snowfall. Both these factors would tend to cool the earth by reflecting sunlight, and hence offset the greenhouse effect.

Thunderstorm prediction. According to the National Transportation Safety Board, bad weather causes 47 per cent of fatal aviation accidents. Meteorologists Theodore Fujita of the University of Chicago and Fernando Caracena of the National Oceanic and Atmospheric Administration (NOAA) reported in November 1977 that their analysis of three accidents that took place during take-off or landing showed that they were associated with downbursts—intense downdrafts that are part of thunderstorms.

Downbursts, caused by cold air sinking through a warmer environment and enhanced by the weight of heavy rain, spread out horizontally when they hit the ground. This causes zones of strong shifting winds called wind-shear

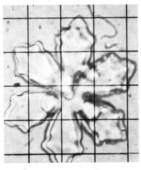

Meteorologist Norihiko Fukuta tests new organic cloud-seeding agents in a plastic cloud chamber, eight stories high, *top*. Agents producing more big ice crystals, *above*, may be better rain producers.

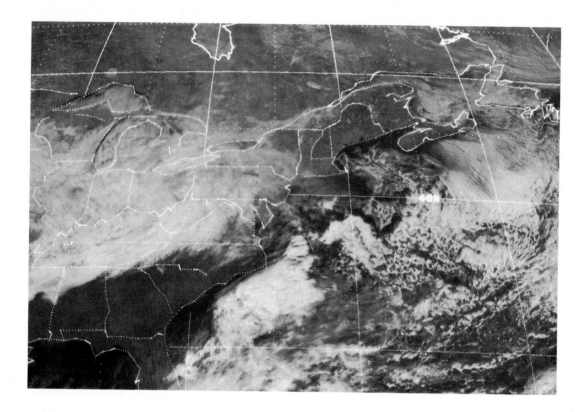

Meteorology

Continued

Pictures beamed to earth by a meteorological satellite helped weathermen accurately forecast a February blizzard that paralyzed the U.S. Atlantic Coast. A low-pressure system began off North Carolina, *above*. It moved up the East Coast in a counterclockwise pattern, *above right*. Then it met a cold-air mass over land that triggered the snowfall.

lines. Downbursts are difficult to observe and even more difficult to predict because they move rapidly – 65 to 95 kilometers (40 to 60 miles) per hour – and may cover up to 10 square kilometers (4 square miles).

Advances in radar technology have revealed amazing details of severe thunderstorm circulation. Doppler radars send out a radio signal that is reflected by precipitation particles in the storm. By measuring the change in frequency of the reflected signal, observers can calculate the particles' velocity toward or away from the receiver. If two Doppler radars are measuring the same particles from different angles, the velocity components in all three dimensions can be calculated.

R. Michael Hardesty, Alfred J. Bedard, Jr., and their colleagues at the Wave Propagation Laboratory in Boulder, Colo., reported in September that such new instruments and remote-sensing devices are being put to immediate and practical use to reduce the number of weather-related aircraft accidents. For example, two systems have

been installed at Dulles Airport near Washington, D.C., to give warning of thunderstorm downbursts and winds.

A Doppler radar system can measure the wind profile in the 500 meters (550 yards) closest to the ground either by acoustic signals in fair weather or by microwave signals when it is raining or snowing. A wind profile is a graph on which wind speed and direction are plotted along one axis and height is plotted along the other. Thus, wind speed can be determined at any height.

This system provides a continuous profile of low-level winds. However, because each downburst is confined to such a small area, one sensor might miss an important disturbance. To increase the surveillance area, a network of 125 barometers has been installed around the airport. Downbursts associated with severe thunderstorms are accompanied by rapid rises in surface pressure. Therefore, the barometers can provide immediate warning of an approaching pressure rise and associated weather.

Reducing tornado toll. Another significant use of Doppler radar is in the

Meteorology

Continued

early detection of tornadoes. Donald W. Burgess of NOAA's Severe Storms Laboratory in Norman, Okla., reported in March 1978 that NOAA's experimental system detected every tornado that came within 80 kilometers (50 miles) of Norman. The radar alert came an average of 23 minutes before a tornado was visible—an important advantage when every second counts. Burgess gives credit to the early-warning system for the fact that Oklahoma recorded fewer than half the usual number of tornado deaths in 1977—43 persons died, compared with an average of 114—although the state had almost 200 more twisters than usual.

Meteosat pictures. *Meteosat*, the first European meteorological satellite, was launched from Cape Canaveral, Fla., on Nov. 23, 1977, for the European Space Agency (ESA) and produced its first picture on December 9. Located in a stationary orbit directly above the equator, the ESA satellite is expected to provide both visible-light and infrared pictures of the cloud cover over Europe, Africa, and the Middle East for at least

three years. *Meteosat* is one of a series of satellites that will be launched by various nations taking part in the Global Atmospheric Research Program.

Forecast improvement. Frederick G. Shuman, Director of the National Weather Service, reported in January that weather forecasting is more accurate than it was 20 years ago. He said that bigger and faster computers and updated mathematical techniques for solving the equations that describe the atmosphere are responsible. They have produced a gradual improvement in forecasting wind and pressure patterns at all levels in the atmosphere. But people are more interested in whether or not it will rain than they are in the velocity of winds 5 kilometers (3 miles) above the earth's surface. Progress in local forecasts has been gradual but steady. For example, the percentage of correct answers to the question, "Will it rain at a particular point during a given 12-hour period?" has increased from about 80 to 85 per cent in Boston, Chicago, and Washington, D.C., over the last 20 years. [Richard A. Anthes]

Microbiology

Microbial geneticists Carl Woese and George Fox of the University of Illinois in Champaign-Urbana proposed in November 1977 that they had identified bacteria completely different from all other living organisms. The scientists suggested that these bacteria should be considered to be close relatives to the first living organisms to develop on earth.

Most biologists accept the theory that life originated on earth spontaneously several billion years ago with the creation of a single cell. This first, or primordial, cell eventually evolved into all of the kinds of organisms now inhabiting the earth.

Scientists can follow much of the development of higher plants and animals by studying their fossil records. However, a long period of evolution preceded the earliest known fossils. This period involved the evolution of microorganisms, particularly the bacteria, which are so tiny and fragile that they left no fossil records. Consequently, scientists can only speculate about their evolutionary history.

Geological data reveal that the early earth—up to about 500 million years ago—contained no free oxygen gas. This means that the first life had to be organisms that grew without oxygen. Such bacteria still exist today deep in the soil, in lake and ocean sediments, and in other places where there is no free oxygen. By this criterion alone, several bacteria qualify as candidates for the earliest forms of life. The bacteria identified by the University of Illinois researchers, therefore, had to display more than an ability to get along without oxygen.

Attempts have been made in recent years to classify the thousands of kinds of bacteria on a time scale by comparing the sequences of the chemical constituents that comprise their large molecules. The reasoning behind this approach is that the sequence in such molecules, for example the genetic material or proteins, of closely related organisms will be more similar than the sequences of distantly related organisms. Woese and Fox were using a variation of this basic approach to com-

Two species of the methane-forming bacteria that may be the earliest forms of existing life include one that forms chains of individuals, *below*. The spherical object is the same species in cross section. The other species, *below right*, is caught in the act of reproducing by division.

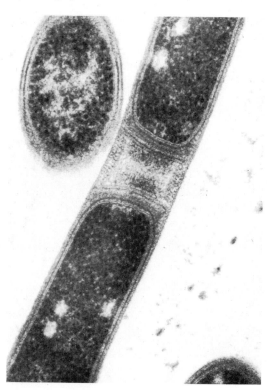
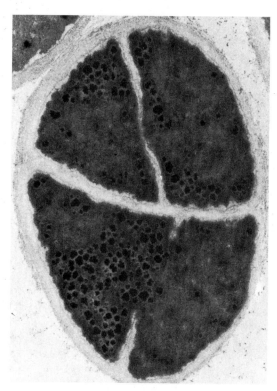

"Of course I don't look familiar—I'm recombinant."

Microbiology

Continued

pare bacteria when they discovered that one group of bacteria differs greatly from all others.

The scientists were studying the sequence of the constituents of a large molecule called 16-S ribonucleic acid. This molecule is part of ribosomes, particles that play a major role in protein synthesis and which are found in the cytoplasm of all cells. Woese and Fox chose this molecule because it is easy to purify, is universally present in cells, and the sequences of its constituents are known to change slowly.

The scientists grew large populations of different kinds of bacteria in separate cultures. Then they broke the bacteria open mechanically and isolated the ribosome particles. After that, they added a material that dissolves 16-S ribonucleic acid and several other substances that were present. They used electrophoresis to obtain pure 16-S ribonucleic acid. In electrophoresis, an electrical current passed through a gel, or jellylike solid material, causes materials added to the gel to separate into their components. The components

then migrate within the gel to characteristic positions from which they can be collected. Next, the scientists added an enzyme called ribonuclease T_1, which broke the pure material into many small fragments. These were separated by electrophoresis and analyzed. The analysis of 16-S ribonucleic acid fragments from different bacteria provided the data to develop an index of similarity of the bacteria.

Woese and Fox found that the similarity index showed all but one group of bacteria to be relatively close together in evolution. The index for the exceptional group is vastly different, however. This group of bacteria happens to be unusual in some other ways also. For example, these bacteria do not contain the chemical substance peptidoglycan, which is found in the cell walls of nearly all other kinds of bacteria. Also, these bacteria use some unusual molecules for reactions involving the movement of electrons to produce energy.

Of particular significance, these bacteria obtain energy through a unique process in which they convert hydrogen

Microbiology

Continued

A cell oozing its way over a glass plate treated by a new technique that covers it with fine gold particles leaves a readily visible track. The track allows scientists to characterize cell motion with little observation.

gas and carbon dioxide gas to methane in the total absence of oxygen.

Geochemical evidence tells us that the primordial atmosphere of the earth had no free oxygen and was composed of hydrogen, carbon dioxide, and nitrogen gases and water vapor. This is a perfect environment for growth of the methane bacteria.

The proposal of Woese and Fox to create a separate kingdom for the methane-forming bacteria, which they have named the archaebacteria, has created quite a stir among microbiologists interested in evolutionary processes. It is intriguing to speculate that these unusual bacteria may be, in effect, living fossils of the earliest kind of cellular life.

Fused bacteria and antibiotics. A novel approach to genetic engineering was reported in July 1977 by microbiologists David Hopwood, Helen Wright, and Mervyn Bibb of the John Innes Institute in Norwich, England, and Stanley Cohen of Stanford University in California. The experiments were especially significant because the kinds

of bacteria studied, called *Streptomyces*, produce more than half of the many kinds of antibiotics used in medicine.

One of the most controversial subjects in microbiology is the controlled transfer of genetic material, and thus permanently heritable characteristics, from one kind of organism to another. Most of these genetic-engineering experiments involve transfer of small amounts of genetic material to a recipient cell followed by formation of many copies of the material and, in some cases, expression of the physiological function of the genes. In most cases, gene function is the production of a specific protein, such as an enzyme.

However, the new work involved genetic material used by the bacteria to make antibiotics. The ability to permanently alter the amounts or kinds of antibiotics produced by a particular species is potentially of great significance to industries that make antibiotics, and, of course, to the public.

The scientists mixed the genetic material of two species of the *Streptomyces* by combining, or fusing, the contents of

Microbiology

Continued

two bacterial cells into one. The first step was to create protoplasts of the two species. A protoplast is a bacterium with its outer, or cell wall removed. Cells surrounded by these tough cell walls could never be fused, but the softer and more pliable protoplasts can.

The scientists carefully digested away the cell walls of the two bacteria species in separate tubes using two enzymes that break down bacterial cell walls. The cells, now bounded only by a fragile cytoplasmic membrane, were then bathed in special solutions to keep them from breaking open. Then the scientists mixed the protoplasts together and placed them on the surface of a special growth medium. This medium contained, in addition to nutrients needed for growth, a chemical called polyethylene glycol, and a high concentration of the sugar sucrose. Both were needed to provide further protection against breaking and to allow fusion to proceed.

After incubation in this special medium, the protoplasts of the two species fused. The new protoplast cells, now a mixture of both parents, than formed a normal cell wall and grew and multiplied as normal bacteria.

When the scientists then analyzed these new bacteria they found them to possess the characteristics of both parents. Thus, a new kind of organism had been formed that had properties of two other organisms. The only plausible explanation is that the genes of the two parent cells were mixed together during the fusion of their protoplasts.

Fusion of protoplasts of antibiotic-producing bacteria promises to be of great significance to the drug industry. For instance, some rare and potentially useful antibotics are produced in small amounts or by species of *Streptomyces* that do not grow well in large industrial-scale facilities. Perhaps the genes controlling synthesis of such antibiotics could be transferred through fusion to a species that grows more easily. There is also the potential for creating strains of *Streptomyces* that produce many antibiotics at one time. This could lead to savings in the cost of antibiotics.　　　[Jerald C. Ensign]

Neuroscience

A brain peptide called Substance P, one of a group of small biochemical molecules that affect brain activity and behavior, may be involved in the transmission of pain. Neuroscientist Tomas Hökfelt and his co-workers at the Karolinska Institute in Sweden showed in July 1977 that Substance P is distributed in about the same locations in the brain and spinal cord as are met-enkephalin and leu-enkephalin. These are the brain peptides that produce opiatelike analgesia, or pain relief. These same brain areas also produce analgesia when electrically stimulated.

Nearly 20 peptides have been found in brain tissue so far. Some of the peptides seem to act like neurotransmitters of chemical messages between cells, modulating, regulating, and interacting with other neurotransmitters in carrying out the activities of the brain and, ultimately, in controlling behavior.

Hökfelt and others studying the mechanism of pain theorize that Substance P and the enkephalins interact to switch on and off the nerve cells and fibers involved in mediating pain. Understanding how they interact, and how to control the interaction, may provide new methods to control pain.

Schizophrenic brains. Schizophrenics and nonschizophrenics seem to differ in the way their brains handle the neurotransmitter dopamine. A team of researchers that included neuroscientists Philip Seeman and Tyrone Lee of the University of Toronto in Canada, Oleh Hornykiewicz of the University of Vienna in Austria, and Wallace W. Tourtellotte of the Veterans Administration Wadsworth Hospital in Los Angeles gave an explanation for this difference in November 1977.

Recent theories of the cause of schizophrenia have centered on alterations in the brain levels of dopamine. After heavy use of amphetamines, some people temporarily develop an acute mental illness that mimics schizophrenia. Since amphetamines are known to influence the release of dopamine from nerve cells, the association seemed clear. But researchers found the same amount of dopamine in both schizophrenics and healthy people.

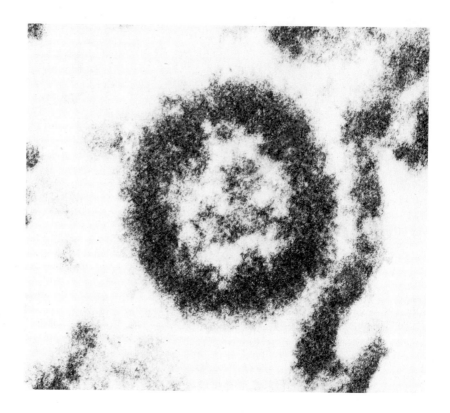

A doughnut-shaped structure has been identified as the "post-synaptic density" of a nerve cell, which receives the impulses sent across the synaptic cleft, or gap, that separates nerve cells.

Neuroscience

Continued

To find out why the two groups process similar amounts of dopamine differently, the researchers compared brain tissues from schizophrenic and nonschizophrenic individuals who had died of nonneurological causes. They found that the brains of the schizophrenics contained more cell receptors for dopamine than did those of the normal people. These dopamine receptors are tiny molecules on the membrane of brain cells that capture and react with dopamine molecules.

This excess of receptors – most of them in the limbic system of the brain, which is involved in emotion – causes the affected brain cells to react as though there were excess amounts of dopamine stimulating them. This overreaction may be involved in the bizarre behavior and paranoid hallucinations of schizophrenic patients.

The stuff of dreams. Psychiatrists J. Allan Hobson and Robert W. McCarley of Harvard Medical School described a new theory of dreaming in December 1977. They suggested that dreaming is probably a direct result of physiological changes in the brain while a person sleeps.

Hobson and McCarley believe that dreaming has psychological significance, but that the direct generator of the hallucinationlike episodes that most of us experience four or five times during a normal night's sleep is physical rather than mental. Their theory is based on studies of electrical discharges from the brain cells of cats during a particular phase of natural sleep called rapid eye movement (REM) sleep. Although the animal is asleep, there are many signs of wakefulness, such as the irregular electrical impulses measured in the brain, changes in muscle tone, and REM. These conditions are similar to changes in humans during dreams.

The researchers implanted tiny electrodes near large cells in a part of the brain stem called the reticular formation and found that these cells seem to play a part in causing REM and irregular electrical impulses, and in generating internal sensory information for the forebrain – the front part of the brain associated with higher brain functions.

Extending the process to humans, Hobson and McCarley theorized that the activated forebrain combines stored memory material with random data it receives from the reticular formation to construct dreams. The result of this combination of sensory and motor stimulation with miscellaneous memories is the sometimes pleasing, sometimes frightening, and usually quickly forgotten experience we call dreaming.

Malnourished brains. The damaging effects of undernutrition on brain development were demonstrated by studies on infant rats published by neuroscientists Patricia McConnell and Martin Berry of Birmingham University Medical School in England in April 1978. Working with newborn rat pups, the researchers carefully controlled the amount of suckling time allowed each pup so that weight gain was limited to 0.5 gram (0.02 ounce) per day. After 30 days, they compared the brains of the undernourished rats with those of rats allowed to feed normally. They examined particularly the dendrites of certain large cells, called Purkinje cells, in the cerebellum. Dendrites are the outgrowths of nerve cells that receive signals from other nerve cells.

The undernourished rats' Purkinje cells were significantly smaller and their dendrites showed much less branching than those of the normal rats. The pattern of branching also differed, which may indicate that their interaction with other cells was altered.

McConnell and Berry then tried to find out if the early feeding deficits could be made up. Infant rats were undernourished in the same way as the earlier group for 30 days and then allowed to eat as much as they wanted. The scientists examined the brains of the now-mature rats at 80 days and compared them with the brains of 80-day-old rats that had eaten normally throughout their lives. They reported that most of the brain defects found in malnourished rat pups were also found in adult rats malnourished as pups. Poor nutrition in young rats during critical periods of early development seems to lead to irreversible deficits in the brain. [George Adelman]

Nutrition

Investigations to determine whether a diet high in fiber helps prevent coronary heart disease continued in 1977 and 1978. Physician J. N. Morris and his colleagues at the London School of Hygiene and Tropical Medicine in England reported in November that they had reanalyzed dietary data taken from more than 300 British workingmen over a 20-year period in a study of various heart-disease risk factors.

They correlated the amounts of fiber types that the volunteers ate with the incidence of heart disease among them. Men who ate more cereal fiber than those in a control group had fewer heart attacks. But men whose fiber came mainly from fruits and vegetables showed no such reduction.

The scientists also found a correlation between a relatively higher-calorie diet and a decreased risk of heart attack among workingmen who were not obese. Their increased intake of food was the result of a more active life.

This seems to support the importance of exercise in preventing heart disease. But the researchers also point out that by eating more, the active workers consumed larger amounts of fiber.

Results seemingly not as favorable to a high-fiber diet were reported by researchers at the University of Oregon Health Science Center in Portland in December. They measured the effects on blood cholesterol and triglyceride levels of diets containing five times as much fiber as the typical American diet, but found no major benefits. Both cholesterol and triglyceride, another type of fat in the blood, have been associated with increased risk of coronary heart disease.

The researchers fed two groups of six healthy volunteers each a diet containing 60 grams (2.1 ounces) of plant fiber for four weeks. For another four weeks, they received a diet containing no fiber. One group's diet was also cholesterol-free. The other group's diet contained 1,000 milligrams of cholesterol from egg yolks. Neither group showed changes in levels of cholesterol, with or without large amounts of dietary fiber.

These results may indicate that fiber works with some other, unknown, fac-

Drawing by Modell; ©1978 The New Yorker Magazine, Inc.

"I think we've finally got it. Natural goodness."

Nutrition

Continued

tor in preventing heart disease. But they could also mean that short-term consumption of fiber will not produce immediate results.

Plants and cholesterol. Scientists have long known that plant sterols, chemicals that are similar to cholesterol, interfere with the body's absorption of cholesterol. Researchers at the Arteriosclerosis Center of the Massachusetts Institute of Technology in Cambridge reported in November 1977 that they used plant sterol to treat 46 patients with Type 2 hyperlipoprotenemia, in which a genetic defect causes high cholesterol levels.

The researchers found a 12 per cent reduction in the patients' blood cholesterol from a level of 349 milligrams per 100 milliters of blood. A cholesterol rating normally ranges between 150 and 250. This was particularly encouraging because it is difficult to lower cholesterol levels in patients with lipoprotein disease by any other method. So the results indicate that the powerful effect of plant sterols may be useful in controlling slightly raised cholesterol

levels in otherwise healthy individuals without changes in their diet.

Biochemist Kenneth K. Carroll at the University of Western Ontario in London, Canada, reported in October 1977 that cholesterol levels may be tied to differences between the way animals metabolize proteins from plants, meat, and dairy products. Carroll found blood-cholesterol levels rose in rabbits fed a cholesterol-free diet containing the milk protein casein as the only major protein source. Their cholesterol levels did not rise when they were fed a variety of plant proteins. Carroll then mixed animal and plant proteins equally and found that rabbits fed this balanced mixture had normal blood-cholesterol levels.

He also found that feeding them a mixture of three parts casein to one part soy protein produced a cholesterol level midway between normal and the high level produced by casein alone. To be certain only protein and not some other substance was involved, Carroll then fed the rabbits predigested protein and purified amino acids — the building

Nutrition

Continued

blocks of protein — in the same ratios and found the same results.

He concluded that the balance of amino-acid combinations that make up the various types of protein helped determine the rabbits' blood cholesterol levels. But it is difficult as yet to relate this finding to humans, because few people consistently eat protein from only one animal source, such as beef. However, some nutritionists suspect that a human diet of mainly animal proteins produces an amino acid pattern similar to that of the casein in Carroll's research, with resulting high cholesterol levels. Scientists are now investigating the importance of balanced plant and animal proteins.

Daily requirements. Researchers at the United States Department of Agriculture's Human Nutrition Laboratory in Grand Forks, N. Dak., reported in March 1978 on a study to determine whether levels of nickel and vanadium in the average U.S. diet are adequate. Scientists have not yet established the exact biological roles of nickel and vanadium. However, studies of biochemical systems in animals diets that are deficient in these minerals show that subtle changes occur.

The government researchers chose nine random sample diets, including such institutional fare as school lunches. The only definitive data that exist on daily nickel requirements are for rats, chicks, and swine. According to the body weights of these animals, 0.05 to 0.08 microgram per gram of dry weight of feed appears to be sufficient. The researchers found that the nine average human diets would yield 165 micrograms of nickel per day, or 0.27 microgram per gram of dry weight of food. If the human requirement is similar to that of the animals, the diets would provide adequate nickel.

The data on vanadium levels were not so encouraging. The average diets contained only 20.4 micrograms of vanadium per day, or 0.032 microgram per gram of dry weight of food. Chicks and rats fed at levels equivalent in terms of body weight to that in the human diet developed signs of vanadium deficiency. [Paul E. Araujo]

Oceanography

Provocative questions about the origin and history of the sea floor, the nature of marine life, currents in the cold Antarctic seas, and problems involving marine pollution challenged ocean scientists during 1977 and 1978.

Probing the sediments. Scientists aboard the drill ship *Glomar Challenger* sought solutions to mysteries about the evolution and movement of the great tectonic plates that lie beneath ocean sediments. From October through December, they drilled holes near the Japan Trench, an area where the floor of the Pacific Ocean appears to be sliding beneath the Japanese islands. Such areas are of particular interest because they are the scenes of frequent earthquakes.

The edge of the Japan plate forms the western wall of the Japan Trench. In the trench, the ocean floor slopes down before sliding under the crustal plate. Scientists had suspected that the sediments and rocks of the western wall would show signs of intense compression. They also expected to see ocean sediments piled up at the base of the islands where they were scraped from the Pacific Ocean floor as it slid under the plate over hundreds of millions of years. They had observed this phenomenon in similar zones off the coast of South America. But in the Japan Trench, they did not find what they had expected.

The western side of the trench had been compressed, but the scientists found no trace of ocean sediments in the rocks. The continental edge and western wall of the trench were covered by sediments made up of material from land and quite unlike the sediments of the deep-ocean eastern wall of the trench. The scientists are analyzing the data from the core samples to determine why the Japan Trench is different from other ocean trenches and what this might mean.

Open-ocean life. Marine biologists devoted attention during the year to the nature and distribution of life in the open ocean. The open ocean is often compared to a desert, a wasteland where food is so scarce that it can support only a limited amount of life.

The Gulf Stream's warm water appears as a dark meandering band that flows between colder (light gray) waters in an infrared image from a weather satellite.

Oceanography

Continued

Biological oceanographers G. Richard Harbison and Laurence P. Madin of the Woods Hole Oceanographic Institution in Massachusetts in late 1977 used underwater breathing equipment to dive to depths of 30 meters (100 feet) in the open ocean and observe the marine life at first hand. In addition, they took photographs and captured specimens in bottles.

Scientific understanding of the life that exists in the open sea had previously come from samples taken with nets. But such samples give only a partial picture of life there. Delicate jellylike organisms, a major part of the open ocean's animal life, are usually destroyed or damaged beyond recognition in the netting operations.

Harbison and Madin's observations provide evidence that the plankton communities in the open ocean are not the thoroughly mixed stew of marine life that appears in the sampling nets. Instead, the living systems of the open ocean seem to be much more structured and complicated than biological oceanographers had previously thought.

They confirmed earlier observations on the diversity, abundance, and probable importance of the jellylike life forms. These organisms, which range from simple jellyfish to complicated vertebrates called salpae, make up most of the animal life in the upper part of the ocean. Salpae, which range from the size of a thumb to the size of a hand, are able to feed on a broad range of animals, from the tiniest phytoplankton (sea plants) to larger crustaceans that are about 2.5 centimeters (1 inch) long. Salpae secrete a sticky substance to make a net that captures passing life, then they roll up and swallow the net along with its contents.

Antarctic sea life. Researchers in December detected signs of life in the cold, dark waters beneath Antarctica's Ross Ice Shelf by lowering television cameras through a hole drilled in the ice 378 meters (1,240 feet) deep. Geophysicist John W. Clough of the University of Nebraska, head of the Ross Ice Shelf Project, reported that on two occasions a fish swam slowly across the field of vision near the bottom. The

Oceanography

Continued

cameras also revealed other signs of life, including tracks, trails, and burrows on the sea floor.

Marine biologist Mary Alice Mc-Whinnie of DePaul University in Chicago reported a number of findings in June 1978 that may affect the rules for the future harvest of krill, the tiny shrimplike animals that abound in the cold seas surrounding Antarctica. Krill is one of the world's largest untapped sources of food. Experts estimate the potential annual harvest of krill at between 45 million and 181 million metric tons (50 million and 200 million short tons). At present, the world's total annual catch of all species of marine animals is about 59 million metric tons (65 million short tons).

Although krill is a potential rival of the soybean as a plentiful protein source for humans and livestock, it is also a primary source of food for some whales, seals, and penguins as well as squid and fish. Because of its important role in the Antarctic food chain, many scientists believe that the unregulated harvesting of krill could have a serious adverse effect on almost all life in the Antarctic waters.

McWhinnie began studying krill in special aquariums set up along the Bellingshausen Sea in November 1975. Antarctic seawater circulated directly into the aquariums, providing a natural environment for the krill.

Contrary to what scientists had believed, McWhinnie found that female krill do not die after spawning. Instead, they shed their skins, continue feeding, revert back to an earlier stage of sexual maturity, and spawn again. Moreover, she found that krill spawn an average of 2,000 to 3,000 eggs. Scientists had previously believed that they spawned from 300 to 800 eggs.

McWhinnie also reported that krill do not feed exclusively on phytoplankton. They eat small animals and even other krill. This finding will force scientists to change their ideas about the growth of krill during winter. They had previously thought that the winter growth of krill was negligible because there is no phytoplankton in the ice-covered waters during the long, dark Antarctic winters.

Finally, the studies suggest that the life span of krill is at least 3 years.

Russian scientists lower a current meter into the Atlantic Ocean as part of a joint U.S.-Russian project to study eddies, water that swirls against the main ocean current.

Barrier reef recovers. Richard Kenchington, a marine biologist at Australia's James Cook University, issued a report in November, easing concern about Australia's Great Barrier Reef. During the early 1970s, observers reported that the Crown-of-Thorns starfish was destroying the reef. But Kenchington reported that the reef does not appear to be in serious danger after all.

Over a five-year period, he dived to count the starfish and examine their effect on the reef. He found that only about one-third of the 2,012-kilometer (1,250-mile) long reef was damaged and 2.6 per cent of it was destroyed. All areas are showing signs of recovery.

Antarctic currents. Scientists taking part in the International Southern Ocean Studies reported in November on their continuing research on the Circumpolar Current, a project begun in 1975. The Circumpolar Current controls most of the water flowing from the South Pacific Ocean to the South Atlantic Ocean.

The scientists have been studying the Polar Frontal Zone, a mass of cold water similar to a meteorological cold front that moves northward in the western Scotia Sea, and also the dynamics of the Antarctic Circumpolar Current in the Drake Passage.

The oceanographers moored buoys equipped with temperature, current, and pressure recorders in the Drake Passage from 1975 through 1977. They used them to take continuous measurements for three 1-year periods. The scientists supplemented these measurements by visiting the area in the summer to take temperature and salt-content measurements at various depths in the Drake Passage and western Scotia Sea.

These studies produced much new information about this important ocean current. They confirmed that there are three distinct bands of relatively fast-flowing water in the Drake Passage, separated by regions of slower-flowing water. The streams, which flow eastward from the Pacific, change their position. The scientists reported that they wander north or south by as much as 100 kilometers (62 miles) in two- or three-week periods.

On the basis of measurements taken over three-week periods during the

Divers, *top*, mark the spot for anchoring a National Oceanic and Atmospheric Administration undersea habitat, *right*, off the Virgin Islands. The government facility is available to qualified marine researchers, who will live in its roomy interior; *above*, at a depth of 15 meters (50 feet).

Oceanography

Continued

summers, the scientists calculated the transport of water through the passage at 124 million cubic meters (4.4 billion cubic feet) per second. Based on the year-long current-meter readings, they estimated that the volume of water transported may vary above or below that amount by 60 million cubic meters (2.1 billion cubic feet) per second. By comparison, the Gulf Stream off the Atlantic Coast of the United States at the same latitude as New York City transports 120 million cubic meters (4.2-billion cubic feet) per second.

Marine pollutants. Chemist Choo S. Giam of Texas A&M University in April identified a group of potential new ocean pollutants called phthalate ester plasticizers. These are used by plastic manufacturers to make products flexible. Giam found the plasticizers in sediments taken from the Gulf of Mexico, in Gulf Coast fish, and in air and water samples from off the Atlantic Coast of the United States. They appear to be as widespread as DDT and chlorinated hydrocarbons. As yet, scientists know little about how they enter the ocean or what effect they might have on marine life.

In an encouraging finding, scientists working in the Southern California Coastal Water Research Project reported in March that wastes have had much less impact on the Pacific Coast than previously feared. Six large sewage systems in southern California pour an average of more than 3.8 billion liters (1 billion gallons) of human waste into the coastal waters each day.

After taking surveys of the organisms in these areas, the scientists concluded that most marine animals, including sport fish, are generally more abundant near the sewage outpourings than in other coastal areas. They also reported that damage done to the coastal ecosystems during the early 1970s by excessive discharges of such chemicals as DDT has begun to abate, and the areas appear to be recovering. The investigators confirmed that chlorinated hydrocarbons are harmful to marine life; on the other hand, they concluded that ordinary human waste is actually a useful nutrient. [Feenan D. Jennings]

Physics

Atomic and Molecular Physics. Physicists around the world continued to study the weak nuclear forces in 1977 and 1978. Teams in the United States, Great Britain, and Russia tested their theories with energy transitions in the element bismuth.

Scientists want to represent nature in the simplest manner possible, to describe all physical laws in a single equation. One attempt to do this is through the unified gauge theories, presented independently in 1968 by Steven Weinberg of Harvard University in Cambridge, Mass., and Abdus Salam of the International Center for Theoretical Physics in Trieste, Italy. Physicists have identified four basic forces of nature: gravity, electromagnetism, the strong nuclear force, and the weak nuclear force. The unified gauge theories attempt to describe two of these – the electromagnetic and the weak forces – in the same way.

Experiments have shown the Weinberg-Salam theory to be generally correct at high energies, particularly those that involve collisions between high-energy neutrinos – particles that have no mass and no charge – and atomic nuclei. However, attempts to test the theory at lower energies have not succeeded.

The unified theory is difficult to test because the weak force is extremely weak. Fortunately, it has a distinguishing characteristic that may permit it to be detected despite the overwhelming background of the other forces; the weak force is the only one of the four that does not always conserve parity.

In atomic physics, parity is conserved when the forces and their interactions in any system behave the same way in the system's mirror image. In the case of weak interactions, a right-handed system can be distinguished from a left-handed system – its mirror image. In electromagnetic interactions the systems cannot be distinguished.

The predominant force binding electrons to the atomic nucleus is electromagnetic. It is about 10^{14} times as strong as the weak force, thus masking it. Detecting the influence of the weak force requires finding occasions when the strong electromagnetic force will not completely dominate it. This occurs in certain lines in atomic spectra.

Atoms excited by an external source to states of energy above their normal, or ground, state emit the energy in discrete, or quantum, units. This emission can be detected as specific lines in the electromagnetic spectrum. The more intense spectrum lines are the result of transition through the so-called electrical dipole radiation, which changes the spinning atom's angular momentum by one quantum unit during the radiation. Atoms can also undergo magnetic dipole radiation. But this is much weaker than its electrical counterpart, and furthermore, according to the laws of quantum mechanics, it must change the atom's angular momentum in two-unit transitions.

Parity is conserved in both electrical and magnetic dipole transitions. In the presence of pure electromagnetic interactions either, but not both, can occur. But, if nonconserving parity forces are active, both are likely to occur simultaneously. Furthermore, in such a mixed-transition situation, polarized light with a wavelength very close to that of the transition will have its plane of polarization turned through a very small angle.

Searches for such a polarization effect in metal vapors are being performed by E. N. Fortson and his co-workers at the University of Washington in Seattle, C. E. Loving and P. G. H. Sandars at Oxford University in England, and V. N. Novikov, O. P. Sushkov, and I. B. Khriplovich in Novosibirsk, Russia. The experimenters are trying to detect optical rotation of the plane of polarization of polarized light that has passed through a metal vapor. They do this by observing light a few wavelengths away from a known transition.

The University of Washington physicists, for example, measured the absorption of polarized laser light near the 876-nanometer (nm) line in the spectrum of bismuth. The 876-nm line is a magnetic dipole transition, and any optical rotation observed at a wavelength near this line would indicate the presence of electrical dipole radiation that is caused by a parity nonconserving force — the weak force.

The Washington group used a tunable dye laser to produce 50-nanosecond pulses near the 876-nm line. The scientists first polarized the laser light by passing it through a Nicol prism. The light beam then passed through a 1-meter (0.3-foot) tube of bismuth vapor and helium gas. A second Nicol prism then detected rotation in the plane of polarization of the laser light.

The Oxford group used a bismuth line at 648 nm, a region of the spectrum where the stronger and more stable dye lasers were available. However, the 648-nm line is in a region of the spectrum that contains numerous interfering lines caused by bismuth in its molecular form. Work on this line was thus limited to lower densities of bismuth where there are fewer molecules to cause interference.

Autoionizing Rydberg states. One of the first and most fruitful uses of the ultraviolet radiation that is a by-product of synchrotron radiation is the study of autoionizing states in atoms. In an autoionizing state, an atom's electrons have enough energy to allow one of them to escape. But none escape because the energy is shared by two or more electrons. In the presence of some external light source, however, one of these electrons suddenly, typically in 10^{-13} seconds, obtains all of the energy and escapes.

In the fall of 1977, a group of physicists at the Stanford Research Institute in Menlo Park, Calif., used lasers to produce autoionizing Rydberg states in atoms with great efficiency. In Rydberg states electrons have very large orbits, that are far removed from the nucleus. In a typical case, strontium atoms are irradiated by a pulsed laser tuned to excite an electron from its ground state to a relatively low excited state. A second laser is then tuned to raise the same electron to a higher state — the Rydberg state.

A third laser pulse then raises a second electron to an excited state, thus giving the atom sufficient total energy to eject either one of the excited electrons. By applying electrical fields during the first two laser pulses, the physicists can excite specific Rydberg states and can study a number of transitions and associated atomic structures in strontium.　　　[Karl G. Kessler]

Elementary Particles. The rapid pace of surprising discoveries in particle physics in the last five years slackened somewhat in 1977 and 1978, but not before yielding evidence that at least one more elementary particle, or quark, is needed to complete the picture of subatomic matter. In July 1977, a research team at the Fermi National Accelerator Laboratory (Fermilab) near Chicago, headed by Leon M. Lederman of Columbia University, announced the discovery of the heaviest subatomic particle ever observed. It is more than 10 times heavier than a proton, which itself is composed of three much lighter quarks. The team included physicists from Fermilab, the State University of New York at Stony Brook, and Columbia University in New York City. They christened their new particle the upsilon.

Quarks are the basic building blocks of which protons and neutrons, as well as many other subatomic particles, are made. They are found only in combination with other quarks or their antimatter opposites, the antiquarks.

In May 1978, two teams of physicists observed upsilons in head-on collisions of electrons and positrons at DESY, the electron synchrotron laboratory near Hamburg, West Germany. Although Lederman and his colleagues were unable to tell much about the new quark, apart from its huge mass, the DESY researchers should be able to determine additional properties.

The discovery of the upsilon did not come as a complete surprise. In 1977, physicists at the Stanford Linear Accelerator Center (SLAC) discovered a particle called the tau. The tau is a member of another family of fundamental building blocks, similar to quarks, called leptons.

Discovery of the tau brought the number of known leptons to five, while the number of quarks remained at four. Most theories about quarks and leptons require that the two families be equal in size, thus the new quark was expected. The theories also insist that each family of building blocks have an even number of members, so at least one more of each remains to be found. There is

Physicists at Fermilab in Illinois used this massive collection of magnets and electronic detectors to discover a tiny new subatomic particle—the upsilon.

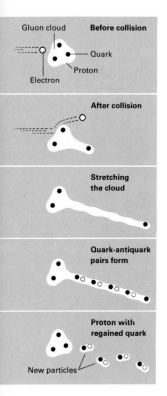

Gluon cloud | Before collision

Quark

Proton

Electron

After collision

Stretching
the cloud

Quark-antiquark
pairs form

Proton with
regained quark

New particles

Bombarding the quarks in a proton to set a single quark free results in a stretching of the gluon cloud of forces and the production of new particles consisting of pairs of quarks and antiquarks. However, no single quark stays free.

already some indirect evidence for the existence of a sixth lepton.

This proliferation of quarks and leptons does not affect our picture of ordinary matter, which involves only the two lightest members of each family, the "up" quark and the "down" quark, and the electron and electron quark. The heavier quarks and leptons are unstable, and spontaneously change into the more common ones very shortly after they are produced.

Quarks in motion. For many particle physicists, however, it was a year of frustration. They had expected that studies of collisions of swift-moving particles, such as protons, would reveal the properties of the quarks of which they are made. If the collision is violent enough, the forces that hold the quarks together have little effect on their motion, at least during the moment of impact. Consequently, the collision of a quark in one particle with a quark in another resembles a collision of two free quarks. The initial motion of the quarks right after the impact should have an effect on the ultimate position of the particles.

The world's two most powerful proton accelerators—the 500-billion electron volt (GeV) machine at Fermilab and the 400-GeV super-proton synchrotron (SPS) accelerator at the European Center for Nuclear Research (CERN) near Geneva, Switzerland—have the energy to show these effects.

However, no one observed clear signs of single-quark collisions in several such experiments at Fermilab and CERN. Either such encounters are rarer than expected, or they are masked by the effects of the motions of the quarks inside the particles. In any event, it seems clear that the study of quarks by this technique will not be as routine as was expected, if the method ever works.

Too much information? Experimenters who study collisions of neutrinos with nuclei experienced frustrations of a different sort—an excess of riches. Neutrino experiments have yielded much of our information on the properties of quarks. Neutrinos are immune to the force that binds quarks inside protons and neutrons, so they can easily penetrate these particles and collide with individual quarks. When they do so, they usually transform one kind of

quark into another, yielding a rich harvest of new types of particles.

These experiments, however, are far from simple. They require massive complicated particle detectors weighing tens or hundreds of tons. Even so, the data obtained are so crude that it is hard to be sure exactly what is being observed.

When a neutrino transforms a quark, a lepton is emitted. If the quark is one of the heavier, unstable types, it quickly transforms itself back into an ordinary quark, a process that often produces an additional lepton. Experimenters on both sides of the Atlantic have reported observing two, three, and even four leptons under these conditions.

Two-lepton events, which are relatively common, are easily understood in terms of the production and subsequent decay of a single heavy quark. But the rarer three- and four-lepton events suggest a complex cascade of transformations that may prove difficult to unravel. This is heady wine for experimenters using these neutrino detectors. They are discovering new effects faster than theorists can understand them.

In particle theory, however, the picture is much clearer. A simple theory of the force that holds quarks together in an unbreakable embrace came of age in 1977. The theory is known as quantum chromodynamics (QCD). It arose from the ideas of a number of young theorists, expecially Gerhard 'tHooft of the University of Utrecht in the Netherlands, David I. Gross and Frank Wilczek of Princeton University, and David Politzer of Harvard University.

The mathematical development of the QCD theory is in its infancy, and much work remains before complete analyses of particle phenomena are possible. Still, its basic features are well established, and it has successfully explained a number of the puzzling features of quarks.

According to the QCD theory, the force between quarks is transmitted by particles called gluons, which are very similar to the photons, or quanta of light, that transmit ordinary electrical and magnetic forces. For example, like photons, gluons always move at the speed of light. Unlike photons, however, gluons can exert forces directly on each other.

A magnetic spectrometer developed at Lawrence Berkeley Laboratory will
be used to study ions and other molecular species, as well as liquid metals.

Physics

Continued

One peculiar effect in quarks is that, unlike other fundamental forces, the force between them is weaker when they are close together than when they are far apart. QCD explains that each quark is surrounded by a cloud of gluons, and the interaction of these clouds at a distance produces a strong attraction between the quarks. When they move close together, however, the clouds neutralize one another and the force diminishes.

The theory also seems to provide a natural explanation of why quarks are never seen alone. The explanation is analogous to the fairy tale "The Sorcerer's Apprentice." In this story, an apprentice magician tries to stop a bewitched broom that has gone berserk by chopping it with an ax. But every time he hits it, each splinter that he knocks loose becomes a new broom.

According to QCD, the same thing happens when one tries to knock a quark out of a proton. Its gluon cloud clings to clouds from the other quarks, and is stretched out into a long, narrow string. The energy required to stretch the cloud must be so great that new quarks and antiquarks can be produced by the conversion of energy to matter. The gluon clouds of these new quarks stick to one another, and to the quark that was originally hit, producing new quark combinations. Therefore it is futile to simply hit a quark harder; one merely produces a longer string and more new particles, but never produces a free quark.

The theory insists that all combinations of quarks must contain equal mixtures of all three colors; by analogy with color mixing, these states are "white." The combination of a quark with an antiquark is like the mixture of a color with its opposite, or complementary color, another way to produce white. Consequently, the only quark combinations allowed contain either three quarks, which compose the proton, for example, or one quark and one antiquark, which produce a meson. Mesons are unstable because any combination of matter with antimatter will quickly annihilate itself, producing lighter forms of matter — photons or leptons. As a result, no meson is able to last more than a few billionths of a second.   [Robert H. March]

Nuclear Physics. One of the dominant features of the behavior of the nucleus of the atom is that, in certain modes of excitation, it undergoes vibrations similar to those that occur in a drop of liquid. A drop of water, when distorted into the shape of a prolate spheroid and released, oscillates between prolate and oblate shapes. The frequency of this oscillating state, called a quadrupole mode, depends on the size of the drop in a particular way. Similarly, an atom's nucleus will oscillate at frequencies having some dependence on its size.

For this liquid-drop comparison to be valid, theorists have insisted that a so-called breathing mode must also exist in which the nucleus remains spherical and simply expands and contracts in radius — a monopole mode. The energy of this monopole mode depends only on the size of the nucleus and its compression modulus — the energy required to change its volume.

In November 1977, David Youngblood and his collaborators at Texas A & M University in College Station reported the first complete identification of this special oscillation in the nuclei of the atoms of two elements.

The breathing mode has previously eluded detection because it had been lost in a background produced by other, stronger oscillations. Exciting a nucleus electromagnetically, or by bombarding it with protons, sets up modes in which nucleons — protons and neutrons in the nucleus — slosh back and forth out of phase with each other. The Texas A & M physicists used alpha particle projectiles that do not excite these modes to any degree. By observing only the angles of alpha particles scattered off the nuclei in the forward direction, where the breathing mode should dominate all other modes, the scientists clearly detected breathing modes in lead and samarium nuclei.

As a result of this success, Frederick Bertrand and his collaborators at Oak Ridge National Laboratory in Oak Ridge, Tenn., reanalyzed previous data on proton-scattering from gold, tin, zirconium, and nickel. They proved that the energy required to establish monopole excitation has the liquid-drop dependence on nuclear size. In addition to substantiating the theory of breath-

"I think you should be more explicit here in step two."

Physics

Continued

ing modes, the discovery has provided data on the compression modulus of nuclear matter. It is about 200 million electron volts (mev).

Where the neutrons are. During 1977 and 1978, three new techniques demonstrated great promise for determining the distribution of neutrons in the atomic nucleus.

Physicists have long used the technique of bouncing electrons off nuclei and measuring their scattering angles. This permits the observers to determine precisely the spatial distribution of electrical charge in a nucleus and thus map out the distribution of its protons, which are positively charged. One of the great triumphs of nuclear theory in the last decade has been the ability to predict these proton distributions.

Unfortunately, until recently, there has been very little experimental information concerning the distribution of the neutrons in the nucleus because they have no charge and, thus, have no electrostatic interaction with electrons.

Ingo Sick and his colleagues at Saclay Laboratory near Paris studied neutron density distribution by using the magnetic interaction that occurs between a scattered electron and a nucleon in the nucleus.

Nucleons can be pictured as being distributed in the nucleus in a series of single particle orbitals which have specified energies and special distribution. When all the orbitals with a given energy have been filled, creating a closed shell, the nucleus has many special properties. In particular, there is no magnetic scattering from closed shells, so the process is sensitive only to the nucleon distribution of an incompletely filled energy level. Thus it can be used only with elements with excess nucleons in a new orbital or a deficiency that produces a partially empty one.

The Saclay group reported in May 1977 on experiments in which they compared magnetic-scattering from a neutron orbital in strontium 87 with a corresponding proton orbital in niobium 93. The scientists showed that the shapes and radii of these two orbitals are almost identical, confirming the predictions of scientists.

Another new method of determining the distribution of neutrons is scattering pions with an energy of about 200 mev from a nucleus. At this energy, pions may combine with a nucleon to form a new short-lived particle, or resonance. This makes positive pions interact with protons and negative pions interact with neutrons much more strongly than negative pions interact with protons or positive pions with neutrons. Hence, the angles at which the positive and negative pions scatter from nuclei near the resonance energy should correspond to differences in distributions of the nucleons.

During 1977, physicists at the Swiss Institute for Nuclear Research in Zurich performed high-resolution scattering experiments with positive and negative pions at the resonance energy on carbon, oxygen, silicon, calcium, and lead. Similar high-resolution experiments have been performed at Los Alamos Meson Production Facility in New Mexico. At present, however, the theories about pion-nucleus interactions are insufficient to make a meaningful analysis of the exceedingly rich data.

The third experiment on neutron distributions used proton-scattering. Russian physicists at Gachina in Leningrad used polarized carbon 12 protons at energies of 1 billion electron volts. Los Alamos physicists used 800 mev polarized protons of carbon 12, nickel 58, and lead 208.

If the detailed behavior of high-energy proton-scattering from a single proton and a single neutron were completely understood, then theorists could relate the scattering of a high-energy proton from a nucleus to a particular combination of the proton and neutron densities. Since we know the proton density, we could determine the neutron density. However, we do not know enough about the interactions with a single proton or neutron to successfully analyze such data.

Using polarized protons permits us to simultaneously analyze both the cross section – the probability of scattering in a given direction – and the dependence of the scattering on the alignment of the proton spin. This method significantly diminishes the sensitivity of the analysis to uncertainties in a nuclear interaction.   [John W. Negele]

Plasma Physics. Thermonuclear fusion continued to dominate research in plasma physics in 1977 and 1978, with tokamak devices receiving the most effort. To obtain fusion power, researchers must heat a mixture of deuterium and tritium to a temperature high enough so that the ions and electrons of these hydrogen isotopes will fuse to form helium, giving off energy. The temperature must exceed 100 million° C and the fuel density, in particles per cubic centimeter, times the length of time the fuel is confined, in seconds, must be greater than 10^{14}. No one has yet achieved this combination.

Magnetic-fusion. This work centers around tokamaks in which the plasma is confined in a toroidal, or doughnut, shape by a very high magnetic field. In a tokamak, the plasma is initially heated by the passing of an electrical current through it. This produces a power that is a product of plasma resistivity and current density. A plasma's resistivity decreases as the temperature of the electrons is increased and the current density is proportional to the ratio of the magnetic field strength to the outer radius of the toroid. The mechanical strength of the apparatus limits the magnetic field to less than 100 kilogauss. The toroidal radius must be large enough for the hot plasma to be isolated from the walls of the chamber.

What this all means is that the power that heats the plasma decreases as the reactors are made larger. As a result, physicists are developing other ways to heat the plasma. These include using radio-frequency waves, plasma compression, and the injection of energetic neutral atoms, with neutral injection being developed most vigorously.

In a neutral-injection system, the equipment that produces neutral, or ionized, atoms is located about 5 meters (18 feet) from the tokamak. Here a low-temperature plasma is formed. The plasma ions are pulled through a mesh electrode electrostatically and accelerated to about 50,000 electron volts (kev). These energetic ions then pass through a cloud of hydrogen gas that adds an electron to each ion, forming a beam of 50 kev neutral atoms. These are directed through a connecting pipe to the tokamak plasma. Since the neutral atoms are not deflected by the tokamak magnetic field, they penetrate deeply into the tokamak plasma, thereby heating it.

Using this method, physicists led by Harold P. Eubank at Princeton University in New Jersey used the Princeton Large Torus (PLT) tokamak to produce the highest ion temperatures, 27 million° C, or 2.2 kev, ever achieved in a tokamak plasma. With neutral-beam injectors developed at Oak Ridge National Laboratory (ORNL) in Tennessee by a team under O. William Morgan and Halsey H. Haselton, the Princeton group injected about one megawatt of neutral-beam power into the PLT plasma.

In addition to achieving record temperatures, these experiments produced about 10^{12} neutrons per pulse when deuterium beams were injected into a deuterium plasma. The number of neutrons is proportional to the amount of energy output and this yield is comparable to previous achievements in magnetic fusion and about 1,000 times greater than the yield from present experiments using lasers. The neutral-

beam power on PLT will soon be increased to about three megawatts, which should increase the plasma temperatures to about five kev and neutron yields to about 10^{14} neutrons per pulse.

In other tokamak experiments with neutral-beam heating, scientists at ORNL used their ORMAK and scientists at Fontenay-aux-Roses in France used their TFR to produce slightly lower ion temperatures.

There are two types of new tokamaks under construction. Medium-sized tokamaks, which will begin to operate late in 1978, will use plasmas of non-reacting hydrogen. These devices include the ISX-B at ORNL, the Doublet III at Gulf General Atomic Corporation in San Diego, and the PDX at Princeton University. Designers will try to maximize the plasma pressure – and hence the thermonuclear power output – by changing the cross section of the plasma from a circle to vertically elongated cross sections, such as an ellipse. In addition, the PDX will optimize the purity of the plasma by using magnets to channel the outer

Improved designs of fusion-power reactors have brought us closer to the three-part goal of increasing the heat, fuel density, and the confinement time that will make energy from fusion a reality.

The Steps to Fusion Power

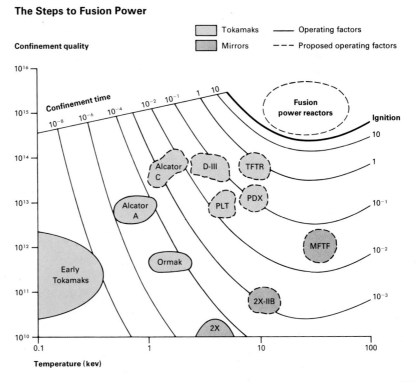

surface of the plasma into a remote plasma disposal chamber. This should reduce losses associated with impurities picked up from the walls of the toroid.

The second, larger type of tokamak is scheduled for operation in the early 1980s. The major U.S. device is the Tokamak Fusion Test Reactor (TFTR) being built at Princeton under the direction of Paul J. Reardon. By 1982, TFTR will have a plasma current of 2.5 million amperes, five times that of present tokamaks, and will heat the plasma to temperatures of 50 million°C to 100 million°C by injecting 30 megawatts of neutral-beam power into it. The objective of TFTR is to demonstrate that it is possible to produce a fusion power output of 30 megawatts or more.

Scientists from the European Economic Community (Common Market) are concentrating on the Joint European Torus (JET), which will be built near Oxford, England. JET uses a vertically elongated plasma cross section to produce plasma currents of about 4-million amperes.

Russian physicists are focusing on a large, slightly elongated, plasma cross-section tokamak called T-20 that will have 4 million amperes of plasma current. It is scheduled to begin operating in the late 1980s. The T-20 will use superconducting magnetic coils and will have very long plasma pulses (about 100 seconds).

Laser fusion. Shiva, the world's highest-power laser-fusing facility, began to operate in the spring of 1978 at Lawrence Livermore Laboratory (LLL) in Berkeley, Calif. In laser-fusion devices, an intense laser beam is aimed at a pellet made of deuterium and tritium. The beam vaporizes the surface of the pellet, driving it toward the center to create the required density, temperature, and confinement time.

The LLL laser system, under the direction of John L. Emmett, has 20 separate arms for the laser beams that will be fired simultaneously at a deuterium-tritium target about 200 microns in diameter. Each laser arm consists of a neodymium-glass laser that produces a pulse of about 500 joules in 10^{-10} seconds. The 20-laser system has been pulsed to 26 terawatts (10^{12} watts) producing 7 by 10^9 neutrons from a single target.   [Dale M. Meade]

Solid-State Physics. A new class of semiconductors based on the organic polymer, polyacetylene, was discovered by a group of scientists at the University of Pennsylvania in Philadelphia in 1978. These semiconductors are of potential value for making solar cells — devices that can convert sunlight directly into electricity.

A conventional solar cell is made of two types of purified silicon. One type is "doped with" — minute quantities are added — an impurity that gives it an excess of free electrons carrying negative charge, or n-type. The other type is doped to give it an excess of holes — fewer electrons — carrying positive charge, or p-type. The two positive and negative materials combine at a p-n junction, which sets up an electric barrier at the junction. This separates positive and negative charges induced by light and leads to an electrical current. See ELECTRICITY FROM THE SUN.

Polyacetylene is a plastic material consisting of chains of carbon and hydrogen atoms in which the chemical bonds between the carbon atoms are not all occupied. As a result, the chains of atoms have unattached electrons with the potential to conduct electricity. In the early 1970s, Hideki Shirakawa and his co-workers in Japan discovered how to grow polyacetylene in relatively crystalline form. While visiting the University of Pennsylvania, the team found a way in which controlled amounts of one of the halogens, such as bromine, could be added to the polyacetylene. These "impurities" act as donors of, or acceptors from, electrons in the acetylene chain.

The scientists then found that the electrical conductivity of the polymer changed from that of a rather good insulator for the pure polyacetylene to the conductivity of a moderately good metal as concentration of the impurities was increased.

Amorphous silicon is another material with promise for photovoltaic devices. The highly purified silicon usually used in semiconducting devices is a crystal. Crystalline silicon cells provide solar electricity where their relatively high cost can be justified, such as in spacecraft. Amorphous silicon is more like glass than a crystal. It promises to make cheaper solar cells possible.

Physics

Continued

Two laser beams generate patterns of heat waves in a crystal. A third laser beam then detects the heat vibrations, called "second sound," that provide information about the atomic structure of the crystal.

In 1975, Walter Spear and Peter LeComber of the University of Dundee in Scotland found that they could increase the conductivity of amorphous silicon by making the material with small amounts of phosphorus hydride (PH_3) or boron hydride (BH_2).

David E. Carlson and Christopher Wronski of the RCA Corporation's David Sarnoff Research Center in Princeton, N.J., used materials prepared in this way to build a demonstration photovoltaic cell from amorphous silicon. They were able to achieve efficiencies of up to 6 per cent.

Not-so superfluid helium. One of the wonders of condensed-matter physics has been the phenomenon of superfluidity of liquid helium as it is cooled to nearly 2°K. (-271°C). Superfluidity is a phenomenon in which a small "bucket" of a liquid, when cooled below its superfluid transition temperature and set into rotation, will rotate essentially forever. It will not be slowed by viscous drag as is a normal fluid.

Theoretical work by Russian physicist Lev D. Landau and two Americans, chemist Lars Onsager and physicist Richard P. Feynman, explained the mechanism of superfluidity in the 1950s. According to the laws of quantum mechanics, a certain proportion of the atoms in the superfluid helium are arranged in such a way that the normal vibrational energy of heat cannot destroy rotation once it is established. The only way the superfluid can be slowed down—apart from heating it above its transition temperature—is to make the circulation so rapid that small whirlpools, or vortexes, are set up in the helium by imperfections in the walls of the container (see CURRENTS IN CHAOS). The fluid in the center of these vortexes turns out to be in a more normal state where the usual mechanisms of viscosity can act to slow down the rotation.

Experiments in 1978 by Kenneth Telschow and Robert B. Hallock of the University of Massachusetts in Amherst and David J. Bishop and John D. Reppy of Cornell University in Ithaca, N.Y., showed that liquid helium can be made to flow in very thin films—with

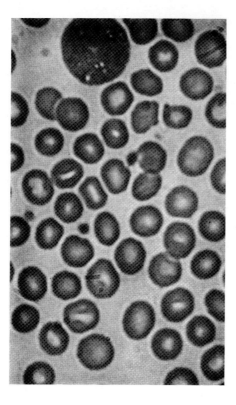
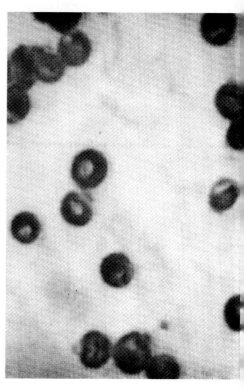

Resolution of red blood
cells in an optical
microscope, 1,000 times
magnification, *right*, is
equaled by an acoustic
microscope, *far right*,
that operates at an
acoustic wavelength
of 520 nanometers.

Physics

Continued

thicknesses only the size of a few atoms. Indefinite superflow then becomes partially spoiled. Although the thin-film helium continues to flow as a superfluid when the temperature is below the transition temperature, the flow does not persist. Instead, a weak viscosity develops that increases as the velocity of the fluid decreases.

In March, a group of theoretical physicists from Cornell and Harvard universities and Bell Telephone Laboratories and another group at Stanford University, the Institute for Advanced Study in Princeton, N. J., and the Xerox Research Laboratories in Palo Alto, Calif., described this apparent partial breakdown of the laws of superfluidity. The scientists observed that because the films are only a few atoms thick, minute regions will be excited because the temperature is slightly above absolute zero. This leads to the spontaneous creation of counter-rotating whirlpools in the film.

When the films move, the hydrodynamic forces acting on the vortexes tend to make them fly apart. This leads

to viscous drag, which increases as the velocity of the fluid increases. As a result, pairs of counter-rotating vortexes are pried apart. Thus, when it is reduced to an atomically thin film, a superfluid is only a partial superfluid.

Acoustic microscopy. The use of ultrasonic waves at gigahertz frequencies—1 gigahertz is 1 billion cycles per second—to produce images of microscopic objects was pioneered by Stanford University scientists Ross A. Lemons and Calvin F. Quate in 1974 through the invention of a scanning acoustic microscope. In 1978, Victor Jipson, also of Stanford, and Quate succeeded in operating the "sound microscope" at an ultrasonic frequency of 3 gigahertz. At this frequency, the acoustic wavelength is 520 nanometers, (billionths of a meter), which corresponds to the optical wavelengths of green light at the center of the optical band. Operating at this frequency and with improved acoustic lenses, the microscope has reached a resolving power comparable to that of the light microscope. [Sebastian Doniach]

Psychology

David H. Hubel, Torsten N. Wiesel, and Michael P. Stryker of the Harvard Medical School in Boston reported in February that they had developed a new technique for studying the visual cortex, the part of the brain that interprets what we see.

The first response to incoming visual stimulation occurs in the retina. As the stimulation moves along the visual pathways, responses occur in cells in the lateral-geniculate, a part of the thalamus, and finally responses take place in the cells of the visual cortex.

We know that individual nerve cells at the two lower levels of the visual pathway respond best to circles or spots of light. Individual nerve cells in the visual cortex, however, appear to respond best to edges or bars of light. Also, these shapes may have to have a specific orientation in space and move in a specific direction at a specific speed in order for an individual cortical cell to respond to them.

The spatial orientation of the stimulus is particularly important. For example, a cell may show a large number of consecutive responses per minute to a horizontal bar, but the number of responses per minute may decrease as the orientation of the stimulus gradually changes from horizontal to vertical. No measurable response may occur when the stimulus is vertical. Another cell may react in the opposite way.

Hubel, Wiesel, and Stryker hypothesized that all cells in the visual cortex that respond to a particular orientation are clustered together, rather than scattered randomly throughout the cortex. However, the grouping of cells by their responsiveness to a given spatial orientation had never been demonstrated anatomically. The researchers used a new technique that is based on the fact that nerve cells absorb and metabolize sugar when they respond. They used ^{14}C 2-deoxyglucose, a synthesized form of sugar that cells absorb as they respond, but cannot metabolize. The sugar, therefore, remains trapped inside the responding cells. Because of this, a radioactive tracer attached to the sugar permits identification of the cells that have responded.

Infants only 2 or 3 weeks old can copy an adult's facial gestures. This ability in very young infants may force revisions in theories on child development.

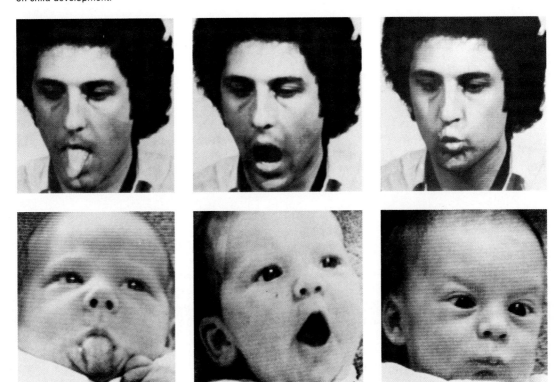

Feeling Heart Dogs

Sonny, a 19-year-old patient at Ohio State University (OSU) Psychiatric Hospital, was delighted with his new therapist. She was resilient, friendly, good-humored, even playful. She offered Sonny love, attention, and acceptance without criticism. In fact, the only problem Sonny had when they were together was keeping the therapist off the couch.

Sonny's therapist, Arwyn, was a wire-haired fox terrier. Sonny and Arwyn were among the participants in a special Pet-Facilitated Psychotherapy (PFP) program we initiated several years ago at OSU.

Pet dogs may help to fulfill two basic psychological needs – the need to love and be loved and the need to feel that we are worthwhile to ourselves and to others. The success of PFP is based on the idea that many psychiatric patients may accept the love of a friendly, non-threatening dog or cat before they can share love with a fellow human.

Our involvement in PFP grew incidentally out of attempts to develop conditions in animals that were similar to psychological disorders in people. We established a "dog ward" in our psychiatric hospital where the animals lived under pleasant, hygienic conditions. The patients could hear the dogs bark, which led to our program.

Some of the patients, especially the alienated, uncommunicative adolescents, broke their self-imposed silence after hearing the barking and asked if they could play with the dogs or help care for them. We permitted this, and it was so helpful to us, the patients, and the dogs that we started research to determine the effectiveness of PFP.

Our study involved many of the hospital staff. Hospitalized patients who had failed to respond favorably to traditional forms of therapy participated. PFP was not proposed as a substitute for other forms of therapy, but as an additional means of helping patients learn to get along with other people.

We began by asking patients whether they liked pets and, if so, what kind. Often the mention of a dog or cat would start a lively conversation. Then the dogs – and, in a few cases, cats – were brought in. Sometimes a patient would visit with several dogs in the kennels and choose one of them. The

type of dog chosen and reasons for the choice gave us a good deal of insight into a patient's feelings. We worked with five types of dogs as co-therapists: wire-haired fox terriers, border collies, beagles, a Labrador retriever, and a German shepherd-husky hybrid.

We found that uncommunicative patients responded well to lively wire-haired fox terriers. These friendly pets appealed strongly to lonely people who craved affection. One patient showed a surprising preference for an extremely shy, unattractive collie because "I felt that this dog needed me." Some energetic patients enjoyed Whiskey, the strong, active, aggressively loving German shepherd-husky.

Patients selected for PFP were withdrawn, self-centered, and uncommunicative. Some were almost mute and so unhappy that they would not leave their beds. They lacked self-esteem and acted as helpless as infants.

As a patient began to assume more and more responsibility for the care of a dog, improvement became obvious. Patients progressed from walking a dog, first on the ward and later outdoors, to coming to the kennel regularly to groom it. Some began to run with their dogs, adding exercise and emotional satisfaction to their daily routine.

This assumption of responsibility for the care of the dogs developed self-confidence in the patients and gradually transformed them from irresponsible, dependent, psychological invalids into self-respecting, responsible individuals.

Early fears that some patients might become so attached to their pets that they would continue to ignore people and become even more withdrawn proved to be unfounded. After the initial stages of PFP when the patient related exclusively to the pet, the dog became a socializing link. Other patients took a great interest in the idea of using a pet as a co-therapist. The staff responded well to pets and to the idea of pet therapy. We observed a widening circle of warmth and approval.

Whenever possible, we made videotape recordings of interactions involving patient-dog-therapist combinations. The tapes served two purposes. We could analyze the interactions systematically. Also, we used the recordings as a form of feedback therapy.

Therapist Samuel A. Corson rewards a colleague, a terrier, for helping patients at Ohio State University Psychiatric Hospital.

Patients who had no interest in watching television would often watch their own social interactions with intense interest, and then discuss them with the human therapist.

Of the 50 patients studied, PFP was unsuccessful with only three, because they did not accept their pets. All the rest showed some improvement, and many showed marked improvement.

After our pilot study lost its funding in 1975, we began a research program at Castle Nursing Homes in Millersburg, Ohio. Despite the many differences between a nursing home and a psychiatric hospital, we found that PFP produced similar results in both. To the dogs used as therapists in our previous study, we added dachshunds, cocker spaniels, Doberman pinschers, and poodles—most of them miniatures and toys. The pets helped residents and staff communicate, and helped to improve the overall morale of the institution. The strength of a community replaced the weakness of detached, unhappy, and self-pitying individuals.

The dogs contributed in many ways to the elderly people's well-being. One overweight resident lost 14 kilograms (30 pounds) in one month when she began walking and running with her dog. And exercising a dog naturally leads to getting around the neighborhood, and making friends.

The animals also helped to involve the aged in other rejuvenating activities. For example, shortly after being given a pet dog, 78-year-old Jed, who had been living incommunicative and self-isolated in the nursing home for about 20 years, began to draw pictures of dogs and show them off. Eventually, the walls in Jed's room were covered with much-admired drawings.

In all our studies, the pets served their purpose admirably. They did not monopolize the patients' affection, but rather strengthened their self-reliance and psychological well-being. It may be worthwhile to consider providing institutionalized old people, psychiatric patients, and other lonely souls with dogs or cats to act as continuing therapeutic helpers.

The PFP dogs serve a function comparable to that of seeing eye dogs. So we think of them as "feeling heart" dogs.   [Samuel A. Corson]

The Harvard researchers injected three anesthetized macaque monkeys with a substance containing the synthetic sugar-radioactive tracer combination. As long as visual stimulation enters the eye, the retina and the visual pathways beyond it will respond, even though the subject is unconscious.

Each monkey was exposed to 45 minutes of visual stimulation of one or both eyes by moving or stationary black lines on a white background. Held in a restraining device, the animal was forced to focus its eyes on the slide-projected pattern.

After the monkeys were sacrificed, the scientists examined sections of their cortical tissue by autoradiographic methods. They confirmed that cells that respond to the same orientation are arranged systematically and that they are separated by a constant distance from other groups of cells that respond to a different orientation.

This technique will enable researchers to observe more closely the relationship between cell groups responding to the same orientation and other parts of the visual system. It also will lead to a better understanding of the evolution of the visual system and may provide information about some of the perceptual defects observed in children who have been deprived of visual stimuli.

Lights of love. Robert R. Jackson of the University of California, Berkeley, reported in November on courtship patterns of the jumping spider. Unlike most other spider species, the jumping spider has excellent vision. Also, its feeding and courtship patterns differ from those of other spider species.

Rather than trapping its prey in a web as other species do, the jumping spider actively hunts and captures it. And while other spider species primarily mate on the web of a receptive female, the jumping spider often mates away from the web, and uses its small nestlike web, which is built in dimly lighted places such as under rocks, primarily for shelter. Other aspects of its courtship pattern also differ from those of other spider species.

Jackson examined the behavior of adult and subadult jumping spiders in red light, such as that used in photographic darkrooms, and in normal white light. The first experiment he did

DOUGHERTY

Psychology

Continued

showed that the jumping spider's vision is impaired in red light. Food-deprived males placed in a container with live flies captured the flies in normal white light. In red light, however, the spiders did not hunt the flies and fled from them in cases of accidental contact.

Jackson's second experiment showed that the male's pattern of courtship behavior depended upon whether it was possible for the male and the female to see each other. The male jumping spider normally displays two courtship patterns. If the male and female meet outside her nest, he faces her and dances in a linear or zigzag pattern while waving two of his front legs back and forth. But if a male jumping spider happens upon a nest in a dimly lighted place, he will climb onto the web of the nest and probe it and vibrate part of his body so rapidly that he appears to be blurred. If a receptive female is in the nest, she will come out of it, and they will mate successfully.

Males placed in containers where females had been living used the dancing courtship pattern and were success-

ful in mating in white light. In red light, however, only the second courtship pattern led to successful mating.

Jackson theorizes that these data may be relevant to other species. He suggests that alternative courtship patterns may evolve when the two sexes are likely to meet in distinctly different environments, when the species has developed behavior patterns suited to these different environments, and when ecological factors favor the development of various behavior patterns.

Ladies' choice. Cathleen R. Cox, then at Stanford University, and Burney J. LeBoeuf, of the University of California, Santa Cruz, reported in March that the behavior of female elephant seals affects mate selection.

Their data provide strong support for a neglected aspect of the theory of sexual selection proposed by Charles Darwin in 1871. Darwin hypothesized that both competition among males for access to a female and a female's choice of only one or a few males were determining factors in sexual selection. However, most efforts since then to

Psychology

Continued

identify the variables involved in sexual selection have focused on competition among males. When researchers have studied the female's role in choosing her mate or mates, they have found it difficult to determine why a female will mate with one male and refuse to mate with another, and to find out what precisely the female does to affect the process of mate selection.

Cox and LeBoeuf found some answers to this puzzle when they studied elephant seals that live on Año Nuevo Island, off California, during their breeding season. The seals are organized into female harems controlled by one or more dominant males, usually full-grown adults. Small harems, 40 females or less, usually have a single dominant adult male, while several high-ranking males may live with a larger harem. The male social hierarchy is established by fighting and threatening. Low-ranking males and subadult males remain at the edge of a harem, and seldom mate.

The researchers also noted that females arriving early in the season tend to settle close to a dominant male and to chase off later-arriving females.

Cox and LeBoeuf's observations indicate that a female usually emits continuous vocal threats and attempts to escape as the male tries to mate with her. These behaviors cause nearby males to respond, and if one of them is of a higher rank, he will probably drive away her suitor and try to mate with her himself. The higher the social rank of the male, therefore, the less likely it is that another male will interrupt his attempt to mate, and the more likely it is that he will mate successfully.

The female's threats and other mating behavior appear to increase the probability that she will mate with a high-ranking male, one of the strongest and fittest, which makes it more likely that her offspring will be healthy and will grow up and reproduce.

Cox and LeBoeuf suggest that the transmission of genes that will make the greatest contribution to the next generation is influenced by the behavior patterns of both the female and male elephant seals.   [Sally E. Sperling]

Public Health

Accumulating evidence has further expanded the list of health hazards related to smoking cigarettes. The Collaborative Perinatal Study of the National Institute of Neurological and Communicative Disorders and Stroke issued reports in August 1977 indicating that smoking substantially increases the risk of damage and death to unborn babies.

One study analyzed 18,000 pregnancies and strongly linked cases of premature separation of the placenta from the uterus, miscarriage, abortion, premature birth, and stunted growth to cigarette smoking by the mother. The study found a close relationship between the number of cigarettes the mothers smoked and the percentage of short, underweight, or small-headed infants. Moreover, low birth weight is four times as common if the mother is a smoker, and birth weight correlates directly with overall fetal survival. Not only are these deficiencies present at birth, but they persist in children up to 4 years of age.

Companion studies reported at the same time were carried out in Cleveland under physicians Paul and Betty Kuhnert. They demonstrated that mothers who smoke and their infants have significantly high levels of lead in their blood. Although doctors do not know how serious the biological hazards of higher lead levels are, researchers point out that they have no known beneficial effects.

Johns Hopkins University epidemiologists Mary Meyer and James A. Tonascia reanalyzed data from Canada's long-term Ontario Perinatal Mortality Study and found sharp evidence of increased mortality shortly after birth associated with smoking mothers. There were 701 fetal deaths and 655 deaths shortly after birth among the 51,490 births studied. Their report in August indicated that the risk of death was directly related to the amount of smoking the mother had done. Their data also suggested that the risk of their babies being stillborn was twice as great for smoking mothers.

Recent data on the harmful effects of smoking on women is not limited to fetal death. Epidemiologist Hirshel Jick

A computerized health appraisal printout shows a 50-year-old male how he can improve his life expectancy by changing his life style.

Public Health

Continued

and his associates in the Boston Collaborative Drug Surveillance Program reported in June 1977 that smoking women undergo menopause significantly earlier than nonsmoking women. They suggest that the cause may be either nicotine's depressant effect on central nervous system hormone production or the stimulation of liver enzymes that increase the breakup of steroid hormones.

Leptospirosis. Human infection with leptospirosis, characterized by fever, jaundice, occasional liver damage, and a death rate of 10 per cent, has been relatively rare in temperate climates, although the microbe is common in animals. However, in November 1977, physician E. Donald Andrew and pathologist Guy R. Marrocco of Cooley Dickinson Hospital in Northampton, Mass., described three human cases in western Massachusetts.

Leptospirosis interrogans is frequently found in foxes, field mice, and opossums. It can also infect livestock, and it is livestock that have been implicated in the current outbreak. Three dairy farmers – a father, his brother, and his son, who work together – developed sudden chills, fever, headache, nausea, vomiting, and diarrhea. The illness lasted two or three days in the father and son, while the 52-year-old brother's illness was longer and included other symptoms, such as lethargy, confusion, and evidence of kidney failure. His condition improved quickly and he was free of symptoms within a week after treatment with the antimicrobial drug ampicillin.

Leptospirosis infection of domestic livestock, including cows, has occurred with increasing frequency in the United States. The bacteria appear in cow urine and apparently survive in the soil or in farm ponds and may infect humans through mucous membranes or skin cuts or in contaminated food. Because annual cattle vaccination against leptospirosis is no longer required, animal transmission is likely to increase. Common milking techniques also tend to increase human contact with the cows, and farm ponds are increasingly used for recreational purposes. Thus conditions are ripe for more frequent outbreaks of human leptospirosis. Vigilance in detecting the disease in farm communities and prompt treatment are important, but animal vaccination and the frequent testing of herds is the only way to protect human beings against the disease.

Pesticides in milk. An excessive amount of dieldrin in commercial milk was reported by Suffolk County (N.Y.) Commissioner of Health Mary McLaughlin and her associates at the county health department in March 1978. Chlorinated hydrocarbons such as dieldrin have been widely used pesticides since 1945. Because they are chemically stable, insoluble in water, and last a long time, these insecticides, which can cause neurological damage in humans, are particularly hazardous when used in agriculture. Despite strict control of their use by the Food and Drug Administration (FDA), the risk of human exposure to these insecticides, particularly through dairy products, continues to pose a serious public health threat to consumers.

During regular testing of milk samples in May and June 1975, the FDA detected 10 times the acceptable levels of dieldrin in the milk of a Suffolk County herd. Intensive investigation failed to reveal any explanation for this, and when dieldrin levels returned to normal, the milk of that herd was again permitted to be sold.

Excessive amounts of this toxic substance in the herd's milk reappeared in the fall of 1975. An investigation revealed that some leftover alfalfa, which had been used before the first incidence of dieldrin in the milk, had been fed to the cows. Alfalfa has often been treated with this pesticide, and this batch was the source of contamination.

The cows were treated with phenobarbital and activated charcoal, which quickly cleared their systems of the dieldrin. The phenobarbital activates liver enzymes that break down the fat-soluble pesticide into a water-soluble form that is excreted in the urine. The charcoal absorbs dieldrin in the stomach and prevents its entry into the bloodstream. [Michael H. Alderman]

Science Policy

Overall support for science and technology increased in 1977 and 1978. Under President James Earl Carter, Jr., federal funds for research and development received a substantial increase in the federal budget. Legislation that some scientists feared would hamper biological research failed to materialize and opinion polls in both the United States and Europe showed that science continues to command a high degree of public support.

Science budget. Basic research received a healthy 11 per cent increase in the budget that Carter sent to Congress in January. Although about 6 per cent must be allowed for inflation, the budget still represents real growth.

President Carter's State of the Union message on Jan. 19, 1978, stressed the importance of science to the nation's economic well-being, national security, and ability to solve domestic problems. "I am determined to maintain our nation's leadership role in science and technology," Carter declared. In his budget for fiscal 1979 (Oct. 1, 1978, to Sept. 30, 1979), Carter requested about

$27 billion for research and development—$3.6 billion for basic research, $6.3 billion for applied research, and $17.2 billion for development.

The National Science Foundation (NSF) would get $940.9 million for basic science, a $70-million increase. A total of $2.8 billion was proposed for the National Institutes of Health (NIH) for medical research. However, this $4.2-million increase barely covers the cost of inflation. The National Aeronautics and Space Administration (NASA) budget would go up 7.5 per cent to $4.37 billion. The Office of Management and Budget (OMB) allocated the largest part of this budget to space science, followed by space applications and aeronautical research.

Recombinant DNA. The issue of how to regulate recombinant-DNA research was still unresolved by mid-1978. Congress was unable to pass a bill because the members could not agree on what to put in it. Furthermore, a number of scientists were exerting pressure on the congressmen. Bills that called for strong legislation in regulat-

Social Genes?

The annual meeting of the American Association for the Advancement of Science in Washington, D.C., proceeded uneventfully until demonstrators interrupted a session on Feb. 15, 1978, to pour water over the head of a Harvard zoologist, Edward O. Wilson. This was the latest incident illustrating the highly emotional controversy that began in 1975, when Wilson published *Sociobiology*, a college-level textbook.

A biology textbook seems an unlikely focus of political dissent, especially since the author's principal scientific interest is the social behavior of ants and other insects. But after studying their social systems, Wilson decided to write a book devoted to social behavior itself. And here the controversy arises.

Wilson and other sociobiologists theorize that certain kinds of social behavior, like physical traits, evolved through the process of natural selection and are governed by genes passed from generation to generation. The social behavior thus evolved is of a type that will best ensure the survival of the genes. The sociobiologists propose that this also includes at least some part of social behavior in humans, ranging from jealousy and fear of strangers to kindness and cooperation.

Any discussion of a possible genetic basis for human behavior is a political minefield. If human behavior is shaped only by learning and experience, it can be improved in accordance with political ideals, making social progress possible. On the other hand, if human behavior is genetically determined, the way people behave in society is fixed and no social progress can be made. For example, a group known as the Social Darwinists proposed in the late 1800s that Charles R. Darwin's theory of evolution applied to society as well. They claimed that, in the struggle for survival, the most fit became rich and powerful. Therefore, the social classes and institutions that had "evolved" were necessarily the best.

But the new science of sociobiology has had some noticable successes in explaining behavior in evolutionary terms, particularly the altruistic behavior found throughout the animal kingdom. For example, worker ants produce no offspring; they exist only to serve the community and help raise the queen's offspring. It is difficult to explain the evolution of such behavior in terms of survival of the fittest.

Sociobiologists explain that what is at stake is not the survival of the individual animal but its type of genes. Every individual shares some of the same genes in common with its kin. Worker ants, which are all sterile females, are actually sisters of the queen and have a great many genes in common. From the genes' point of view, there is survival value in behavior that helps the animal's close relatives survive, because they will pass these genes along to their offspring.

Wilson and other sociobiologists do not claim that everything humans do is genetically programmed. But they believe that some of what is regarded as distinctively human behavior may be explained in evolutionary or genetic terms. For example, why would you risk your life to save a stranger? Sociobiologists theorize that the "calculating" gene in its struggle to survive provides the evolutionary motive. The stranger or one of his friends might one day save the life of you or your child, once again increasing the gene's chances of survival.

Wilson's textbook is a convenient focus for politically committed scientists who see great dangers in linking genetics with human behavior. These scientists fear that the new discipline of sociobiology may prove fertile ground for political and social ideas that claim a basis in genetics, such as theories that some races have inferior intelligence.

Sociobiologists agree that scientific ideas about genetically linked human behavior may be used for political ends. But the answer, they believe, is to stop the perversion of scientific ideas, not the scientific study. They also deny any necessary link between what is and what should be. Because the reproductive urge may have a genetic basis does not mean that everyone should have as many children as possible.

Discussion of the genetic basis of human behavior is fraught with intellectual pitfalls and political dangers. Sociobiology may someday revolutionize the social sciences, but agreement on how much of human behavior is learned and how much inherited seems far in the future.   [Nicholas Wade]

ing DNA research began to lose support to alternative proposals questioning the degree of potential dangers in DNA research.

One interested scientist was molecular geneticist Stanley N. Cohen of Stanford University in California who argued that there should be no legislation. This feeling is shared by other scientists active in recombinant-DNA experimentation. They believe that the current research practices of molecular biologists are adequately safe. Microbiologist Harlyn O. Halvorson of Brandeis University in Waltham, Mass., led a group favoring legislation that would have prevented state and local authorities from writing their own safety rules. On the other side, some scientists believe the risks involved are substantial. Some of them belong to Friends of the Earth, an environmental group that spearheaded a movement to persuade Congress that strict DNA-research regulations are necessary.

Recombinant-DNA research involves inserting genes from other organisms into bacteria. The technique presently is governed by voluntary adherence to the NIH guidelines, drawn up by an NIH committee to deal with the possible hazards of the technique. The guidelines set up elaborate and cautious rules to guard against bacteria being endowed with new and possibly harmful properties.

However, the guidelines applied only to federally supported research, not to projects carried on in industry and elsewhere. Congress tried to frame a law in 1977 that would make the NIH guidelines legally binding on all researchers in the United States, but as of mid-1978 had not been able to reach an agreement on a bill.

Local authorities took up the issue, and some of them favored even stricter safety rules than those set by the NIH. Biological researchers are deeply disturbed at the prospect of both local and federal interference in a traditionally unrestricted enterprise. Thus they are continuing efforts to assure legislators that the risks of the research have been exaggerated, and that excessive government regulation would do more harm than good.

The NIH guidelines have been broken twice. In December 1977, the federal government ordered Charles A. Thomas, Jr., to suspend his genetic research at Harvard Medical School because the school failed to obtain a required memorandum of understanding – a pledge to abide by the NIH guidelines. This was the first time the NIH had halted gene-splicing studies because of a procedural violation. Earlier in the year, at the University of California, San Francisco, researchers broke the NIH rules by using a biological component – bacteria that is proved safe for experiments – before it had been certified by the NIH director.

Although public involvement has been a painful and time-consuming experience for the scientists involved, they seem to have gained political support for their research. Research at Harvard had been stopped pending approval by a local citizen committee, but their objections have been satisfactorily resolved. Princeton scientists developed their own modified guidelines to avoid such a confrontation.

An NSF survey conducted in 1976 and released in 1978 found that scientists in the United States enjoy a public esteem second only to physicians. Of the people surveyed, 71 per cent said that science and technology have changed life for the better; only 7 per cent believed the change has been for the worse. And 60 per cent considered government decision makers most at fault when science and technology cause problems; only 12 per cent blamed scientists or technologists directly. These conclusions are significant because some scientists have blamed public hostility toward science for many current problems.

In Europe, a similarly supportive attitude toward science was found. In nine European countries, 69 per cent of the people surveyed believed science to be "one of the most important factors in the improvement of our daily life."

The Department of Energy. President Jimmy Carter signed a bill on Aug. 4, 1977, establishing the Department of Energy (DOE). DOE has some 20,000 employees and a $10.6-billion budget. It was built around three former agencies – the Federal Energy Administration, the Federal Power Commission, and the Energy Research and Development Administration. The sec-

President Carter tours the gaseous diffusion facility at the Oak Ridge National Laboratory in Tennessee in May to emphasize his strong support for peaceful uses of nuclear power. Accompanying him is deputy plant manager Kenneth W. Sommerfeld.

Science Policy

Continued

retary of DOE is James R. Schlesinger, former White House energy adviser.

A five-member federal energy commission within the DOE is delegated to set rules for the transportation and sale of natural gas and electricity. The DOE also has marketing authority over electric power, controls the rate of energy production on public lands, and has jurisdiction over oil-shale reserves.

DOE's debut was clouded by congressional delay on approving the President's energy bill. DOE's budget request of $11 billion for 1979 reflected a shift away from the high priority accorded to development of breeder and light-water nuclear reactors to conservation measures such as providing funds to weatherize the homes of low-income families and encouraging local governments to make their buildings energy-tight. In other respects, the budget continued to provide for enormous investments in nuclear power, a source of considerable frustration to the advocates of solar energy.

Sun Day observances, organized by Solar Action Incorporated of Washing-

ton, D.C., were held on May 3, 1978, across the United States. Sun Day was conceived by Denis Hayes of the Worldwatch Institute, the chief organizer of Earth Day in 1970, to support solar technology as a practical means of obtaining energy. Congress and President Carter endorsed Sun Day, but environmentalists complain that the Administration has shown no inclination to increase solar-energy research.

The desirability of solar energy is undoubted, but its prospects are hard to assess. Covering roofs with photoelectric cells of the type used to power satellites is possible in 1978, but a 30-fold reduction in price is necessary to make the technology a reality.

Forecasters continue to differ widely about the feasibility of solar energy. A report commissioned by the Ford Foundation in 1977 predicted that solar energy would not contribute significantly to U.S. energy supplies until "rather far into the 21st century." However, an estimate issued in May 1978 by the Council on Environmental Quality argued that solar energy could provide 25

Science Policy

Continued

per cent of the nation's energy needs by the year 2000. See ELECTRICITY FROM THE SUN.

Nuclear energy problems. Nuclear energy prospects dimmed in 1977 and 1978. The U.S. nuclear industry, capable of producing about 30 reactors a year, received orders in 1977 for only two. Cancellations have outnumbered orders since 1975, and the trend of deferring any new orders has become widespread – there were 44 deferrals in 1977. Problems that once seemed trivial have become menacing obstacles. According to the Atomic Industrial Forum Incorporated, the reactors that were supposed to operate reliably 80 to 90 per cent of the time do so only 50 to 60 per cent of the time. Construction costs have climbed steadily. The cost of uranium fuel is five times what it was in mid-1973, and the cost of enriching uranium, necessary before it is used in a reactor, has more than doubled. There is still no long-term solution in sight for the problem of how and where to store nuclear wastes.

A nuclear installation in the United States was picketed by the Clamshell Alliance – an antinuclear group. On April 30, the demonstrators moved onto the construction site of a nuclear power generating plant in Seabrook, N.H., refusing to leave until plans to build the plant were abandoned.

On March 21, construction had been halted, pending a review of the plant's cooling system by the Nuclear Regulatory Commission (NRC). The Alliance hoped to halt work permanently.

One person was killed and about 100 were injured in July 1977 in Creys-Malville, France, when 20,000 antinuclear demonstrators battled police at the site of France's first commercial breeder reactor, which uses plutonium. Opponents argue that plutonium is extremely deadly and no safeguards can ensure public safety. Groups have also organized in France, West Germany, and Sweden to oppose nuclear power.

Oppressed scientists. The National Academy of Sciences (NAS) adopted public protest as a weapon in its effort to aid scientists in other countries who are suffering political persecution. The NAS has usually made such representations privately, in the belief that quiet diplomacy was most effective. But it changed its policy in 1977 by forming a Committee on Human Rights. The committee's first act was to draw attention to the plight of eight scientists being oppressed for their political beliefs – two in Russia, one in Uruguay, and five in Argentina.

Committee members later visited Argentina, where they were received by President Jorge Rafael Videla, and Uruguay, where they were permitted to visit a scientist in jail. The group returned with "a realistic but not necessarily optimistic view of what private groups can accomplish in advocacy for human rights."

NAS can bring more pressure to bear on the Soviet Union than on Latin American countries, where it has few scientific ties. When scientist Yuri F. Orlov was sentenced to seven years in prison in May on charges of defamation of the state, NAS President Philip Handler issued an unprecedented public warning: "We have repeatedly informed Soviet authorities that the issue of human rights threatens to erode the willingness of American scientists to cooperate with their Soviet counterparts." If other dissident scientists are imprisoned, Handler said, "Soviet-American relations will have been profoundly damaged."

Orlov, who is a high-energy physicist, headed an unofficial group that monitored Russia's compliance with the human rights portion of the Helsinki agreements of 1975.

Scientist-administrators. Arthur C. Upton became head of the National Cancer Institute (NCI) in July 1977. Upton is a radiation biologist who submitted a report critical of the NCI's mass-screening program for breast cancer the previous March. Upton said on May 21, 1978, that the NCI is returning to the view that cancer research should be based on wide-ranging investigation. The NCI previously advocated planned and blueprinted research.

At the U.S. Geological Survey, Director Vincent E. McKelvey stepped down in what some scientists feared was a political firing. This was the first time the head of the survey had changed with a new administration. Geologist Henry W. Menard of Scripps Institution of Oceanography succeeded McKelvey. [Madelyn Krzak]

Space exploration acquired a greater international dimension in 1977 and 1978. In the United States, the National Aeronautics and Space Administration (NASA) completed space-shuttle approach and landing tests and began training 35 new astronauts for shuttle missions. Russian cosmonauts set a new record for the longest manned mission in space. Japan announced in March 1978 it would explore the Moon, Mars, and Venus; and China in January launched and recovered its third reentry vehicle. French and German contractors continued ground-testing of the Ariane heavy launch rocket they are building for the European Space Agency (ESA).

Shuttle progress. A new era of U.S. manned space flight was heralded with a series of test flights in which the space shuttle orbiter *Enterprise* was mounted atop a Boeing 747. The *Enterprise* flew five successful glide tests between August and October 1977. It separated from the jumbo jet at altitudes ranging from 6,705 to 7,925 meters (22,000 to 26,000 feet) and glided to landings in California's Mojave Desert. Astronauts Fred W. Haise, Jr., and Charles G. Fullerton alternated as commander and pilot of the shuttle with astronauts Joe H. Engle and Richard H. Truly.

The *Enterprise* was then ferried atop the 747 in March 1978 to the Marshall Space Flight Center in Huntsville, Ala., for vibration testing. The shuttle's solid rocket boosters and the main propellant tank were also sent to Huntsville for tests. See SPACE GOES COMMERCIAL.

The shuttle's first orbital flight test, originally scheduled for March 1979, was rescheduled for June 1979 because of problems in the main rocket engine. John W. Young, a veteran of Gemini and Apollo space missions, was named as commander and Robert L. Crippen, a rookie astronaut, as pilot of the first shuttle mission.

Meanwhile, 35 new astronaut candidates, including six women, three blacks, and a Japanese-American, were chosen to begin training at the Lyndon B. Johnson Space Center near Houston in July for space-shuttle missions. There are four crew categories for rou-

Aboard the *Salyut 6* space station, Georgi Grechko, left, one of the cosmonauts who set the 96-day manned space-mission record, joins in a medical experiment with visitors Alexei Gubarev, right, and Vladimir Remek, center. A Czechoslovak, Remek is the first traveler in space who is neither a Russian nor an American.

Space Exploration

Continued

tine U.S. shuttle missions – commander, pilot, mission specialist, and payload specialist. The specialists will supervise the mission's scientific tasks.

In addition, two American and three European candidates for payload specialist on the first *Spacelab* mission in 1980 began the final selection process at the NASA and ESA center.

Russian record. The U.S. man-in-space record of 84 days set in February 1974 aboard *Skylab 4* was broken on March 16, 1978, when two Soviet cosmonauts, Lieutenant Colonel Yuri V. Romanenko and engineer Georgi M. Grechko, returned from a 96-day mission aboard the *Salyut 6* space station. Preliminary medical reports indicated that the cosmonauts had suffered loss of muscle tissue, but were otherwise in good condition.

Salyut 6, the first space station with facilities for docking two spacecraft, was launched on Sept. 29, 1977. Russia's first attempt to reach it, the *Soyuz 25* mission, failed on October 10 because of a malfunction in the *Soyuz* docking mechanism. Romanenko and Grechko docked their *Soyuz 26* craft with the station on December 11 and performed a series of scientific tasks, ranging from photographing the earth to studying the effects of long-term weightlessness on their bodies.

While in orbit, they were visited by *Soyuz 27* cosmonauts Vladimir A. Dzanibekov and Oleg G. Makarov in January 1978, and by Alexei A. Gubarev and Vladimir Remek, a Czechoslovak, in March in *Soyuz 28*. Remek was the first spacefarer from a country other than Russia or the United States. In addition, the Russians in January launched an automated Soyuz-type craft that docked with the station, bringing up cargo that included fuel, fresh fruit, and letters from home. The space freighter also brought up a small furnace, which the cosmonauts used in experiments on making new metal alloys.

The *Skylab* is falling. Tracking networks in mid-1977 began warning that *Skylab*, the big U.S. space station launched in 1973, is losing altitude faster than expected. Although 80 per cent of the *Skylab* orbit is over ocean, it also passes over major cities – including Washington, D.C., Chicago, and Los Angeles – and uncontrolled re-entry poses a serious threat.

In an attempt to avert a calamity, NASA planned a rendezvous between *Skylab* and space shuttle on its second orbital flight, tentatively set for October 1979. The crew, Haise and Jack R. Lousma, began training for this mission early in 1978. They planned to fly close to *Skylab* and send a remotely controlled rocket, carried up in the orbiter's cargo bay, to dock with the space station. The rocket would either boost *Skylab* to a higher orbit so that it would remain aloft for a few more years or send it to a controlled splashdown in either the Pacific or Indian oceans. The decision on whether to send *Skylab* up or down depended on its altitude at the time of the shuttle mission.

But, on June 11, NASA controllers completed a series of maneuvers that changed the position of *Skylab* so that it will fly small end forward, parallel to the earth. This position reduces atmospheric friction, and NASA engineers believe the craft will remain in orbit until late 1979.

Skylab's loss of altitude is caused by increased sunspot activity that heated the upper atmosphere and caused it to rise to a higher altitude. This resulted in increased atmospheric friction that slowed the orbital speed of *Skylab*, and the craft began to drop.

***Cosmos* crash.** Pointing up the disaster potential from falling space debris, a Russian ocean-surveillance satellite, *Cosmos 954*, crashed in western Canada on Jan. 24, 1978. Fortunately, this area is sparsely populated. Radioactive debris from the satellite's uranium fission-power reactor was strewn over a wilderness area near Great Slave Lake. See ENVIRONMENT.

Voyager probes. NASA, in 1977 launched two 825-kilogram (1,820-pound) probes toward Jupiter and Saturn – *Voyager 2* on August 20 and *Voyager 1* on September 5. Controllers confronted a series of problems on both craft. *Voyager 2*'s experiments boom, carrying cameras and other data-gathering equipment, jammed when they tried to extend it; and *Voyager 1*'s scan platform, on which the television cameras are mounted, became stuck and could not be extended. After NASA technicians corrected these

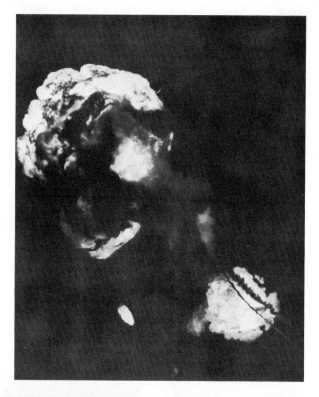

problems, *Voyager 2*'s radio receiver failed. The controllers temporarily lost contact with the probe. However, they were able to activate a backup receiver aboard the craft.

Voyager 1 is due to make its closest approach to Jupiter in March 1979; to Saturn, in November 1980. The *Voyager 2* craft will make its closest approach to Jupiter in July 1979 and to Saturn in August 1981.

Launch failures. The remainder of the year's launch schedule at Cape Canaveral, Fla., was marred by three failures. Critics said this reflected a decline in quality control. A NASA Delta rocket carrying an ESA communications satellite blew up 57 seconds after launch on September 13.

Sixteen days later, a NASA Atlas-Centaur exploded 55 seconds after lift-off. It carried a commercial communications satellite for the International Telecommunications Satellite Consortium (INTELSAT). The second stage of an Air Force Titan 3-C, bearing a pair of military communications satellites, failed on March 25, 1978, and a safety officer destroyed the vehicle. These launch failures totaled losses of $171.4 million, according to NASA and Air Force reports.

Investigators blamed the Delta failure on a defect in the propellant of one of nine solid-fuel motors strapped on the rocket. They blamed the Atlas explosion on corrosion of a vital piece of plumbing in the fuel pump. The cause of the Titan 3-C rocket failure was not fully determined.

International participation in space science and technology dominated the NASA launch schedule. In 1977, NASA launched 11 international satellites but only five U.S. satellites. The international list included communications and meteorological satellites for the North Atlantic Treaty Organization, INTELSAT, ESA, Indonesia, Italy, and Japan.

A new U.S. Pioneer probe was launched toward Venus on May 20, 1978. Another Pioneer probe was scheduled for launch in August.

Soviet news sources hinted in February 1978 that the Soviet space agency had developed a reusable space shuttle similar in its delta-wing shape to the U.S. space shuttle. [Richard S. Lewis]

Atlas-Centaur rocket carrying a communications satellite, *left,* blows up seconds after liftoff from Cape Canaveral, Fla., *top.* The debris, *above,* was collected for investigation.

Technology

Small but innovative and practical advances in technology during 1977 and 1978 helped improve health and comfort and reduce energy bills.

Pacemaker monitor. Biophysicist Albert A. Auerbach, electrophysiologist George Katz, and electronics engineer Sidney Steinberg of Medalert Corporation, a New York City medical-engineering firm, were granted a patent in October 1977 on a highly sophisticated pacemaker. Pacemakers are battery-powered devices that are implanted in a heart patient's chest to stimulate and regulate heartbeat with a tiny electrical charge.

The new pacemaker detects the heart's response to the electrical charge and increases the current if necessary. Furthermore, it can diagnose its own malfunctioning and cause a harmless irregularity in the patient's electrocardiogram to alert the doctor to the malfunction. The device can also be monitored from the doctor's office by telemetry while the patient is elsewhere.

Lithium batteries. In June 1977, the National Semiconductor Corporation of Santa Clara, Calif., introduced a long-lasting lithium battery designed to replace the standard $1\frac{1}{2}$-volt silver-oxide cells in light-emitting diode (LED) watches. The lithium batteries are flatter, so watches in which they are used can be very thin. The battery forms the back of some National Semiconductor watches. The company claims the lithium battery should last about two years.

Digital synthesizer. Scientists at Bell Telephone Laboratories in Murray Hill, N.J., in October unveiled a computerized digital sound synthesizer. The synthesizer can help composers create and write music and is a major step toward artificial-voice machines that convert speech to binary digits, or bits—a series of 0s and 1s. It will also serve as a laboratory tool for analyzing sound and digital sound transmission.

The device can orchestrate and perform musical scores as fast as they are composed, simulate and play up to 30 musical instruments at a time, create musical sounds never heard before, and instantly change the pitch of either a human voice or a musical instrument.

In demonstrating the synthesizer, a Bell Labs scientist spoke into a micro-

A new electronic plant probe monitors soil, emitting sounds that tell when the plant needs water or fertilizer.

phone, and the device instantly shifted the pitch to make him sound first like Donald Duck, then Popeye.

The synthesizer's pressure-sensitive keys are linked to a computer that divides each sound into its various frequencies and processes them in digital form in up to 200 million operations per second. The computer recognizes how hard the key is struck, and how long it is held, then controls timbre, tempo, or any other musical command.

As composers play, they can see the music "written" on a television screen, relieving them of the tedious work of hand notations. Bell Labs is using the machine in an experiment with digitized synthetic speech for recorded telephone announcements.

Artificial speech. In November 1977, the American Hospital Supply Corporation of Chicago began marketing two versions of a nondigital artificial-voice machine called Handi-Voice to aid persons who have lost the ability to speak through injury or disease. Both versions resemble calculators, weigh 1.8 kilograms (4 pounds), and cost $2,000.

Each device has a computer memory that can store up to 40 words, phrases, and sounds that can be combined to form more words. Numerical codes are used to program one model to utter complete sentences. The other has 128 keys labeled with words and pictures. See ELECTRONICS.

Energy savers. While energy technology took giant strides in such industrial fields as coal gasification, smaller and less glamorous devices evolved to help the homeowner cut down on utility bills. Thermographic heat scanners became smaller, lighter, and much less expensive. These cameralike scanners detect heat loss through windows, roof, or walls in the form of infrared radiation. A new system called ThermAtrace was announced in August by Barnes Engineering Company of Stamford, Conn. It is a portable, 4-kilogram (9-pound) device that is used like a camera to take infrared pictures. Unlike earlier systems, ThermAtrace provides a recognizable photograph of the structure, with colored lines superimposed to indicate temperature variations.

The unit has a mirror that allows ordinary light to pass through it but

A camera developed to take pictures at night, *above*, uses special optical glass fibers to intensify light entering the lens. It produces clear pictures taken by artificial light, *top right*, or moonlight, *right*.

Technology

Continued

reflects infrared light. The reflected infrared light focuses onto a detector and is converted into an electronic signal that lights up an LED to produce the graphlike traces over the image.

The light bulb received an energy-saving face-lift in 1978. Researchers at the Massachusetts Institute of Technology developed a chemical film for the inside surface of an incandescent bulb to reflect infrared light into the bulb's center. This will keep the filament hot and reduce the amount of electricity needed to keep it glowing. Meanwhile, the General Electric Company introduced a fluorescent bulb that produces 10 per cent more light than a conventional one. See ENERGY.

Safe sprays. Two new substitutes were introduced to replace ozone-damaging propellants in fluorocarbon aerosol sprays — Aquasol in January 1978 and the Selvac sprayer in June 1977. Aquasol uses carbon dioxide as the propellant. There are three layers in the can — the gas propellant on top, water underneath, and the product to be sprayed. Pushing the button forces

the water and the product into the spray valve through a tube. At the same time, the gas moves into the valve through a separate tube. The product mixed with water and the gas come together in a special chamber, from which the spray emerges.

The Selvac sprayer eliminates the need for propellants. The product is contained inside an elastic bladder made of a butyl-rubber membrane enclosed in a tough elastic that maintains a steady pressure on the product, contracting as it is used up. Pressing a button at the top opens a valve and releases the spray.

3-D images. University of Utah scientists announced in September 1977 that they had developed a device for creating a three-dimensional illusion in transmitted two-dimensional images. A computerized optical system projects several two-dimensional images, one behind the other, on a TV screen to create the three-dimensional effect. The system could be used in such areas as air-traffic control or X rays for internal medicine. [Edward Moran]

Transportation

Transportation concerns continued to be dominated by safety and energy considerations during 1977 and 1978. The United States government sponsored a program to explore the feasibility of electric passenger vehicles, but there was little other interest in new technology. Instead, efforts focused on making existing transit systems and equipment conform to stricter safety and fuel-efficiency standards.

Railroads. The rising accident rate on U.S. railroads commanded attention. The Office of Technology Assessment reported in May that accidents caused by faulty roadbeds had increased 106 per cent between 1966 and 1974. Lack of maintenance and filling freight cars with heavier loads to improve cost efficiency were partly to blame. The number of derailments soared because existing roadbeds could not take heavier loads.

The Department of Transportation (DOT) imposed new deadlines for improving the nation's fleet of more than 40,000 tank cars. DOT said that new coupling systems designed to improve safety must be installed by December 1978, and protective flame-retardant coating must be put on all tank cars capable of carrying hazardous materials by December 1979.

The new coupling systems consist of protective shelves at both the top and bottom of the coupler, rather than only the bottom shelf used on conventional couplers to make disconnection easier.

Tank-car owners have two safety-shielding options. One consists of a 1.3-centimeter ($\frac{1}{2}$-inch) steel envelope around the entire car. Sandwiched between the car and the shield is a 1.3-centimeter layer of asbestos covered with aluminum foil. An alternative protection system is composed of a 1.3-centimeter steel protective shield at the front portion of the car plus a chemical coating around the entire unit. One coating consists of encapsulated water bound to the car by thick paint. The other is an ablative compound—a material that will expand in intense heat to form a foamlike shield around the car.

The Federal Railroad Administration (FRA) launched a program in 1978 to repair and upgrade portions of the 1,770 kilometers (1,100 miles) of track in the Northeast Corridor Rail System, which runs from the New England region to Washington, D.C. Concrete ties are being used along the sections that are to carry passenger trains at 193 kilometers (120 miles) per hour. Because concrete ties last longer than wooden ties, the track maintains its alignment and gauge, or distance between the rails, longer. Also, rail wears more slowly on concrete ties. These facts combine to keep the track in better condition, thus reducing the chance of derailment. Although concrete ties have been used in Europe and Japan, they have had only limited tests in the United States.

While U.S. railroads struggled to update existing equipment, there were reminders of the brief fling with high-technology rail schemes that began in the late 1960s. Japan announced that an electric rail car was clocked at a record 300 kilometers (187 miles) per hour in a test early in March 1978. The test car, which is suspended above the track by magnetic force, was expected to exceed 483 kilometers (300 miles) per hour in 1979. The United States abandoned a similar program in 1975.

Automobile safety. Highway accidents dropped sharply after the 1973 oil embargo forced adoption of a national speed limit of 89 kilometers, or 55 miles, per hour (mph), but the rate began to climb again in 1977. The National Transportation Safety Board reported that 46,880 persons died in traffic accidents in 1977, an increase of 1,357 or nearly 4 per cent over the previous year. This is partly a result of more vehicle-miles being driven and, to an undetermined extent, a result of motorists ignoring the 55-mph speed limit.

Secretary of Transportation Brock Adams ruled on June 30, 1977, that airbags or some equivalent passive-restraint system must be installed on all standard and luxury size cars beginning with the 1982 model on 1983 intermediates and compacts, and on 1984 subcompacts and minisize cars.

Airbags are devices that inflate in front of passengers and keep them from being thrown against the dashboard in a collision. Stored under the dashboard, the bags are activated in about 40 milliseconds. Cylinders of stored gas are triggered mechanically or electronically to inflate the bags when the vehi-

Transportation
Continued

cle hits anything at a specific impact intensity. Adams cited estimates that airbags would save about 9,000 lives per year. Automobile manufacturers had opposed airbags for more than 10 years, but withdrew their opposition after Congress defeated resolutions aimed at overturning Adams' decision.

Electric cars. The Electric and Hybrid Vehicle Research, Development, and Demonstration Act was passed in mid-1977. It is aimed at reducing petroleum demands by replacing many passenger and light-utility cars with electrically powered vehicles. Two demonstration fleets of electric and hybrid vehicles are to be tested by private, commercial, and government users. A hybrid vehicle is one that uses a conventional gasoline engine for start-up and in situations requiring a strong power source, but switches to electrical power for normal driving. The first fleet of 2,500 vehicles will be produced in 1980 followed by 5,000 in late 1982.

Public transit. Public urban-transit systems continued to purchase conventional buses, but there was renewed interest in the streetcar system. Streetcars and trolley cars, once the backbone of public-transit systems, ran on steel rails and usually drew their power from electric wires strung overhead. Most U.S. cities abandoned them after World War II because of the inflexibility of their routes and because their rails hampered other traffic.

Now called standard light-rail vehicles (SLRV), they have regained their appeal. The new vehicles retain the overhead wire-trolley mechanism, but operate on track systems that are less expensive to install and require less right of way than the heavy-rail systems under construction or now operating in such cities as San Francisco, Washington, D.C., and Atlanta. Recent studies show that streetcars use less energy than buses and are more adaptable to changes in traffic patterns than are heavy-rail systems.

Even Detroit, the home of the automobile, resurrected a limited downtown streetcar system in 1977, and Boston launched a major program to modernize its system. [James R. Wargo]

Zoology

A South American zoologist in December 1977 reported an unusual case of chemical mimicry. William Eberhard of the Universidad del Valle in Cali, Colombia, found that the bolas spider uses more than sharp aim to capture prey. The spider gets its name from the similarity of its technique to the way South American cowboys swing and throw a bolas — two steel balls tied to the ends of a length of rope — to entangle the legs of a moving animal. The spider swings a sticky ball of its silk at the end of a silk strand at passing insects. When the ball hits and captures an insect, the spider descends a silk line, paralyzes its prey, and feeds.

Eberhard conducted his research in sugar-cane fields on the Universidad del Valle campus. He used the light from automobile headlamps to observe his subjects, female spiders living in a barbed-wire fence, at night. Eberhard reported that moths seem to be attracted to a waiting spider, in some cases even making repeated passes very close to their enemy. Experiments revealed that the spider secretes an odorous attractant when it is hunting. The attractant is carried downwind by air currents. Moths, especially a group called noctuids that live in sugarcane fields, fly upwind when they smell the odor, lured toward the spider. But why would a moth be attracted to its doom by the odor of a spider?

Eberhard found a clue to the answer. He reported that nearly all moths caught by the bolas spiders are males. Male moths locate potential mates by heading toward a female-produced odor called a sex pheromone, and the substance that the bolas spider secretes is similar to the pheromone.

Eberhard also found that the spider positions itself with its legs facing downwind so that when a male moth detects the sex pheromone and flies upwind toward its source, the spider is in position to swing the bolas at its prey.

This hunting strategy is a form of mimicry, a means by which one animal species benefits by imitating an attribute of another.

Deer-wolf détente. L. David Mech, a wildlife biologist at the North Central

Zoology

Continued

Forest Experimental Station near Harris Lake in Minnesota, reported in October 1977 on a newly discovered aspect of wolf behavior. Mech learned how the characteristics of wolf-pack territoriality might explain the delicate balance that is maintained among coexisting populations of deers and wolves.

Wolf packs in northeastern Minnesota live in adjoining territories, each covering about 130 square kilometers (52 square miles). Buffer zones about 2 kilometers (1¼ miles) wide run between these territories, and wolf-pack members seldom enter these zones. Deer are not aware of wolf-pack territory boundaries and live throughout an area that may cross several territories.

Mech studied one pack of wolves for seven winters, and found that the pack members killed fewer deer in the buffer zone than within the territory. Only when they became desperate for food did the wolves of this pack, as well as others he observed, kill substantial numbers of deer in the buffer zones.

Mech theorizes that buffer zones between predator territories help to maintain the predator-prey system. Because wolf packs avoid the zones, deer in those areas survive and form a reservoir for maintaining and replenishing deer populations that are depleted within the wolf territories.

Lacewing masquerade. Biologists Thomas Eisner, Karen Hicks, Maria Eisner, and Douglas Robson of Cornell University in Ithaca, N.Y., recently uncovered an instance of unusual insect strategy. They reported in February 1978 that the larva of the green lacewing uses a most extraordinary disguise to remain unnoticed among the woolly alder aphids upon which it feeds.

The aphids feed on plant juices and excrete excess carbohydrate in a fluid called honeydew. Ants protect "flocks" of aphids in order to maintain a source of carbohydrate for their colony, fighting any aphid predators ferociously.

The ants can easily maintain their watch because the aphids are covered with a white, fluffy wax, secreted as dense tufts of filaments, that makes them conspicuous against the dark branches of alder bushes. Lacewing

A bolas spider, *right*, releases a drop of attractant that lures moths. When a moth draws near, the spider swings its sticky silk ball, *far right*, to catch the doomed moth.

"You know what I hate? Picking up those little mice with my feet."

Zoology

Continued

The long-whiskered owl, new to scientists, was spotted high in a forest in the Peruvian Andes. Christened *Xenoglaux loweryi*, the bird has fringes of feathers on the sides of its head that are unique.

larvae, which are gray and bristled and have rather large sickle-shaped mandibles, or biting organs, would normally be quickly observed by ants and culled from a flock of aphids.

However, the Cornell team discovered that some of what appeared to be alder aphids on a bush were really green lacewing larvae covered with patches of waxy fluff. Further investigation in the laboratory showed that the larvae did not produce the wax themselves. Instead, they pull wax tufts from the aphids and place it on their backs. Using quick movements of its mandibles, a larva can build its fluffy shield in less than 20 minutes.

When larvae with waxy tufts and larvae with no tufts were put into aphid herds, the ant guards bit and removed undisguised insects. On the other hand, disguised insects were inspected and then ignored. The lacewings not only look like alder aphids, but they perfect their act by pressing themselves closely in among the aphids, moving very seldom so that guard ants do not notice them. The researchers compared the

strategy of lacewing larvae to "wolves in sheep's clothing," their disguise permitting the lacewing larvae to fool the guardians of their prey.

Singing sparrows. Donald Kroodsma of the Behavioral Sciences Department of Rockefeller University in New York City reported in May on experiments with song sparrows that confirmed earlier findings.

Zoologists study birdsong and other signals in an effort to discover whether they are learned or genetically controlled. Most people accept the fact that body shapes and sizes are genetically controlled, but how genetic information can determine the notes of a song is more difficult for scientists and others to understand.

In 1966, biologist James Mulligan of St. Louis University reported that male song sparrows hatched and raised by captive canary parents developed the species-specific song of the song sparrow. Mulligan qualified his work, however, stating that the songs of birds raised separate from others of their own kind are "approximately" normal, but

Rhesus Ban Threatens Research

Hundreds of biomedical and psychological research projects in the United States that use rhesus monkeys as stand-ins for human beings may have to be stopped or severely curtailed because the government of India banned further export of all primates, effective on April 1, 1978. Most of the rhesus monkeys used in U.S. laboratories have been imported from India, including about 12,000 of the 14,000 used in experiments in 1977.

The rhesus monkey has become the standard laboratory primate because of its convenient size – 5 to 10 kilograms (11 to 22 pounds) – and its ability to adapt relatively well to laboratory housing. In the early 1950s, many rhesus monkeys were used to develop and produce the Salk polio vaccine, which was declared safe and effective in 1955. They are still used in testing the safety of each batch of polio vaccine.

The Rh factor in blood, discovered in 1940 through research using rhesus monkeys, was named "Rh" for the monkey. Rhesus monkeys are also used widely in studies of how the nervous system functions. They are among man's closest relatives in the animal kingdom, and their brains more nearly resemble the human brain than do those of most other animals. Rhesus monkeys are also used to study atherosclerosis, or hardening of the arteries. These animals develop atherosclerosis very much as do humans when they are fed diets high in fat and cholesterol.

Another major use of rhesus monkeys is in reproduction studies. Old World monkeys and apes have a menstrual cycle similar to that of humans. Rhesus monkeys are also used to study behavior, infectious diseases, and the effects of toxic substances.

The simple fact that they have been used so much in laboratory work makes rhesus monkeys valuable in research. Scientists can use data compiled earlier by other scientists as a starting point in their quest for new knowledge.

Several countries bordering on India, such as Bangladesh, Nepal, and Pakistan, have rhesus monkeys. However, they probably do not have enough to replace the Indian supply. Some research can use the closely related cynomolgus monkey found in Indonesia, Malaysia, and the Philippines.

India began reducing the number of rhesus monkeys exported in 1974 due to the depletion of the monkey population. At that time, the U.S. Department of Health, Education, and Welfare started several projects to breed rhesus monkeys. It hopes that by 1980 there will be 6,000 rhesus monkeys born annually as a result of these projects.

Major breeding colonies are on two islands, one in the Florida Keys and the other off Puerto Rico, where troops of monkeys are allowed to roam free. The animals are provided with food and water and are watched carefully so that special needs and medical care can be given if needed. Other breeding programs are conducted in large pens, or corrals, that hold groups of about 50 monkeys, and in smaller pens that hold groups of about 10 animals.

Rhesus monkey females give birth to only one offspring per year. Twins are rare. In the breeding colonies, the young animals are left with their parents until they are 2 or 3 years old.

Until 1973, Indian hunters trapped wild rhesus monkeys in forests, on farms, and in villages where this highly adaptable animal lives, and shipped some 30,000 to the United States each year. The quota was cut to 20,000 in 1974 and to 12,000 in 1975.

A number of factors probably played a part in India's decision to stop exporting the animals. The government gave no official reason. Because many Hindus, including Prime Minister Morarji Desai, oppose the killing of animals, exporting monkeys for scientific research has always posed religious and political problems in India. But a more compelling reason for the ban may have been the wide publicity in India given to the use of some rhesus monkeys to test the destructive capability of U.S. weapons, particularly the effects of neutron irradiation. Such testing was interpreted as a violation of a 22-year-old agreement that monkeys would not be used in atomic-blast experiments.

U.S. military officials say that they had no knowledge of such an agreement, and members of the Interagency Primate Steering Committee, the group that arranged for the supply of rhesus monkeys, say they did not know the monkeys were used in military experiments.   [Charles McPherson]

Zoology

Continued

An aphid-guarding ant, *top*, attacks a green lacewing larva trying to feed on the aphids. Another larva dons a disguise, attaching the aphid's white, waxy "wool" coat to its own bare back, *above*. Larvae using this ruse often go undetected by the ants.

may lack the richness and complexity found in the songs of males raised by parents of their own species.

Unfortunately, the primary theme of this study—that song sparrows produce basically normal songs without ever hearing the songs of their own species—has persisted, but the fact that Mulligan qualified his theory was forgotten. Kroodsma's recent analysis of his song sparrows' efforts clearly showed deficiencies in their songs, especially in the duration and frequency of certain notes and phrases. But his findings confirmed Mulligan's earlier work.

An interesting new discovery made by Kroodsma is that song sparrows reared by parents of other species incorporate parts of the songs they hear as they mature into their own melodies. Sparrows that are reared in total isolation develop certain aspects of their songs that are actually more true to type than the songs of birds that are reared with canaries.

All of these observations strongly suggest that song development, at least in song sparrows, is in part inherited, or genetically controlled. But learning is necessary to fine-tune the melodies, ensuring that the songs are the same from one generation to the next. Because songs are used for communication between individuals, it is important that they be preserved intact.

Battling bluegills. Psychologists David Chiszar and David Henderson of the University of Colorado in Boulder reported in 1977 on territorial aggression among bluegill sunfish. The fish, a common U.S. pond dweller, aggressively drives intruders away from its territory, especially during the spring breeding season.

The researchers found that after a bluegill had spent one week alone in a 95-liter (25-gallon) aquarium, it would attack any fish put into the tank. Chiszar and Henderson used this experimental arrangement, called the prior-residence effect, to investigate how aggression is related to sex and size of both inhabitant and intruder.

In their first series of experiments, Chiszar and Henderson kept a male or a female bluegill in a tank for one week during the nonreproductive season, then put another bluegill of either sex into the tank. They reported that the

fish reacted aggressively when they met. The tests showed that males and females are equally aggressive.

Since both sexes are equally aggressive and females have shown they can dig and protect their own nests, the researchers wondered why males build the spawning territories. Henderson and Chiszar suggested that males build the nests because they come into the reproductive condition and move to shallow water to spawn before females do. The investigators also studied the effect of size on aggressiveness. They reported that larger residents are more aggressive and that an intruder's size does not affect a resident's behavior. In fact, small residents dominated large intruders, indicating that greater size or age does not automatically confer an advantage. However, many large residents killed intruders, while smaller residents learned to live with them.

These results may help to explain the interactions between bluegills in heavily populated ponds. Like many other fish, bluegills living in crowded waters become stunted, a response that probably lowers their nutritional requirements. But stunting may also allow bluegills to coexist in overpopulated ponds. Extremely aggressive bluegills would be less likely to develop, and small residents would be more tolerant of other fish.

Strange new owl. John O'Neill and Gary Graves of the Louisiana State University Museum of Natural Science in Baton Rouge reported that they had discovered a bird previously unknown to scientists. They sighted the bird, which they named the long-whiskered owl, in a forest high on the eastern slopes of the Andes Mountains in northern Peru.

The bird is a member of the typical owl family *Strigidae*, but it was given its own genus and species because it has several unique features. Long, delicate facial feathers fringe its head, and long bristles start at the base of its bill and grow up between its eyes to form a fanlike crest.

The tiny owl has been given the scientific name *Xenoglaux loweryi*. *Xenoglaux* means amber-eyed stranger and *loweryi* is in memory of George H. Lowery, Jr., former director of the LSU museum.   [William J. Bell]

A poisonous moray eel, *above*, rests with its head exposed. The body markings of a plesiopod fish, *right*, mimic the moray eel so effectively that its predators tend to leave it undisturbed.

People
In Science

The rewards of scientific endeavor range from winning a Nobel
prize to successfully competing in a national science talent
search. This section, which recognizes outstanding scientists, also
recognizes the students who may someday follow in their footsteps.

Edward
E. David, Jr.

By Daniel S. Greenberg

Working in areas ranging from communications to energy, this versatile engineer has found time to help students learn about the challenging opportunities in technology

With an array of many of the nation's scientific leaders standing behind him and an attentive crowd of onlookers to the front and sides, President Richard M. Nixon stood at a microphone in the sunswept White House Rose Garden. Next to him was Edward E. David, Jr., a 45-year-old research executive from Bell Telephone Laboratories.

A gesture from the President quieted the crowd, and David placed his hand on a Bible to take the traditional federal oath of office. He thus became the sixth man in history to serve in the post of presidential science adviser. It was Sept. 18, 1970–a happy day, long before the storms of Watergate. The appointee, looking youthful and trim, perhaps due to his obsessive, year-around devotion to tennis, appeared relaxed and confident. Although he was unknown to most Americans, David had built an international reputation in the world of science, particularly in electronic-communication science and engineering, and he had been elected to both the National Academy of Sciences and the National Academy of Engineering. Following the ceremony, David, flanked by his wife, Ann, and his teen-age daughter, Nancy, chatted congenially with the press, and accepted congratulations from friends and colleagues.

He could not realize then that he was being thrust into the most difficult situation of his career. Two years later, he would leave the Administration in sadness and frustration. He had brought to the job a lifelong conviction that would prove incompatible with politics and politicians. He firmly believes that problems are best approached directly and solved by openly arriving at the best available decision. As he now puts it, "I was attracted to science and technology because there are no hidden motivations. It's all on the merits."

David, who was born in 1925, became interested in science early in life. The only child of a stockbroker in Atlanta, Ga., David recalls that he was "turned on" to science when he was 7 years old through membership in the Georgia Mineral Society. Through that society he became acquainted with professors from Emory University and Georgia Institute of Technology (Georgia Tech) who aroused his interest in natural science.

At the monthly meetings of the society, David heard lectures by mineralogists. At the age of 8, he read a paper to the society, the youngest member ever to do so. To this day, his interest in mineral collecting holds firm. He maintains in his home several striking displays of rock forms he has found throughout the world since taking up the hobby. No one in David's close family—one uncle, three aunts, and two cousins—was involved in science. Yet they encouraged his interests, in line with their belief in education and scholarship.

David was very deeply distressed as a youth by reports of Nazi persecution of Jews before World War II. The incredible stories he heard as a teen-ager of how German Jews first lost their citizenship rights because of Hitler's anti-Semitic hatred, then were herded into concentration camps, and finally systematically exterminated burned in his consciousness. "I got started seriously with science," he recalls, "because I felt that the persecution of the Jews reflected all sorts of aberrations in society. Science has a rationality to it."

After attending Emory in Atlanta and the University of Georgia in Athens, David graduated with a bachelor of science degree in electrical engineering from Georgia Tech in 1945. Then, after serving as an ensign in the United States Navy, he was accepted for graduate study at the Massachusetts Institute of Technology (M.I.T.) in Cambridge.

At M.I.T., David earned his doctorate degree in 1950, along with a reputation as a persistent and skillful worker. His college roommate, John G. Truxal, now director of the National Coordinating Center for Curriculum Development at the State University of New York, Stony Brook, says of David: "He drives himself as hard as anyone I've ever known. When he decides on a goal, he gets there."

The author:
Daniel S. Greenberg is the editor and publisher of *Science & Government Report.*

That determination was not limited to scientific pursuits. While he was still a student at M.I.T., David decided he wanted to marry a childhood acquaintance, Ann Hirshberg, who was then studying English literature at nearby Wellesley College. They had known each other for many years in Atlanta, but had never dated. At that time, she had little interest in science and was an avid horse enthusiast. They were married in 1950. David says that her support and advice are at the root of his success.

Another goal David set for himself was to work for Bell Telephone Laboratories, the research arm of the Bell Telephone System. Bell Labs is one of the largest scientific enterprises in the world. Its research projects range from electronics to the study of molecular structures and concepts in higher mathematics. Its staff reputedly enjoys a freedom of inquiry that is unusual in industrial research.

"Unfortunately," David recalls, "the Lab was hiring very few people that year, and I wasn't among those that they had chosen for interviews. I mentioned this to my thesis adviser, and he said he'd see what he could do. That's how I got an interview and was hired."

When David joined Bell Labs in Murray Hill, N.J., in the fall of 1950, it was generally assumed that a first-rate engineer could successfully deal with almost any engineering problem. So David's specialty in microwave electronics was ignored, and he found himself assigned to Project Jezebel, a secret U.S. Navy project on underwater sound. The project's goal was to design systems that could distinguish the sounds made by hostile submarines from natural background noises. That effort was remarkably successful, and even today the system that David's research team developed is an essential element in the Navy's antisubmarine capability.

In this work, David became associated with John R. Pierce, whom he describes as "my mentor and very close friend." Pierce's contributions to electronic communication have earned him a worldwide reputation as a prolific genius. For example, he is the originator of communication-satellite technology.

"People were scared to death of John Pierce," David recalls. "He's truthful to the point where it's brutal. His judgments are entirely on the merits, and he's got no hidden motivations. Those qualities frightened a lot of people but, remember, I was drawn into science because it's based on merit. John and I got along fine."

Pierce, now a professor at the California Institute of Technology in Pasadena, corroborates that recollection of working with David at Bell Labs. "I first met Ed when the acoustics work was assigned to my lab. What impressed me was that he was quick on the pickup, he was adaptable, and he'd tackle anything."

According to their Bell colleagues, Pierce and David were an ideal pair. "John had a rare kind of scientific genius, really in a class by himself," a co-worker recalls, "but he lacked rapport with other researchers. Ed, on the other hand, had a knack for getting along with

As director of research for Exxon Corporation, Edward E. David, Jr. (fourth from left at the table), holds meetings regularly to assess scientific developments, and must also check closely on laboratory work, *opposite page.*

people, for orchestrating their research, for listening to a brief explanation of what they were doing and then dropping a few suggestions that were right on target for solving a problem–and doing this in a way that made them feel it was their own idea."

David was put in charge of all Bell acoustics research in 1956, including fundamental work on speech and hearing, a field of acoustics that had been in the scientific doldrums for many years. He and his group were soon pioneering in what Pierce describes as "the earliest exploration of the computer as a means for simulating complex sound-processing equipment." The practical consequences of this research ranged from vast cost and time savings in the design and development of many types of electronic sound-producing devices to a low-cost artificial larynx for people with damaged vocal cords.

David and Pierce wrote *Man's World of Sound* in 1958, a book that was well received and is still a useful text on acoustics. "Because neither of us knew very much about this subject," Pierce now says wryly, "we wrote a book." However, there is some foundation for this statement. Both men agree that their research in preparation for the writing provided them with an education in the mysteries of how living organisms produce and perceive sound.

David was clearly established as a fast-rising star in the highly competitive world of electronics research when he was appointed in 1962 to head computer-science work at Bell Labs. In that post, he helped pioneer the time-sharing techniques that have greatly expanded the use of computers. Three years later, he became executive director of

Bell's communication-systems division, heading a staff of 200 workers who were engaged in research on computer science, communication, and electronic switching.

Despite the heavy demands at Bell Labs, David nevertheless found time, starting in 1966, to collaborate on another book, this time with his M.I.T. roommate, Truxal, then teaching at the Brooklyn Polytechnic Institute. The work was an ambitious undertaking—the development of a specially devised curriculum for high school students, aimed at giving them technological literacy.

David was convinced that too few young people were receiving an opportunity to acquaint themselves with the goals and products of engineering. He wanted to develop what Pierce describes as "a course that would teach high school students to understand man's artifacts and use them intelligently, rather than fear them."

"I had plenty to do at Bell," David recalls, "but I felt that engineering education was falling by the wayside. High school students were getting little or no exposure to it, and the best of them were going into the physical sciences instead of engineering. I felt a responsibility to my profession and to what it can do for society." He remembered how membership in the Georgia Mineral Society had helped him in his early years, and he knew that early training would help students to develop interest in the engineering profession.

The David-Truxal book, which was supported by the National Science Foundation (NSF), is *The Man-Made World; A Course on Theories and Techniques that Contribute to our Technological Civilization.* Completed in 1969, it is more than a high school textbook on engineering and technology; it offers a complete program of study, with teachers' guides and work projects. More than 1,000 high schools throughout the United States were using this curriculum in 1978.

Despite all these professional activities, David for years has found time almost every day to indulge his passion for tennis. He also skis, at times competitively, and has won silver and bronze medals at ski meets in Vermont. In addition, he is a serious amateur photographer. Though he seldom rides horses and she seldom plays tennis, Ed and Ann David share many interests. One is world travel, and they have crisscrossed most of the globe together.

At the beginning of 1970, in his 20th year at Bell Labs, David was widely viewed as a good prospect for the top job in that highly esteemed organization. There was little reason to expect that he would tear up his roots and depart for the unknowns of governmental service in Washington, D.C.

It is frequently difficult to determine how presidential appointments come about, since the President and his aides are usually deluged with recommendations when it becomes known that they are seeking a recruit. Nevertheless, William O. Baker, David's boss, who later became president of Bell Labs and was probably one of the few scientists with whom President Nixon felt at ease, might have been the major force behind David's appointment. Baker was a member of the Presi-

With his wife holding the Bible, David takes the oath, in 1970, as Science Adviser to President Richard M. Nixon from Associate Judge Austin Fickling.

dent's Foreign Intelligence Advisory Board, a supersecret body that counseled the White House on U.S. intelligence operations. And in addition to being a distinguished scientist, Baker had for a long time been an active Republican.

Baker strongly advocated U.S. scientific and technological supremacy, and was greatly concerned over deteriorating relations between the Nixon Administration and the scientific community. The great difficulties were eating away at the nation's scientific efforts where it hurt most—in diminishing funds for training young scientists and conducting scientific research. In addition, the White House science office, officially known as the Office of Science and Technology (OST), had lost most of its influence over research policy and nuclear arms-control policy, long a major concern of the scientists who were associated with the OST.

Baker strongly believed the White House needed a science adviser in whom the President would have confidence. "I made a suggestion to Mr. Nixon," Baker recalls, "that he appoint Ed David to the post. Others may have made that suggestion, too," he modestly adds. "I stressed that Ed had an international outlook, which appealed to Mr. Nixon, who was then pursuing détente with the Russians."

Furthermore, David was not a member of the old guard; he had been a government consultant briefly, but he had never been a member of the President's Science Advisory Committee, as had all previous

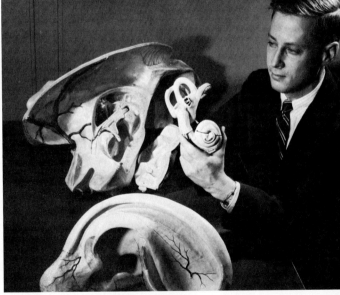

Ed David checks the speech input to an analogue digital converter, *left,* as part of his work in directing research at Bell Labs. The work required an understanding of the human ear, *above.*

One of the Davids' two pet terriers, Punch, romps in the snow, *above*, as the family takes a walk on the New Jersey farm. They are adding a room to the farmhouse, *opposite top*. In stables nearby, Ann keeps Dusty, one of her four horses, *opposite bottom*.

presidential science advisers. His appointment would represent a break with the past, and presumably would heal the rift between Nixon and the scientific community.

David says he accepted the post because "I was fascinated by the challenge. I went down to Washington and spoke to some of the President's senior staff. I told them I wouldn't take the job if the idea was to de-emphasize science and technology. They said that was fine. I said I wanted to make science and technology useful for the country, and they agreed. I didn't see Nixon until after I took the job, but when I did, he told me that he needed help and he agreed that we had to put science and engineering to work for the country. It all looked good and promising. It wouldn't be boring, I knew. I don't like boredom. It is the only thing I've ever thoroughly despised."

Incidentally, David feels no strong preference for either of the two major political parties. Though he is sometimes referred to as a Republican, he says the label was first applied at the time of his appointment in the Nixon Administration.

The 28 months that David spent as Nixon's science adviser were difficult and tumultuous. "I rarely saw the President alone, but I saw him often in groups, such as Cabinet meetings or special meetings on particular topics. What became apparent at once was that he had no

concept at all as to what science was about, no idea of the processes of science and technology, of what they can do and on what time scale. Politicians operate within a time scale related to elections every two and four years. Research doesn't work that way."

An even greater problem, David soon learned, was the political environment. "Washington is a nest of sharks," he explains. This led him to formulate David's Law: "In a closed system, such as the White House, influence is conserved. What one gains, another loses."

Primarily, David's job was to advise the President on how science and technology could be used to benefit the nation. He and his aides also were to evaluate all federal scientific and technological programs and help to develop new programs and policies.

Vexing problems soon confronted him. The Administration had little sympathy for his argument that basic research was suffering from financial malnutrition. Also, White House aides pressured him to do something to quiet the former science adviser to Dwight D. Eisenhower, Harvard chemist George B. Kistiakowsky, and others who were publicly opposed to a major Nixon objective, developing an American supersonic transport plane. In addition, David was besieged with demands by Senator Edward M. Kennedy (D., Mass.) and other members of Congress to greatly expand the government's cancer-research program, regardless of the advice of the best biomedical researchers. To make things worse, David was surrounded by close Nixon aides who were skeptical of the value of the White House science office.

Physicist Lee A. DuBridge, who preceded David as Nixon's adviser and had also served as an Eisenhower adviser, had been gradually excluded from important White House deliberations and then dismissed because his counsel did not please the Nixon Administration.

Yet, David managed some successes. As job shortages began to afflict the scientific community in 1971, he prevailed upon the White House to budget $42 million to help unemployed scientists and engineers find jobs. And, concerned over the lack of work for new science graduates, he initiated a program to provide hundreds of fellowships and research posts in federal laboratories. His office prepared the first presidential message on energy, proposing an extensive energy research program that still seems appropriate in 1978.

Nixon had appointed Ed David because he was a practical man—a career engineer who believed that engineering had a great deal to offer the United States. But, in terms of professional and personal values, David was very much in agreement with his academic predecessors in the White House science post. He wanted to hire the best people, regardless of how they might be viewed by other members of the Nixon Administration. He recalls, for example, that M.I.T.'s Jerome Wiesner offered to resign from his at-large membership on the President's Science Advisory Committee, a post he held by virtue of being a former White House science adviser.

A man with many outside interests, Ed David has been collecting mineral specimens since he was 8 years old. He holds one he found during a recent trip to England. He is also an avid tennis player.

"Wiesner thought his presence would be an embarrassment to me," David said, referring to the fact that Wiesner, his thesis adviser at M.I.T., was prominently associated with Democratic circles in the university community. "But I told him that a resignation would give the wrong signal. I felt that we needed good science and engineering advice, not Republican or Democratic advice."

The Administration was increasingly suspicious of the scientific community. So the difficulties mounted as time went by. In September 1971, almost a year to the day after David had been sworn in, Nixon suddenly announced that he was appointing William M. Magruder of the U.S. Air Force, a nonscientist and close associate of John D. Ehrlichman, as a special presidential assistant who would be responsible for finding ways to use science and technology to stimulate the economy. Magruder had previously been the chief of the defunct supersonic transport project, and many observers interpreted the Administration's appointment of Magruder as a political move designed to appease the dissatisfied supporters of that project.

David's response to the Magruder appointment was to offer Magruder complete staff support and cooperation. "They were organizing a political reaction to scientific and technical problems," he says, "and I figured I would do whatever I could to contribute some rationality to the process."

After lengthy studies, Magruder proposed spending about $2 billion on new initiatives that would have displaced efforts by private industry. Nixon's budget planners rejected virtually every Magruder proposal, and the effort came to nothing.

But Magruder's failure was no consolation to David. He immediately organized a salvage effort, which resulted in the first presidential Message on Science and Technology. It pointed out the importance of innovation in solving national problems in energy, health care, economic growth, and other fields.

Later, David's relations with Henry A. Kissinger resulted in trips to Germany, Japan, Poland, Russia, and other countries to encourage international efforts in science. The comprehensive U.S.-Russian science agreements were arranged on these trips and were signed in Moscow and in Washington, D.C.

Despite these efforts, rumors circulated in late 1972 that Nixon would soon abolish the White House science office. In December 1972, David recalls that he was summoned from a space launch at Cape Kennedy, Fla. (now Cape Canaveral), to talk to Nixon's top aides at Camp David, Maryland. It was clear that the OST was to be abolished, and they offered David the chairmanship of the Atomic Energy

David's responsibilities at Exxon range from discussions with an engineer analyzing metal failure in machinery parts, *right,* to the evaluation of tests at a pilot plant for oil refining, *opposite page.*

Commission (AEC), with the tacit understanding that he would preside over its dismantling. The plan was to reorganize the AEC under the proposed Department of Energy and Natural Resources.

"I had already had one horse shot out from under me, and I wasn't looking for another round of the same," David recalls. "So I thanked them and made plans to quit." He resigned on Jan. 3, 1973, and not long afterward Nixon announced that OST was to be abolished and some of its functions reassigned to the NSF.

David then returned to industry, taking a challenging post as executive vice-president for research, engineering, and planning with Gould, Incorporated, in suburban Chicago. Gould is a diversified manufacturing company that makes many types of industrial and automotive batteries, power switches, metallurgical products, and the Navy's only modern ship-launched torpedo. Gould's directors had decided to develop a broad, systems-oriented approach to its industrial-research management, and wanted David because of his work at Bell Labs. As Bell's President Baker noted, "Ed's experience at Bell was initially in a specific field of research, but eventually he took on broader responsibilities and became one of our leading people in bringing together a wide variety of talents and fields of knowledge to bear on complex problems."

Charged with building up Gould's research capabilities, David presided over the construction of a multimillion-dollar research laboratory in Rolling Meadows, Ill. In four years he doubled the research activities, which contributed to the company's tripling in size.

Over a weekend lunch, Ed David asks a question of Mary Ann Sembrot, his executive assistant, while his wife and Peter Denes, an electronic-speech scientist, listen. Later he catches up on some reports and other work in his home office.

In February 1977, he resigned from Gould and hung out his shingle in downtown Chicago as an industrial consultant, telling friends and acquaintances that he expected he'd be doing that for many years, if not indefinitely. "It's exciting, different, and never boring," he said. But just a few months later, he became the target for some of the professional recruiters for top-level science positions.

"I never thought it would happen," David says, "but they came to me with an offer I couldn't refuse. I don't mean the money, though that's not bad. I mean the job."

In July 1977, he became president of the biggest nongovernment energy-research organization in the United States, the Exxon Research and Engineering Corporation located in Florham Park, N.J. It is a $250-million-a-year affiliate of the Exxon Corporation. Rapidly diversifying into nonpetroleum energy sources and seeking new businesses for the coming post-petroleum era, Exxon wanted a leader from outside the energy field. It fixed its sights on David. Like Gould, Exxon wanted someone who had a comprehensive way of approaching problems, who could coordinate the work of researchers in many different fields.

"At first I thought, 'No,'" said David. "But the more I thought about it, the more I realized that here was an opportunity to do everything I believe in – to apply science and technology in a rational way for the good of the country. To seek safe, economical, sensible solutions to our country's most serious problems is what I've been interested in all my professional life."

The job is a demanding one. But with support for building up the research program, and his performance measured in terms of scientific and technical accomplishment, David finds life more rational than in the crisis-ridden times when he was the President's science adviser.

David and his wife are happy to be back in New Jersey, where they live on a 29-hectare (65-acre) rural estate in Bedminster, about half an hour's drive from his office. In addition to the sprawling, renovated farmhouse, there are stables where Ann keeps her four horses, plus several others that she boards for friends and neighbors. Their daughter, Nancy, is a senior at Princeton University.

Ed David has continued throughout the years to serve the broader science community. For example, in 1978 he accepted the presidency of the world's largest interdisciplinary scientific organization, the American Association for the Advancement of Science. And his interest in engineering education has never abated.

"I think this is one of the most exciting and promising periods for a young person to be going into research," he says. "The powers of science and technology are greater than ever, but so are the problems that our society faces. In energy, environment, resource management, health, space, and a whole variety of fields, we now have an opportunity to solve some of the most difficult problems that mankind has ever faced. And it is through science and technology that we will do it."

Science Talent Search

By William J. Cromie

Forty of the brightest high school science students gather in Washington, D.C., for the final round of an annual nationwide hunt for promising scientists

It would be a grueling and challenging week for the 40 high school students checking into the Mayflower Hotel in Washington, D.C., on March 2, 1978. Finalists in the 37th Science Talent Search, they would face intensive questioning from a panel of eight judges, including a Nobel laureate, two physicians, a mathematician, an engineer, a chemist, a physicist, and a psychiatrist. The contestants would set up exhibits in the Great Hall of the National Academy of Sciences (NAS), and talk to the press and hundreds of visitors. And they would deal with mounting tension as they awaited the judges' choices.

Yet, none of the contestants would have missed this opportunity. The 10 winners would share the bulk–$60,000–of the $67,500 in scholarships provided by Westinghouse Electric Corporation. And all the contestants would have a lively, enjoyable week despite the stress. Many had never before visited Washington. They would meet the President of the United States, congressmen, Nobel prizewinners, and distinguished scientists. They would visit historical monuments, great museums, and famous laboratories. In the evenings, they would go to interesting restaurants, the ballet, and Georgetown discothèques.

For the judges, it would be a tough week, too. They would have to decide among 40 fine young scientists who had been picked from

almost 1,000 contestants nationwide. The judges would interview them, examine their work, then pick the 10 they thought would become the most innovative scientists in the next 10 to 20 years.

Julie W. Pan, 17, of Flushing in Queens, N.Y., was a typical contestant. She is a member of the National Honor Society and the Honor Roll of the Mathematical Association of America and served as president of the math society at Stuyvesant High School. Pan plans a career in molecular biology. Becoming one of the 40 finalists assured her of $250 and a recommendation for admission to the college of her choice. Like the other students, she would be evaluated on the basis of her school record, interviews with the judges, and a research project. Pan's project involved studying a fruit fly chromosome that causes genetic changes in other chromosomes.

Another contestant, Sarah E. (Sally) Dennis, 17, a senior at John Marshall High School in San Antonio, Tex., won a first-place award at the 1976 International Science and Engineering Fair (ISEF), and was one of two students to represent the United States at the 1976 Science Fair of the Americas in São Paulo, Brazil. Her project covered four years of research on substances used to fix dyes to natural fibers.

John D. Rainbolt, 17, a top biology student at William Chrisman High School in Independence, Mo., also competes in football, track, and wrestling and works 20 hours a week at a hospital. He received a summer research grant from the National Science Foundation (NSF) in 1977 to work at the University of Texas in Austin on the sex life of butterflies, the subject of his Science Talent Search project.

While Rainbolt studied butterflies, William H. (Bill) Collins, 17, of Canoga Park High School, in the Los Angeles suburb, built a seismometer and digital computer that placed him in the finals. He used these instruments to determine how ground movements produced by earthquakes and underground nuclear tests affected a building.

The author: William J. Cromie is a free-lance science writer and executive director of the Council for the Advancement of Science Writing.

Pan, Dennis, Rainbolt, and Collins had submitted the results of their research—along with transcripts, test scores, personal information, and letters of recommendation—to Science Talent Search officials by mid-December 1977. They qualified, along with 963 other students. Then 10 evaluators, representing various fields of science, selected the Honors Group, the best 300 applicants. These received certificates and recommendations to schools of their choice. The field was then further narrowed to the 40 who went to Washington.

The national search has been conducted since 1942 by Science Service, a nonprofit organization in Washington, D.C., devoted to increasing the public understanding of science. Westinghouse not only provides the money needed for the scholarship funds, but also finances the administration of the Science Talent Search.

The 1978 judging began immediately after a welcome luncheon on Thursday, March 2, at which students met the judges and introduced

Joseph Dougherty of Virginia, left, and Philip King of New Jersey, try to relax as they await judging sessions, *left.* New Yorker Michio Hirano talks to two judges, *below left.* Philip Handler, left, president of the National Academy of Sciences, and Nobelist Glenn T. Seaborg question Frank Hansen of Illinois, *below.*

themselves to one another. The schedule called for every finalist to spend 15 minutes with each of two panels of three judges, plus 15 minutes with Stuart Hauser, assistant professor of psychiatry at the Harvard School of Medicine in Cambridge, Mass. The eighth judge, Glenn T. Seaborg, who shared the 1951 Nobel prize in chemistry and is president of Science Service, talked informally to the students at mealtimes, as they exhibited their projects, and on other occasions.

"During the interviews, we attempt to find the most innovative and imaginative kids," explained physician David Axelrod, chairman of the judges and director of research at the Infectious Disease Center, New York State Department of Health. "The information we get by talking with them is as important as the research projects they do. We attempt to determine if their thinking is broad and basic, not hung up on a particular technology or narrow perspective. Sometimes we ask questions we think they cannot answer, or those that have no answer, to see how they handle the situation."

Physicist Rosalyn S. Yalow speaks to the young students about the work that brought her a share of the Nobel prize for physiology or medicine in 1977.

"Interacting with the judges and other finalists becomes a mellowing experience for some kids," said Brigid Leventhal, head of the Pediatric Oncology Division at Johns Hopkins Hospital in Baltimore. "They have outperformed their peers in school and may think they are very special persons. But when they meet the other finalists and are questioned by the judges, they realize this may not be so."

"Lines of communication among the contestants become established very quickly," Hauser said. "You see this when you start getting the same answers to the same questions, even when the answers are wrong. I don't try to trick the students. My object is to assess how broad a student is in his or her thinking. My questions are directed at determining how well they can move from idea to idea and not get stuck on one line of thought."

Some of the finalists dreaded their 15 minutes with Hauser, who quickly became known as "the shrink." A few thought this interview was fun but one boy complained that he had been "torn apart psychologically." "Remember to keep eye contact and watch your body movements carefully," coached one girl. "Don't scratch your left ear more than your right," joked another.

Julie Pan felt a "quiet tension" when she talked with the judges. She rated the experience as more difficult than interviews for admission to college. "It's hard to plan for the judging because you don't know what they'll ask," she said. "They asked me if intelligence is hereditary. No one knows the answer to that one. I replied that, on the basis of my research, I believe that some link probably does exist between intelligence and genes."

The Pan family provides support for the idea that intelligence at least can run in a family. Her father teaches mechanical engineering at the New Jersey Institute of Technology, a 20-year-old brother is a physics and chemistry major at Harvard University, and a 23-year-old sister studies electrical engineering at the Massachusetts Institute of

Technology. Pan describes her mother, an auditor, as "a very strong lady who pushes us kids all the time. She and my sister never stop encouraging me to do better." Pan also gets inspiration at school. "There is a fantastic atmosphere at Stuyvesant," she said. "The faculty and students boost you to incredible accomplishments."

Pan had a full day on March 2. After a judging session, she went to Capitol Hill to visit her congressman, Benjamin S. Rosenthal (D., N.Y.). Then she accompanied the 13 other New York winners to see Senator Jacob K. Javits (R., N.Y.). Javits congratulated the students, posed for photographs with them, and then asked if they had any questions. He may have regretted that overture. Why, one student asked, do some students receive high school diplomas when they read at the fourth-grade level? Pan and other students insisted that charges of discrimination against minorities leveled at New York City's top science high schools were unfounded. The finalists also quizzed Javits about racial quotas in medical schools receiving federal funds. He promised to look into the points they raised.

That evening, conversation centered on the judging. "I didn't handle that interview very well," was a familiar lament. "We talked about physics and calculus," one student said, "and I would like to have stayed longer." Another did not like the interview. "I felt as if my life was under a microscope," he complained. Rainbolt was worried, "They asked me the volume of the earth and I blew it." His companion quickly rattled off the formula for calculating the volume of a sphere when you know the diameter. Rainbolt eyed him glumly. To relax, some students browsed in a bookstore, while others looked for a discothèque. Many talked until early in the morning about everything from mathematics to whether God exists in a human form.

They rose early on Friday, March 3, some to keep appointments with judges, others to visit scientists in the Washington area. All the

On a tour of National Institutes of Health laboratories, Judith Bender of Hawaii asks a scientist about his research, *below left.* Another researcher describes several neurochemical research projects to John Rainbolt, *below.*

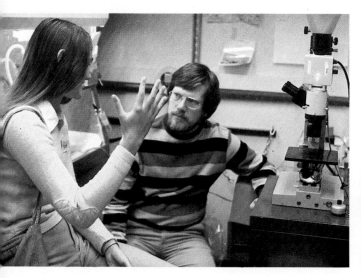

finalists had opportunities to talk with scientists working in the fields they plan to enter. For example, Rainbolt plans to do research in neurobiology and is interested in the chemistry of the brain. He met Janet Passonneau, chief of the Laboratory of Neurochemistry at the National Institutes of Health (NIH) in Bethesda, Md., and they discussed his research project on subtropical *Heliconius* butterflies. Rainbolt analyzed the chemistry of the sperm capsules of these colorful insects and found that the sperm is contained in a ''balloon'' of water and amino acids, the nitrogen-containing compounds that combine in various ways to form proteins. As the female is fertilized, she absorbs the amino acids, which supply her with additional energy that she will need to lay her eggs.

Passonneau told Rainbolt she had done research on moth hormones as a graduate student. She took him on a tour of her laboratory, and showed him research projects on brain metabolism, hibernation, and ischemia—the obstruction of blood vessels. She then introduced him to scientists doing research in which he is interested. Several other finalists, including Pan, visited other scientists at NIH.

Over lunch, the scientists asked the students how they decided on careers in science. Rainbolt said that biology had fascinated him for as long as he could remember. ''My advanced biology teacher helped me a great deal in my junior year,'' he added. ''He is a natural motivator who reinforces your interest and makes you want to do more.'' With the teacher's encouragement, he applied for, and received, an NSF grant to do summer research. ''I really enjoyed spending those nine

William Collins explains his seismometer to an interested audience, *below.* Ohioan Donna Pickrell's exhibit, *bottom,* showed how chromium and iron are absorbed by plants. Julie Pan, second from left, *below right,* asks fellow New Yorker Robert Klerer about his computer project.

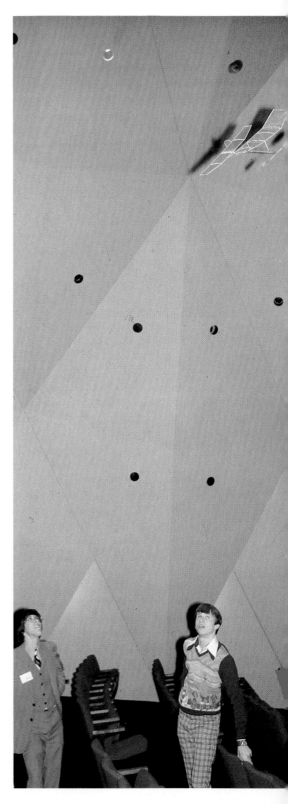

Peter Sanborn, left, and Mark Drela watch Sanborn's model plane, used in his experiment on the physical properties of rubber bands, soar through the auditorium of the National Academy of Sciences.

weeks at the University of Texas last summer. Being on my own, I learned as much about myself as I did about butterfly sperm capsules. Everyone treated me like a graduate student. It was tough coming back home and being just another high school kid again."

Rainbolt is more than just another bright high school student at Chrisman High, however. He was named the most valuable offensive back on the school football team in 1977, and was once selected Player of the Week in the Kansas City metropolitan area. He runs the 100-yard dash in 10.2 seconds and can bench-press 136 kilograms (300 pounds). He likes painting, poetry, sailing, and hiking, and he also took and processed all the butterfly photographs used in his project exhibit.

On Friday afternoon, a van brought crates, boxes, and trunks from the hotel to the Great Hall of the NAS. It was time for the contestants to set up their exhibits. As the exhibits went up, everyone got a clearer picture of the competition they faced. Collins put up his display, then strolled around to look at the other projects. "There are some obvious winners here," he commented, "but I think I've got a good chance."

Collins built an electronic seismometer that measures and records on magnetic tape the vibrations, or seismic waves, produced by earthquakes. The seismic waves change the frequency of an audio signal on the magnetic tape. These changes can be read much like the wavy lines on a conventional seismometer. The seismometer won first prize at the Los Angeles County Science Fair and third prize at the California State Science Fair in 1976. Collins then decided to find a practical application for his instrument and use it as a project in a national science competition.

He built a digital computer to analyze the seismic-wave frequencies recorded by the seismometer. With this combination, he studied the tremors produced by a powerful distant earthquake, a smaller local one, and an underground nuclear test in Nevada. He also recorded the natural vibrations

John Rainbolt works in his high school laboratory, *right,* continuing his research on the *Heliconius* butterfly. Sally Dennis' laboratory is her kitchen at home, *below,* where she tests the characteristics of dyes.

of a 14-story building to determine if the structure would vibrate at the same frequency as the ground movements produced by natural or man-made quakes. If so, the building's shaking would be amplified, increasing the possibility of structural damage. Collins did, in fact, discover that a nuclear test produced a sharp increase in ground vibrations at almost the same frequency as the natural movement of the building–$1\frac{1}{4}$ cycles per second. He believes that his technique can be used to calculate and predict the effect of earthquakes on buildings.

Sally Dennis arrived late in the afternoon to set up her display, wooden boards holding samples of dyed wool and other fibers. She had analyzed and compared various mordants–chemicals that bond dyes to textiles. She became interested in this as a Junior Girl Scout in the fifth grade. "Some friends of mine did projects with dyes, and I loved the beautiful, vivid colors they obtained," she recalled.

Dennis began collecting a variety of bark, berries, flowers, leaves, and roots that produce dyes. She worked in the kitchen at home, her mother encouraging the experiments despite the smell and mess. She once cooked oleander leaves, unaware that the fumes are poisonous. The vapors made her grandmother sick and the young science student a great deal more cautious.

Dennis particularly enjoyed her judging interview with Hauser. "I'm going to be a psychologist, so we had a lot to talk about," she explained. "I love watching people and animals and wondering why they are so kind or so rotten to each other. We have eight cats and two dogs at home, and I enjoy figuring out their personalities. I intend to get a double degree, in psychology and business. The business world is challenging, and in industrial psychology you can start out working on your own ideas instead of building on someone else's research."

On Friday evening, the finalists heard talks by Seaborg and Rosalyn S. Yalow. A researcher at the Veterans Administration Hospital in the Bronx, N.Y., Yalow shared the 1977 Nobel prize for physiology or medicine for developing radioimmunoassay, a method of using radioisotopes to study biological systems and measure minute quantities of various substances in these systems.

Yalow received her doctorate in physics and never took a course in biology. "What you learn in school is only part of what you do in life," she told the students. Seaborg probably agreed. He went against convention when he published a new version of the periodic table, which classifies elements according to their chemistry. As a result, he was able to predict the existence of five new elements, which he subse-

Science is not the sole interest of Rainbolt and Dennis. He has his own photo lab, *top left,* and competes in athletics, *above left.* She enjoys doing needlepoint, *above,* and studies modern dance, *top right.*

quently discovered and for which he won the Nobel prize. The students were thrilled to hear the stories of major discoveries from the scientists who made them, and they peppered Yalow and Seaborg with great numbers of questions.

The judges completed their interviews and selected the winners late on Saturday morning, March 4. "There was good agreement among us," noted Seaborg, "and we discussed the students until our decisions were unanimous." "Some kids stand out at both ends," remarked Russell D. Johnson, a chemist with Operations Research, Incorporated. "It's easy to pick out the best and the worst, but the ones in-between involved a more difficult process of elimination."

But the students would not know the results until Monday evening. Collins rated the questions the judges asked him as "surprisingly tough." He felt tense during the judging and could not estimate how well he had done. Pan was satisfied with her performance in front of the judges, and she felt that her chances were "pretty good." Dennis had begun to feel gloomy about her prospects. Rainbolt commented, "I'm a long way from last, but I may be just as far away from first."

Over and over you heard the same story: "My mind went blank. The judges ask you a question and you know the answer, but you can't

Senator Jacob K. Javits, (R., N.Y.) beams as he meets the New York contestants, *below.* All the young students pose for a traditional group portrait on the Capitol steps, *bottom left.* Some of them view the space shuttle exhibit at the National Air and Space Museum, *below right.* For many, the White House talk by President Jimmy Carter, *bottom right,* climaxed the eventful week.

At the crowded awards banquet, presidential science adviser Frank Press speaks of national science goals and the potential contributions of young scientists.

think of it. After you close the door, or when you're riding in an elevator, the answer jumps into your mind. Is that a lousy feeling!"

On Saturday afternoon, officials opened the exhibits to the public. Scientists, teachers, students, and others crowded the hall to view the projects and ask questions. The contestants explained their research over and over again, sucking on hard candy and sipping soft drinks to keep from becoming hoarse. They perspired under the bright, hot lights set up by television crews. Westinghouse distributes television films of the winners to their hometown stations, and the Washington news media also covered the finalists.

Michael S. Briggs, 17, of High Point High School in Adelphi, Md., had one of the most interesting exhibits. He attracted mathematicians and game buffs with a solution to a problem long thought to be unsolvable. When two people play a game such as checkers, mathematics can be used to determine the best moves each player should make. However, no general solution exists for more complicated games such as chess or for games played by three or more persons, because there are so many combinations of possible moves. Briggs became interested in the problem after reading an article on computer-played chess and developed an approximate solution for all games and numbers of players. "If you play your best game, this method maximizes the least amount you can expect to win," Briggs told his audiences.

A quiet boy with a quick smile, Briggs spends much of his spare time studying astrophysics. He also enjoys making stained-glass ornaments and reading novels and science magazines. He plans to study physics at Princeton University, and hopes to teach and do research in either physics or astronomy.

The finalists ate at a French restaurant on Saturday night, then went to see the New York City Ballet perform *Jewels* at the John F. Kennedy Center for the Performing Arts. They slept late, attended

First-place winner
Michael Briggs, at right,
and a second-place
winner, Joseph Tanzi,
face the news cameras,
above, after the banquet.
At a final party, *above
right,* Briggs receives
congratulations and
checks news coverage.

church, or went sightseeing on Sunday morning. In the afternoon, they returned to their exhibits in the Great Hall, where the crowd was even larger than on Saturday.

Late in the afternoon, the finalists began disassembling and packing their projects. They relaxed that evening at an Italian restaurant and watched Henry Winkler in the movie *The One and Only.* Too keyed-up to sleep, many stayed up after the movie to talk, read, or go dancing.

On a brisk Monday, March 6, the group walked from their hotel to the White House. Croatians and Serbs, protesting the arrival that day of President Josip Broz Tito of Yugoslavia, were gathering on Pennsylvania Avenue and police had closed off much of Lafayette Park facing the White House. Foot, mounted, and motorcycle police were assembled to control the crowds and prevent trouble. The scene heightened the drama of visiting the President.

The students heard talks by the heads of federal research organizations, such as the NSF and the National Aeronautics and Space Administration. The meeting had been arranged by geophysicist Frank Press, science adviser to the President and director of the Office of Science and Technology Policy.

President Jimmy Carter told the finalists he had read summaries of their projects and admitted he did not understand some of them. The President mentioned his own interest in science. Referring to the demonstrators outside the White House and the day's main problem, a nationwide coal strike, he said there were times when he wished he had remained in nuclear engineering. He wished the students success in the future, and shook hands with some of them.

The finalists were thrilled. Many found it hard to believe that they had visited with the President of the United States. "I'll remember this the rest of my life," said one. Most of them noticed that the President appeared somber.

Monday evening finally came. The students dressed for a reception and the awards banquet in the hotel's grand ballroom. They heard remarks by Seaborg; Edward G. Sherburne, Jr., director of Science Service; George F. Mechlin, a vice-president of Westinghouse Electric Corporation; and an address by Press. Then Axelrod announced the winners, beginning with the fourth-place awards.

As he began to read the names, the suspense mounted–but only up to a point. "The kids usually pick the same winners as the judges, though not in the same order," one judge pointed out. One student most of the participants selected had not been called for second prize. He was Michael Briggs. And that was the name that Axelrod finally announced as winner of the $10,000 first prize.

A judge explained their choice after the banquet. "Mike Briggs is not significantly different from the others, just a shade ahead of them. His project was a nice piece of math, conceived and done completely on his own. In person, he knocked us over. He answered everything we asked him, and is equally knowledgeable in math, physics, and astronomy. He has the kind of broad scope and imagination that makes a good scientist."

The row of telephone booths outside the banquet hall quickly filled with students calling home. The faces of the finalists reflected relief, disappointment, happiness, and bitterness. Quickly, they changed into comfortable clothes to attend a farewell party at Science Service headquarters. They drank pop, ate potato chips, and vented nervous energy in loud, animated conversation. Winners were heartily congratulated. Losers tried to put the competition out of their minds. More than one could not discuss his or her feelings without tears.

"I'm not crushed," Julie Pan said. "Winning would have been a happy surprise, but not something I really expected. I got an awful lot out of the experience–my first trip to Washington, the chance to see and talk to the President, congressmen, and scientists. I made some good friends."

Bill Collins was pragmatic. "Being one of the top 40 still means a lot. You get a good recommendation to the college you want to enter, and having this in your record should help get other financial aid."

"I wouldn't believe any of the 30 who said they weren't disappointed," Sally Dennis declared. "It's a little ego-crushing and it teaches you a lot about yourself."

John Rainbolt said he knew he didn't make it after they announced the third-place winners. "Sure I'm disappointed, but I've got no regrets. I feel honored to have made it this far. I intend to do research, and I wanted to know how I compare with others who have the same goal. Now I know, and I feel good about it."

The Winners

First Place, $10,000 scholarship:
Michael S. Briggs, 17,
  Adelphi, Md. (Mathematics)

Second Place, $8,000 scholarships:
Philip G. King, 18,
  Rumson, N.J. (Computer Science)
Joseph P. Tanzi, 17,
  Cranston, R.I. (Computer Science)

Third Place, $6,000 scholarships:
Judith L. Bender, 17,
  Honolulu, Hawaii (Biology)
Michael P. Mathis, 17,
  Scarsdale, N.Y. (Mathematics)
Samuel A. Weinberger, 15,
  New Rochelle, N.Y. (Mathematics)

Fourth Place, $4,000 scholarships:
Lawrence R. Bergman, 16,
  Bayside, N.Y. (Biology)
Ann T. Piening, 18,
  Bethalto, Ill. (Astronomy)
Daniel S. Rokhsar, 17,
  Staten Island, N.Y. (Physics)
Jay B. Stallman, 16,
  Forest Hills, N.Y. (Biology)

Alternates (to receive awards if winners are unable to accept):
Robert J. Klerer, 17,
  Irvington, N.Y. (Computer Science)
Mary E. Kroening, 18,
  San Diego (Computer Science)
Information about the 1979 Science Talent Search can be obtained from Science Service, 1719 N Street, NW, Washington, D.C. 20036

Ilya Prigogene discusses his work on nonequilibrium thermodynamics, for which he was awarded the Nobel prize for chemistry in 1977.

Awards And Prizes

A listing and description of the year's major awards and prizes in science, and the men and women who received them

Earth and Physical Sciences

Chemistry. Major awards in the field of chemistry included:

Nobel Prize. Ilya Prigogene, a Russian-born professor at the Free University of Brussels in Belgium, won the 1977 Nobel prize for chemistry. Prigogene received the $145,000 award for "his contributions to nonequilibrium thermodynamics, particularly the theory of dissipative structures." Prigogene's work increased the understanding of how living things use energy.

Prigogene spends part of each year at the University of Texas in Austin as director of the Center for Statistical Mechanics and Thermodynamics.

Cope Award. Orville L. Chapman, professor of chemistry at the University of California, Los Angeles, won the Arthur C. Cope Award given by the American Chemical Society (ACS) in 1978. Chapman received the award for his contributions in the synthesis and characterization of compounds that set new boundaries for the structural theory of organic chemistry, his research on chemical communications mechanisms in flying insects, and his studies on unusual and important organic systems. The award includes a $10,000 prize, a gold medal, and a $10,000 grant-in-aid for research.

Priestley Medal. Melvin Calvin, a professor of chemistry at the University of California, Berkeley, was awarded the Priestley Medal by ACS for distinguished service. Calvin's research revealed the chemical steps in photosynthesis, on alternative energy sources, and on the origin of life on earth.

Physics. Awards recognizing major works in physics included:

Nobel Prize. Two Americans and a Briton were awarded the 1977 Nobel prize for physics. Sharing the $145,000 award were Philip W. Anderson of Bell Telephone Laboratories in Murray Hill, N.J., and Princeton University, professor emeritus John H. van Vleck of Harvard University; and Sir Nevill F. Mott of Cambridge University in England.

Anderson and Mott independently made discoveries that led to development of electronic switching and memory devices made from such materials as glass, rather than from more expensive crystal materials. Van Vleck was cited for explaining the magnetic properties of solids and how "a foreign ion or atom behaves in a crystal."

Bonner Prize. Two Russian nuclear physicists shared the 1978 Tom W. Bonner Prize. Sergei Polikanov of the Joint Institute of Nuclear Research in Dubna and V. M. Strutinsky of the Institute of Nuclear Research in Kiev shared the American Institute of Physics award for their significant contributions to the discovery and explanation of isomeric fission, the splitting of nuclei with almost identical properties.

Buckley Prize. George D. Watkins of Lehigh University received the 1978 Oliver E. Buckley Solid State Physics Prize. Watkins was honored "for outstanding contributions to the understanding of radiation-induced defects in semiconductors by the imaginative use of experimental techniques and theoretical models."

Comstock Prize. Raymond Davis, Jr., of the Chemistry Department at the Brookhaven National Laboratory in Upton, N.Y., was awarded the $5,000 Cyrus B. Comstock Prize in 1978 for his determination of the intensity of neutrino radiation reaching the earth.

Franklin Medal. Cyril M. Harris, a Columbia University professor of acoustics and electrical engineering and past president of the Acoustical Society of America, received the Franklin Medal on November 2. Harris was honored for his contributions to acoustical science and engineering and for his design of such concert halls as New York City's Metropolitan Opera House and the Kennedy Center for the Performing Arts in Washington, D.C.

Lawrence Memorial Award. Five American scientists were honored with the Ernest O. Lawrence Memorial Award in 1978. The Department of Energy award, for meritorious contributions to the development and conservation of sources of energy, went to:

James D. Bjorken of the Stanford Linear Accelerator Center in Palo Alto, Calif.; John Emmett of the Lawrence Livermore Laboratory in California; F. William Studier of the Brookhaven National Laboratory in Upton, N.Y.; Gareth Thomas of the University of California, Berkeley; and Dean Waters of the Oak Ridge National Laboratory in Tennessee.

Professor emeritus John van Vleck of Harvard accepts congratulations after his share in the Nobel prize for physics had been announced.

Chemist Melvin Calvin, winner of the Priestley Medal in 1978, is now studying the possibility of obtaining automobile fuel from plants.

Earth and Physical Sciences

Continued

Michelson Medal. Albert V. Crewe, dean of the University of Chicago's Physical Sciences Division, won the Albert A. Michelson Medal for his invention of the scanning transmission electron microscope.

Oersted Medal. Wallace A. Hilton, chairman of the Physics Department at William Jewell College in Liberty, Mo., for 30 years, won the Oersted Medal in 1978. The award, given by the American Association of Physics Teachers, honors outstanding teachers of physics.

Waterman Award. Richard A. Muller of the Lawrence Berkeley Laboratory in California won the National Science Foundation's (NSF) Alan T. Waterman Award in 1978. Muller will receive $50,000 annually for three years for research. He was honored for his innovative research.

Geosciences. Awards for important work in the geosciences during the year included:

Carty Medal. John N. Mather, professor of mathematics at Princeton Uni-

versity, won the John J. Carty Medal in 1978. The $5,000 National Academy of Sciences (NAS) award is for outstanding accomplishment in any field of science.

Day Medal. Samuel Epstein of California Institute of Technology (Caltech) won the Arthur L. Day Medal in 1978. Epstein received the Geological Society of America (GSA) award for research on the solar system's early history.

Day Prize. John Verhoogen, professor of geology and geophysics at the University of California, Berkeley, received the $10,000 NAS Arthur L. Day Prize and lectureship for his fundamental work on the thermodynamics of the earth's core and mantle and contributions to scholarship in earth sciences.

Vetlesen Prize. Geophysicist J. Tuzo Wilson, director general of the Ontario Science Center in Toronto, Canada, was awarded the $50,000 Vetlesen Prize. Wilson was honored for his work in the development of the plate tectonic theory, which describes the earth's crust as a shell of floating plates.

Life Sciences

Physicist Rosalyn S. Yalow, a researcher in nuclear medicine, shared the Nobel prize for physiology or medicine.

Medicine. Major awards in medical sciences included the following:

Nobel Prize. Three American scientists were awarded the 1977 Nobel prize for physiology or medicine. Rosalyn S. Yalow received half the $145,000 prize for developing radioimmunoassay, a clinical and research technique for determining how many of various hormones are present in the body. Roger C. L. Guillemin and Andrew V. Schally split the remaining half of the prize for their research into the production of peptide hormones in the brain.

Yalow is director of the research laboratory at the Bronx Veterans Administration Hospital and a professor at the Mount Sinai School of Medicine of the City University of New York. Guillemin is a resident fellow of the Salk Institute for Biological Studies in San Diego. Schally works at the New Orleans Veterans Administration Hospital and Tulane University.

Gairdner Awards. Five medical scientists won $10,000 Gairdner International Awards in September 1977 for outstanding contributions to medical science. The winners are:

K. Frank Austen, Harvard Medical School, for research on the inflammatory response; Sir Cyril A. Clarke, Nuffield Unit of Medical Genetics, Liverpool, England, for work on preventing hemolytic disease in the newborn; Jean Dausset, Blood Disease Research Institute in Paris, for research on histocompatibility antigens and the study of genetically determined diseases; Henry G. Friesen, University of Manitoba Faculty of Medicine in Winnipeg, Canada, for work on lactogenic hormones and the identification of human prolactin; Victor A. McKusick, the Johns Hopkins University School of Medicine in Baltimore, for his work on clinical genetics.

Lasker Awards. Five European scientists received the 1977 Albert Lasker Medical Research Awards. The Lasker Awards are presented annually for outstanding research.

Swedish scientists Inge G. Edler and C. Hellmuth Hertz shared the $15,000 clinical medical research award for their pioneering work in using ultrasonic vibrations to diagnose heart disorders and other serious illness. Edler is associate professor of medicine at University Hospital in Lund, Sweden. Hertz is head of the Department of Electrical Measurements at the Lund Institute of Technology.

Two Swedish scientists and one from Great Britain shared the $15,000 award for basic medical research.

Professor K. Sune D. Bergstrom and Chairman Bengt Samuelsson of the Karolinska Institute's Chemistry Department in Stockholm, Sweden, along with John R. Vane of the Wellcome Research Laboratories in Beckenham, England, shared the award for their discoveries and pioneering research concerning prostaglandins, natural substances in the body that are important in regulating such things as blood clotting, blood pressure, and stomach acids.

Biology. Among the awards presented in biology in 1977 and 1978 were the following:

Carski Award. Noel R. Krieg of the Virginia Polytechnic Institute and State University won the 1978 Carski Foundation Award for Distinguished Teaching. The $1,000 award recognized Krieg's contributions as an excellent teacher. He joined the faculty at Virginia Polytechnic in 1960 and has helped to create a stimulating environment at that institution for graduate studies in microbiology.

Horwitz Prize. Three New York City immunologists shared the Louisa Gross Horwitz Prize in 1977. Michael Heidelberger, his first graduate student at Columbia University, Elvin A. Kabat, and Henry G. Kunkel of Rockefeller University, shared the $25,000 prize for their outstanding research in biology or biochemistry. Heidelberger is considered the father of immunology. The prize is awarded annually by Columbia University.

Lilly Award. David Botstein of the Massachusetts Institute of Technology Department of Biology received the $2,000 Eli Lilly & Company Award in 1978. Botstein was honored for his many accomplishments in molecular biology. The Lilly Award is given annually to honor outstanding scientists under 40 years of age.

Stone Award. Biologist Bruce K. Duncan received the Wilson S. Stone Award in March. The award is given

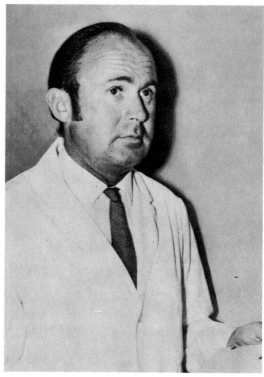

Life
Sciences
Continued

Roger C. L. Guillemin, *above*, and Andrew V. Schally, *above right*, shared half the Nobel prize for physiology or medicine for work on brain hormones.

annually by the University of Texas M.D. Anderson Hospital and Tumor Institute for outstanding achievement in the biomedical sciences by a student in the United States.

Duncan was honored for his innovative work with uracil-DNA glychosidase, the key enzyme that initiates DNA repair of uracil, thereby suppressing mutations prior to DNA replication. Working at the University of Minnesota, Duncan developed a system for synthesizing DNA with variable amounts of uracil in the common bacterium *Escherichia coli*.

Tyler Ecology Award. Russell E. Train, government official and noted environmentalist, won the John and Alice Tyler Ecology Award in 1978. He received the annual $150,000 prize for his efforts to control pollution through education, conservation, and the development of legislation.

Train has had a distinguished career in government and public service. He served as undersecretary in the U.S. Department of the Interior in 1969 and 1970, and was chairman of the Council

on Environmental Quality from 1970 to 1973. He was elected president of the World Wildlife Fund-U.S. in March.

Waterford Biomedical Science Award for 1978 went to Swiss immunologist Niels Kaj Jerne. The $7,500 award, administered by Scripps Clinic and Research Foundation in San Diego, Calif., is for outstanding contributions to biomedical science. Jerne is director of the Basel Institute of Immunology in Switzerland. Jerne was honored as one of the principal architects of present-day immunological theory. His theories have profoundly influenced recent scientific thinking and experimentation.

Weicker Memorial Award. Ernest Bueding, professor of pathobiology, pharmacology, and experimental therapeutics at Johns Hopkins Medical School, won the first Theodore Weicker Memorial Award. Bueding received the $10,000 prize for his research in pharmacology. He is noted for his research on filariasis and schistosomiasis and on the biochemistry and pharmacology of parasitic worms.

Space Sciences

Professor John R. Winckler of the University of Minnesota won the Arctowski Medal for 1978 for his solar research.

Aerospace. The highest awards to be granted in the aerospace sciences included:

Collier Trophy. General Robert J. Dixon and the U.S. Air Force Tactical Air Command received the 1977 Collier Trophy for the development and the implementation of the Red Flag combat-simulated flight-training program for the U.S. armed forces.

Goddard Astronautics Award. Joseph V. Charyk, president of Communications Satellite Corporation, was awarded the Goddard Astronautics Award for his part in developing satellite communications systems.

Reed Aeronautics Award. James T. Stewart, retired U.S. Air Force general, received the Reed Award for his "distinguished and significant contribution" to the development of U.S. military aircraft.

Astronomy. Major awards in astronomy during the year included:

Arctowski Medal. John R. Winckler of the University of Minnesota was awarded the $5,000 Henryk Arctowski Medal for his research on solar modulation and acceleration of high-energy particles and discoveries of solar flare gamma rays and auroral X rays.

Bruce Medal. H. C. van de Hulst, professor of astronomy at Leiden University in the Netherlands, won the Catherine Wolfe Bruce Gold Medal in 1978. The award is given by the Astronomical Society of the Pacific.

Pierce Prize. James M. Moran, Jr., lecturer and radio astronomer at Harvard/Smithsonian Center for Astrophysics, was awarded the Newton Lacy Pierce Prize in 1978 for his contributions to very-long-baseline interferometer techniques. The prize is awarded annually by the American Astronomical Society.

Warner Prize. David N. Schramm, professor of astronomy and astrophysics at the University of Chicago, received the 1978 Warner Prize. He was cited for his incisive and energetic application of nuclear physics to a wide range of astrophysical problems. The $1,000 prize is awarded annually by the American Astronomical Society.

General Awards

Science and Humanity Awards during the year included the following:

National Medal of Science. President James E. Carter, Jr., presented the National Medal of Science, highest United States award for distinguished scientific achievement, to 15 scientists on November 22 in Washington, D.C. Those honored were:

Morris Cohen, Massachusetts Institute of Technology, for his research in metallurgy

Kurt O. Friedrichs, New York University, for mathematics research

Peter C. Goldmark, Goldmark Communications Corporation, for communications sciences

Samuel A. Goudsmit, University of Nevada, for discovery (with George E. Uhlenbeck) of electron spin as source of a new quantum number

Roger C. L. Guillemin, Salk Institute for Biological Studies, for demonstrating the presence of a new class of brain hormones

Herbert S. Gutowsky, University of Illinois, for nuclear magnetic resonance spectroscopy

Erwin W. Mueller, Pennsylvania State University, inventor of field-emission, field-ion, and atom-probe microscopes (posthumous)

Keith R. Porter, University of Colorado, for electron microscopy

Efraim Racker, Cornell University, for research on oxidative and photosynthetic energy in living cells

Frederick D. Rossini, Rice University, for his research in chemical thermodynamics

Verner F. Suomi, University of Wisconsin, for research in meteorology

Henry Taube, Stanford University, for research on reaction mechanisms in inorganic chemistry and in nitrogen fixation

George E. Uhlenbeck, Rockefeller University, for discovery (with Goudsmit) of electron spin as the source of a new quantum number

Hassler Whitney, the Institute for Advanced Studies in Princeton, N.J., for founding the discipline of differential topology

Edward O. Wilson, Harvard University, for studies of insect societies.

General
Awards

Continued

Russian mathematician
Izrail Gelfand, *above*,
shared a Wolf prize and
Peter C. Goldmark, *above
right*, won a National
Medal of Science for
communications sciences.

Founders Medal. John R. Pierce, professor of engineering at Caltech, received the Founders Medal in 1977. The medal is awarded by the National Academy of Engineering.

Pierce was honored for his contributions to electronic communication. He is best known for his part in developing the *Echo I* satellite, which paved the way for using reflecting satellites to communicate over long distances. He also played an important part in developing *Telstar*, first commercial communication satellite.

Wolf Prize. Nine scientists shared five prizes of $100,000 each, presented in 1978 by the Wolf Foundation. Those honored were:

In agricultural science, George F. Sprague of the University of Illinois in Urbana and John C. Walker of the University of Wisconsin shared the prize. Sprague was honored for showing that corn-protein quality could be improved through genetic manipulation. Walker was cited for his work in plant diseases and the role of soil and other environmental factors in them.

In chemistry, Carl Djerassi of Stanford University was cited for his work in developing oral contraceptives.

The mathematics prize was shared by Izrail M. Gelfand of Moscow State University, for work in functional analysis, and Carl L. Siegel of the University of Göttingen in West Germany, for work on the theory of numbers, complex variables, and celestial mechanics.

In medicine, Jean Dausset of Paris, George D. Snell of Jackson Laboratories, Bar Harbor, Me., and J. van Rood of the University of Leiden in the Netherlands shared the prize for work on antigens, which are involved in the immune response of man and animals.

In physics, Chien Shiung Wu of Columbia University in New York City was honored for showing that some otherwise typical symmetries of behavior in physics do not hold in radioactive decay.

The Wolf Foundation was established in Israel in 1976 by Riccardo Sobirana y Lobo, who was born in Germany as Richard Wolf but now lives in Israel.   [Joseph P. Spohn]

Major Awards and Prizes

Award winners treated more fully in the first portion of this section are indicated by an asterisk (*)

AAAS-Rosenstiel Award (oceanography): Henry M. Stommel

AAAS Socio-Psychological Prize: Jonathan Kelley, Herbert S. Klein

A. Cressy Morrison Award (natural sciences): Philip J. E. Peebles

AIP Prize for Industrial Applications of Physics: Robert D. Maurer

American Physical Society High Polymer Physics Prize: Henri Benoit

American Physical Society International Prize for New Materials: John H. Sinfelt

*Arctowski Medal (astronomy): John R. Winckler

*Arthur Cope Award (chemistry): Orville L. Chapman

*Arthur L. Day Medal (geophysics): Samuel Epstein

*Arthur L. Day Prize (geophysics): John Verhoogen

Becton-Dickinson Award (microbiology): John C. Sherris

*Bonner Prize (nuclear physics): Sergei Polikanov, V. M. Strutinsky

*Bruce Medal (astronomy): H. C. van de Hulst

*Buckley Solid State Physics Prize: George D. Watkins

*Carski Foundation Award (teaching): Noel R. Krieg

*Carty Medal: John N. Mather

*Collier Trophy (astronautics): Robert J. Dixon

*Comstock Prize (physics): Raymond Davis, Jr.

Davisson-Germer Prize (physics): Vernon Hughes

Delmer S. Fahrney Medal (telecommunications): William Oliver Baker

Earle K. Plyler Prize (physics): E. Bright Wilson, Jr.

Eddington Medal (astronomy): William A. Fowler

Federation Aeronautique Internationale Gold Space Medal: Michael Collins

Fisher Award (microbiology): Moshe Shilo

*Founders Medal (engineering): John R. Pierce

*Franklin Medal: Cyril M. Harris

*Gairdner Awards (medicine): K. Frank Austen, Sir Cyril A. Clarke, Jean Dausset, Henry C. Friesen, Victor A. McKusick

Garvan Medal (chemistry): Madeleine M. Joullie

Gibbs Medal (chemistry): William O. Baker

*Goddard Astronautics Award: Joseph V. Charyk

Gottlieb Memorial Award (cancer care): Emil Frei III

Haley Space Flight Award: Thomas P. Stafford, Donald K. Slayton, Vance D. Brand

Heath Memorial Award (cancer care): Georges Mathé

Heineman Prize (American Physical Society): Elliott H. Lieb

*Horwitz Prize (biology): Michael Heidelberger, Elvin A. Kabat, Henry G. Kunkel

Howard N. Potts Medal: Godfrey N. Hounsfield

Ives Medal (optics): Emil Wolf

James Clerk Maxwell Prize (physics): John M. Dawson

Kleemeier Award (gerontology): George Sacher

*Lasker Awards (medical research): K. Sune D. Bergstrom, Inge G. Edler, C. Hellmuth Hertz, Bengt Samuelsson, John R. Vane

*Lawrence Memorial Award (atomic energy): James D. Bjorken, John Emmett, F. William Studier, Gareth Thomas, Dean Waters

Leo Szilard Award (physics): Matthew Meselson

*Lilly Award (microbiology): David Botstein

Max Planck Medal (physics): Walter Thirring

Meggers Medal: Mark S. Fred, Frank S. Tomkins

*Michelson Medal: Albert V. Crewe

NAS Award for Distinguished Service: Noel D. Vietmeyer

NAS Public Welfare Medal: Donald Ainslee Henderson

*National Medal of Science: Morris Cohen, Kurt O. Friedrichs, Peter C. Goldmark, Samuel A. Goudsmit, Roger C. L. Guillemin, Herbert S. Gutowsky, Erwin W. Mueller, Keith R. Porter, Efraim Racker, Frederick D. Rossini, Verner F. Suomi, Henry Taube, George E. Uhlenbeck, Hassler Whitney, Edward O. Wilson

New York Academy of Sciences Award: Harry Shapiro

New York Academy of Sciences Presidential Award: Alexander Rich

*Nobel Prize: chemistry, Ilya Prigogene; physics, Philip W. Anderson, Sir Nevill F. Mott, John H. van Vleck; physiology or medicine, Roger C. L. Guillemin, Andrew V. Schally, Rosalyn S. Yalow

*Oersted Medal (teaching): Wallace A. Hilton

Oppenheimer Memorial Prize (physics): S. Jocelyn Bell Burnell

Pahlevi Environment Prize: Thor Heyerdahl

Penrose Medal (geology): Robert M. Garrels

*Pierce Prize (astronomy): James M. Moran, Jr.

Presidential Medal of Freedom: Jonas Salk

*Priestley Medal (chemistry): Melvin Calvin

Richardson Medal (optics): Walter P. Siegmund

*Reed Aeronautics Award: James T. Stewart

Russell Lectureship (astronomy): Maarten Schmidt

Silver Medal in Physical Acoustics: Martin Greenspan

Silver Medal in Psychological and Physiological Acoustics: Lloyd A. Jeffress

Space Science Award: Laurence Peterson

Space Systems Award: Werner von Braun (posthumous)

*Stone Award (biomedicine): Bruce K. Duncan

Texas Instruments Founders' Prize: Richard A. Muller

Trumpler Award (astronomy): Typhoon Lee

*Tyler Ecology Award: Russell E. Train

U.S. Steel Foundation Award (molecular biology): Gunter Blobel

*Vetlesen Prize (geophysics): J. Tuzo Wilson

Waksman Award (microbiology): Howard Green

*Warner Prize (astronomy): David N. Schramm

*Waterford Biomedical Science Award: Niels Kaj Jerne

*Waterman Award (physics): Richard A. Muller

*Weicker Memorial Award (medicine): Ernest Bueding

*Wolf Prize: agricultural science, George F. Sprague, John C. Walker; chemistry, Carl Djerassi; mathematics, Izrail M. Gelfand, Carl L. Siegel; medicine, Jean Dausset, George D. Snell, J. van Rood; in physics, Chien Shiung Wu

Deaths of Notable Scientists

Notable scientists and engineers who died between June 1, 1977, and June 1, 1978, include those listed. An asterisk (*) indicates that a biography appears in *The World Book Encyclopedia.*

*Adrian, Lord Edgar Douglas (1889-Aug. 4, 1977), British physiologist, co-winner of the 1932 Nobel prize for physiology or medicine for his work on the function of nerve cells.

Alikhanian, Artemii I. (1908-Feb. 25, 1978), Russian nuclear physicist who pioneered in identifying atomic particles and the study of cosmic rays.

Barach, Alvan L. (1895-Dec. 13, 1977), physician, a pioneer in respiratory therapy who developed the first practical oxygen tent.

Beams, Jesse W. (1898-July 23, 1977), physicist, who developed the centrifuge principle to separate the fissionable isotope U-235 from uranium.

Begle, Edward G. (1914-March 2, 1978), mathematician who led the "new math" revolution in schools in the United States in the 1960s.

*Best, Charles H. (1899-March 31, 1978), Canadian physiologist who helped Frederick G. Banting isolate the hormone insulin in 1921 for the treatment of diabetes.

Bieber, Margarete (1879-Feb. 25, 1978), German-born archaeologist whose many books include *Copies: A Contribution to the History of Graeco-Roman Sculpture.*

Bodansky, Oscar (1901-Aug. 21, 1977), Russian-born biochemist and physician who pioneered in the use of enzymes to diagnose cancer.

*Conant, James B. (1893-Feb. 11, 1978), organic chemist noted for his work on chlorophyll and hemoglobin. He was president of Harvard University from 1933 to 1953.

Coolidge, Albert S. (1894-Aug. 31, 1977), chemist and physicist whose 1933 treatise on quantum mechanics theories proved that it was possible to calculate with precision the forces that hold atoms together in molecules.

Cotzias, George C. (1918-June 13, 1977), Greek-born neurologist who developed L-dopa therapy for Parkinson's disease in 1970.

Davis, Francis W. (1887-April 19, 1978), engineer who invented a power-steering unit in 1926 that was adopted by the auto industry in 1952.

Eiseley, Loren C. (1907-July 9, 1977), anthropologist and poet noted for his eloquent contributions to the layman's understanding of science in such books as *The Immense Journey* (1957). He said that "man's basic and oldest characteristic is that he is a creature of memory, a bridge into the future, a time binder."

Eliot, Martha (1891-Feb. 14, 1978), physician with the U.S. Children's Bureau for more than 30 years and the first woman president of the American Public Health Organization.

Fieser, Louis F. (1899-July 25, 1977), organic chemist whose research led to the synthesis of vitamin K, cortisone therapy for rheumatoid arthritis, and the incendiary material napalm.

Gödel, Kurt (1906-Jan. 14, 1978), Czechoslovakian-born logician who, in 1931, formulated Gödel's Theorem, which states that certain mathematical theories cannot be proved or disproved with the accepted method of mathematics. He was co-winner of the first Albert Einstein Award in 1951.

Goldmark, Peter C. (1906-Dec. 7, 1977), Hungarian-born physicist and electrical engineer who invented the long-playing phonograph record and a rotating-disk method for color television during his 36 years with CBS. His recent work included the development of electronic video-cassette technology.

Green, George K. (1911-Aug. 15, 1977), nuclear physicist who pioneered in designing and building atomic particle accelerators.

Gregory, Bernard (1919-Dec. 24, 1977), French physicist who organized European research in high-energy physics as director-general of the European Organization for Nuclear Research from 1966 to 1970.

Hardy, Arthur C. (1895-Oct. 31, 1977), physicist who developed the spectrophotometer in 1927.

Heezen, Bruce C. (1924-June 21, 1977), marine geologist who produced spectacular maps of the ocean floor with co-worker Marie Tharp and discovered the globe-girdling extent of the Mid-Atlantic Ridge in 1959.

Hill, Archibald V. (1886-June 3, 1977), British physiologist, co-winner of the 1922 Nobel prize for physiology or medicine for his work on energy exchanges in active nerve and muscle.

Lord Edgar Douglas Adrian

Charles H. Best

James B. Conant

Loren C. Eiseley

Benjamin Lee

Wernher von Braun

Hobbs, Leonard S. (1896-Nov. 1, 1977), aeronautical engineer who headed the development of U.S. jet airliners and B-52 bombers.

Holinger, Paul H. (1906-March 26, 1978), physician who designed the tracheotomy tube and took the first pictures of the interior of the esophagus and bronchial tubes.

Keenan, Joseph H. (1900-July 10, 1977), mechanical engineer whose work on the mechanics of heat brought greater understanding of the subject.

Kessler, Henry H. (1896-Jan. 18, 1978), orthopedic surgeon who developed cineplasty, a technique for the muscular control of artificial limbs.

Kimpton, Lawrence A. (1910-Nov. 1, 1977), chancellor of the University of Chicago from 1951 to 1960. He headed the university's metallurgical laboratory during the Manhattan Project of World War II, when the first manmade atomic chain reaction was produced there.

Kinosita, Riojun (1893-Sept. 7, 1977), Japanese-born physician, one of the first scientists to link smoking and chemical food additives with cancer.

Kleinschmidt, Edward E. (1875-Aug. 9, 1977), German-born engineer whose inventions included the high-speed teletype machine, the stock market's high-speed ticker tape, and the automated fishing reel.

Kompfner, Rudolf (1909-Dec. 10, 1977), Austrian-born physicist who invented the traveling-wave tube used in communications satellites.

Kunitz, Moses (1887-April 20, 1978), Russian-born biochemist noted for enzyme studies in which he proved that enzymes are proteins.

Leake, Chauncey D. (1896-Jan. 11, 1978), pharmacologist, historian, and former president of the American Association for the Advancement of Science who introduced the use of divinyl ether in anesthesiology. His books on the relation of science to ethics include *Can We Agree?* (1950).

Lear, William P. (1902-May 14, 1978), electrical engineer who designed and built the Lear Jet. His numerous inventions include the automobile radio, the automatic pilot for aircraft, and the eight-track stereo cartridge.

Lee, Benjamin (1935-June 16, 1977), Korean-born physicist who headed the theoretical group at the Fermi National Accelerator Laboratory in Batavia, Ill., since 1973. He supported the "gauge" theory linking two fundamental forces – the nuclear weak force and the electromagnetic force.

Magruder, William M. (1923-Sept. 10, 1977), aeronautical engineer who developed the L-1011 jumbo jet. He headed a federal project to develop supersonic aircraft in the early 1970s.

Noyes, Eliot F. (1910-July 17, 1977), industrial designer of such products as IBM's electric typewriter, and architect whose buildings included the United Nations Pavilion at Expo 67 in Montreal, Canada.

Pigman, W. Ward (1910-Sept. 30, 1977), biochemist whose work in polarimetry contributed to our understanding of the properties of sugars. His book *Chemistry of the Carbohydrates* (1948) became a standard textbook.

Pitman, Earle C. (1893-Feb. 18, 1978), chemical engineer who helped develop nylon and smokeless powder. In 1945, he invented a method for smoothing the outer surfaces of aircraft with a rubber coating that helped reduce drag.

Pitts, Robert F. (1908-June 6, 1977), physiologist whose studies of the human kidney and nervous system led to such standard therapy as postsurgical and intravenous fluids and diuretic drugs.

Sporn, Philip (1896-Jan. 24, 1978), Austrian-born electrical engineer responsible for many technological advances in the U.S. electrical utility industry, including initial operation of the first 330,000-volt transmission line.

Thomson, Sir Arthur Landsborough (1890-June 9, 1977), Scottish biologist and ornithologist who was a member of Great Britain's Medical Research Council for 40 years and editor of the *New Dictionary of Birds.*

*Von Braun, Wernher (1912-June 16, 1977), German-born rocket engineer who developed the V-2 missile in World War II to bomb Great Britain. He played a major role in the U.S. space program from 1945 to 1960.

Wolf, Bernard S. (1912-Sept. 16, 1977), radiologist at Mount Sinai School of Medicine in New York City who pioneered in the use of radiology to diagnose disease. [Irene B. Keller]

Assessing Our Petroleum Future

By Betty M. Miller

**To make meaningful plans for the use
of our petroleum resources, we must
keep close track of how much remains**

Very few Americans before 1973 knew or cared how much oil and gas lay beneath the land. As long as most of us could remember, these petroleum resources had been available to run our cars or heat our homes. A few people, most of them geologists in government and industry, had studied statistics on these resources and saw declining production rates for known oil fields, decreasing discovery rates for new fields, and rising exploration and production costs. But their concern was overshadowed by another set of figures—the long-term annual-production rates.

The United States had always been the world's leading oil producer. We pumped more than 1 billion barrels out of the ground in 1929, 2 billion barrels in 1948, 3 billion barrels in 1966, and reached

Oil drilling crews, *above right,* tap rock formations in a search for the petroleum that appraisals by USGS geologists, *right,* indicate is there.

our peak production of 3.3 billion barrels in 1970. Then came the winter of 1973-1974 and the oil embargo imposed by the Organization of Petroleum Exporting Countries. Long lines at gasoline stations, fuel oil shortages in some parts of the nation, and the sudden jump in prices awoke Americans to the fact that much of their petroleum was coming from outside the United States. Suddenly, almost everybody shared the geologists' concern over U.S. oil and gas resources.

As one result, the Federal Energy Administration (FEA) was directed to appraise the undiscovered oil and gas resources of the United States, on land and off the coasts to a depth of 200 meters (660 feet). The FEA mandate came when President Gerald R. Ford signed the Federal Energy Administration Act of 1974 into law. The law required the FEA to prepare a "complete and independent analysis of actual oil and gas reserves and resources in the United States and its outer continental shelf, as well as the existing productive capacity and the extent to which such capacity could be increased for crude oil and each major petroleum product each year for the next 10 years through full utilization of available technology and capacity."

Many appraisals had been made before, most of them by geologists in the petroleum industry who focused on specific areas in which their companies were interested. In addition, the National Academy of Sciences (NAS) was reviewing the methods by which resources were evaluated. And reserve and resource studies were being conducted or contemplated by the Federal Power Commission (FPC) on gas reserves; the Federal Trade Commission (FTC) on ownership and control of oil and gas reserves; and the U.S. Geological Survey (USGS) on oil and gas resources on land and on the outer continental shelf.

The FEA's task was to incorporate this data, as well as new data, into a "master" appraisal. So it turned to the USGS for help. The USGS turned the task over to its Resource Appraisal Group in the Geologic Division. This group was already developing new and improved appraisal methods that would permit geologic data to be collected and evaluated systematically for all U.S. petroleum areas. The USGS published the results of its survey in June 1975. The theme of the report was that less than 50 per cent of the recoverable oil and about 55 per cent of the natural gas in the United States remained to be discovered. At the current U.S. rate of production, this is equivalent to a 35- to 55-year supply. The publishing of this assessment ended any remaining optimism about U.S. oil and gas resources.

Energy directly controls the world's standard of living. It is essential to the new and continuing growth of all nations, so it is of prime importance to domestic and international policies.

The industrial nations' major source of energy is petroleum hydrocarbons, primarily in the form of crude oil and natural gas. About three-fourths of the energy consumed in the United States comes from petroleum. Liquids—gasoline, fuel oil, and lubricating oil—account for about two-thirds and natural gas for about one-third of the total.

The author:
Betty M. Miller is Program Chief of the Resource Appraisal Group of the U.S. Geological Survey.

The trans-Alaskan Pipeline, *above,* carries oil from Prudhoe Bay to the terminal at Valdez, *left.* Such major oil strikes are the result of precise geologic studies of the earth's structure.

There has been a lot of talk and even some action on conserving energy and developing coal, nuclear power, and other alternate energy sources. Nevertheless, most of these sources will not contribute significantly to the energy picture before the year 2000. Until then, we will have to depend on petroleum hydrocarbons.

In order to cope with this, we must know as much as possible about the availability and distribution of our petroleum resources. Such knowledge is a fundamental requirement for a national energy policy. For example, it permits us to estimate, based upon current consumption rates, how much actual time we have in which to develop alternative energy resources.

Estimating America's total undiscovered hydrocarbons requires a broad knowledge of geology and the ability to draw useful analogies between known and unknown geologic conditions. Individual experts or even groups of experts in industry may not have this ability on such a large-scale study. However, the USGS does. To understand why this is so, it is helpful to know a little of the history and purpose of this scientific agency.

President Jimmy Carter, and the first U.S. secretary of energy, James R. Schlesinger, visit an oil rig off the coast of Louisiana as a gesture of their concern for the need to increase U.S. production of oil.

After the Civil War, people migrated to the Western United States in great numbers. This created a need for more detailed knowledge of the topography and the mineral and other resources of the Western frontier. The NAS, which had been commissioned by Congress to study geological surveys of the Western territory, recommended in 1879 that the individual studies be discontinued and that a national geological survey be established. President Rutherford B. Hayes signed legislation on March 3, 1879, that created the USGS as an agency of the Department of the Interior.

USGS scientific and engineering research programs have grown apace with industry in the United States. This growth reflects a continuing and increasing need for USGS research surveys, investigations, and advice about U.S. natural resources. When the USGS was organized, it employed 39 people and had annual funds of $100,000. In 1978, it had more than 9,300 full-time employees and a budget of $433 million.

The NAS had recommended that the USGS should "be charged with the study of the geological structure and economic resources of the public domain." By the second half of the 20th century, Congress had become aware of the importance of the mineral resources of the continental shelf and deep seabed underlying the oceans. Consequently, in 1962, USGS authority was extended outside the public domain, to areas beyond the nation's shores that the secretary of the interior determined "to be in the national interest." Thus, while it has focused its work mainly on the United States and its possessions, the USGS has also become international in the scope of its work.

The work of the USGS is shared by four divisions: topographic, geologic, water resources, and conservation. Resource appraisal is the work of the Geologic Division and has four main elements: land-resource, mineral-resource, energy-resource, and offshore geologic surveys. The last two of these elements are concerned with the problem of energy resources. Energy-resource surveys are basic studies of the geology of specific areas. They include mapping and applied appraisal studies of coal, oil and gas, oil shale, uranium and thorium, and geothermal resources. Offshore geologic surveys provide the significant geologic and geophysical knowledge needed to appraise U.S. resources on the outer continental shelf.

To make the resource appraisal requested by the FEA, the Resource Appraisal Group set out to develop a systematic collection and evaluation of basic geologic and geophysical data from the 102 petroleum provinces throughout the nation. A province, or basin, has a discrete, or separate, geology, and may contain a large number of oil and gas fields. The provinces cover the entire United States plus offshore areas out to a water depth of 200 meters. The Resource Appraisal Group obtained the assistance of more than 70 USGS geologists, each experienced in one or more specific provinces. These experts provided basic geologic and geophysical data and interpretations of the data.

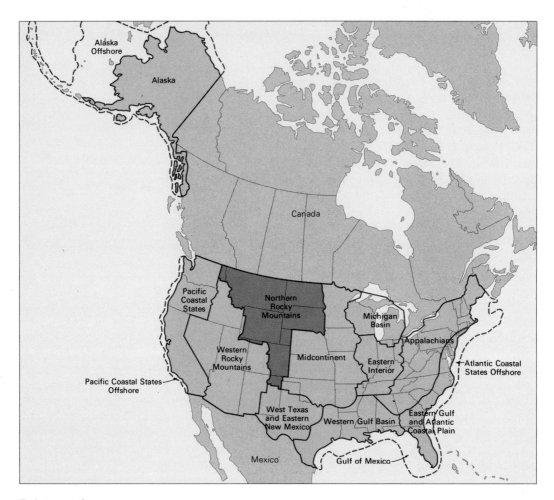

To interpret the geology for petroleum potential, scientists divide the United States into onshore and offshore regions. The regions are further divided into provinces, each having unique geologic structures.

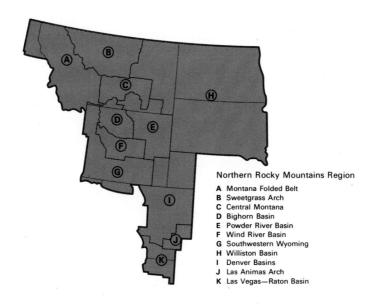

Northern Rocky Mountains Region

A Montana Folded Belt
B Sweetgrass Arch
C Central Montana
D Bighorn Basin
E Powder River Basin
F Wind River Basin
G Southwestern Wyoming
H Williston Basin
I Denver Basins
J Las Animas Arch
K Las Vegas—Raton Basin

As a result, for the first time, large quantities of data were collected and analyzed to compile a national petroleum-resource appraisal. The Resource Appraisal Group used traditional methods of estimating the volume of sedimentary basins, but also did statistical studies that linked each of the 102 provinces. The result is as complete and accurate an appraisal of the remaining undiscovered, recoverable resources of the United States as could be made in the time allotted.

How do geologists know where to look for oil and natural gas? Before answering that question, we need to know some of the basic characteristics of areas where petroleum is found.

The word *petroleum* is derived from the Latin *petra* (rock or stone) and *oleum* (oil)—rock-oil. Petroleum is a common constituent of sedimentary rocks, usually in the form of gas, liquid, semisolid, or solid, or in a combination of these states within a single reservoir. Chemically, it is an extremely complex mixture of hydrocarbons, hydrogen and carbon compounds, with minor amounts of impurities of nitrogen, sulfur, and oxygen.

The fundamental conditions required for petroleum to occur in the earth include:
- The right kind of rock of an adequate thickness;
- Beds containing considerable dispersed organic matter;
- Beds that are porous (full of tiny holes) and permeable (able to pass liquids or gases);
- A suitable environment for organic matter to decay to form oil or natural gas;
- A thermal history of the area favorable to forming petroleum;
- Trapping mechanisms;
- Hydrodynamic conditions favorable for oil and gas to flow through the rock and ultimately be trapped;
- The right timing for the development and flow of petroleum in relation to the development of traps.

An oil or gas "reservoir" or "pool" is not a subterranean cavern filled with oil or gas. It is a porous, permeable rock body, a sort of sponge, lying under an impervious layer of rock—the seal. The reservoir contains oil or gas, or both, that is stored in the interconnected pores in the rock, which has been deformed so that the oil and gas have been trapped over long periods of time. Several pools located in a single geologic feature are called a "field."

Rocks are classified as igneous, metamorphic, and sedimentary. Igneous rock has solidified from molten or partly molten material, such as lava. It is usually very dense, with a crystalline or amorphous texture, and has little or no porosity or permeability. Metamorphic rock is pre-existent rock that has undergone a metamorphosis, or change, that is mineral, chemical, or structural in nature. Such changes are caused by substantial changes in temperature, pressure, shearing stress, and chemical environment deep within the earth. Metamorphic rock also has little or no porosity and permeability.

Sedimentary rock results from the consolidation of loose sediment. It may be a clastic rock, such as sandstone or shale, consisting of mechanically formed fragments of older rock carried from their source and deposited by rivers or lakes, carried in air as dust, or carried by glaciers. It may be a chemical rock, such as salt, gypsum, and some limestones, formed by materials that were once in solutions. Or it may be an organic rock, such as certain other limestones, that consists of the remains or secretions of plants and animals. These are the sediments that petroleum geologists look for.

In some sedimentary rocks, petroleum occurs only in infinitesimal amounts, or is so highly dispersed that it is not economically worthwhile to produce. In other areas, however, sedimentary rocks may contain extremely rich accumulations that are measured in billions of barrels. Petroleum can be found on all the continents, although some places are much richer than others. The richest petroleum area in the world is the Mesopotamian-Persian Gulf—the Arab Middle East.

Sedimentary rocks provide three of the fundamental requirements for the presence of oil: the organic source of petroleum; the porous and permeable reservoir rock; and the sealing mechanism that makes a trap. Therefore, they are the first rocks that geologists look for in evaluating an unexplored region as a possible source of oil and gas. In general, the chances of finding commercial quantities of oil or gas are roughly proportional to the volume of sediments in a potentially productive province. Geologists use the quantity of the sediments, expressed in cubic miles, to compare the potential of different regions.

The best conditions are those where the sedimentary layers have built up to great thickness. Generally, these basins have been the "depressional lows" in the geologic structure. But geophysical forces have uplifted some sedimentary basins, making them plateaus or broad arches. And in other cases, the forces have compressed the basins, making complicated folded and faulted structures.

Many sedimentary basins occur along continental margins and in the foothills and lowlands bordering mountain chains. Geologists believe that there is a total basin area of about 6 million square kilometers (2.5 million square miles) under the United States with potential for crude oil and natural gas in recoverable amounts. Thus, about 70 per cent of the total land area of the United States can be classified as being sedimentary provinces.

The rest of the land holds little or no promise for petroleum. It consists, for example, of complexly folded and faulted mountain systems, made up primarily of igneous and metamorphic rocks. Other areas have crystalline "basement" rocks covering the surface, such as the Precambrian shield area in Minnesota and Wisconsin. And there are areas such as those in Washington and Oregon that are covered by thick sequences of igneous rock as massive lava flows.

Several other factors, including depth, temperature, and pressure, limit where petroleum can be found. Commercial quantities of crude

Probabilities of Petroleum

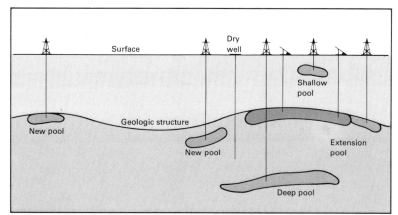

Developed field

Test field

Exploratory drilling

Producing well

A producing oil pool is the best indication that other pools may be found nearby in the geologic structure.

Studying surface rocks is the first step in determining if an area holds promise for petroleum resources.

oil have never been found in the United States much deeper than 6,100 meters (20,000 feet), and they are unlikely to occur in significant amounts below 4,880 meters (16,000 feet). Chemical relations among the compounds of petroleum and natural gas indicate that only the simple hydrocarbons in a gaseous phase can exist at the temperatures and pressures that occur at depths of 6,100 meters or more.

We can be fairly certain, from geologic evidence, that petroleum deposits will eventually be found in many regions that are not now productive, or at greater depths in basins already partially explored. But we can only estimate where and how deep these deposits may be. We can never know for sure the actual location and size of a field until we drill test wells into a prospective trap.

When people think about mineral or energy reserves, they are usually thinking about those that have been discovered and can be extracted economically. However, long-term national planning must be based on estimating the resources not yet discovered. And it must take into account improved recovery methods that could make it economic to extract currently unrecoverable deposits. Thus, petroleum resources must be continuously reassessed as new geologic knowledge is gained, new technology is developed, and economic and political conditions change.

For planning purposes, petroleum resources are classified in terms of both economic feasibility and degree of geologic assurance that the resources are there. It is important to distinguish between "reserves" and undiscovered recoverable "resources." Reserves are identified resources that we know we can recover. They include, in order of decreasing reliability, measured reserves, based on physical evidence in drilled fields; indicated reserves, which are producible, but cannot be accurately estimated; and inferred reserves, whose presence is based more on geologic interpretation than on physical evidence. All these categories are assumed to be economically recoverable.

Resources include these reserves, plus those not considered to be economically recoverable. Resources also include economic and subeconomic recoverable resources that have not been discovered. These are estimated totally from geologic interpretation.

In terms of a producing oil field, the measured and indicated reserves are those within the productive limits of the proven pool and are considered producible under present prices using current technology. Inferred reserves are those that will eventually be added to the fields through extension wells, revised estimates, and new pools. Undiscovered recoverable resources are assumed to exist outside known fields. A successful new well drilled some distance from a known field would confirm that there was petroleum in the undiscovered field, putting it into the reserve category.

Noneconomic resources include oil and gas that is not expected, under any circumstances, to be worth the cost of production. They also include deposits that are considered too small to find or produce.

U.S. Resources and Reserves

Petroleum resources in the United States are classified, *right,* according to relative assurance of existence and the current costs of extracting them. Figures for the two major categories, *below,* are given for 1977.

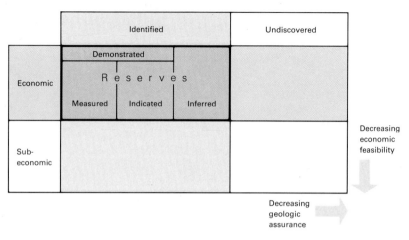

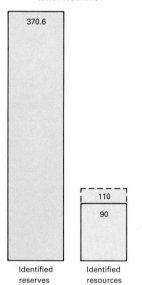

Crude Oil
(billion barrels)

56.8	140
	120
Identified reserves	Identified resources

Natural Gas
(trillion cubic feet)

370.6	110
	90
Identified reserves	Identified resources

The American Petroleum Institute (API) and the American Gas Association (AGA) prepared reserve estimates that are current as of Dec. 31, 1977. The undiscovered recoverable resources were derived by the USGS using a computer analysis of the distributions as 95 per cent and 5 per cent probabilities. This translates to ranges of total undiscovered recoverable oil resources between 50 billion and 127-billion barrels and the undiscovered recoverable gas ranges between 9 trillion and 19 trillion cubic meters (322 trillion and 655 trillion cubic feet).

The API-AGA figures provide a distinction between reserves and resources. First, as of the end of 1977, the total cumulative production of crude oil in the United States was estimated at 115 billion barrels. The measured reserves were 29.5 billion barrels, with 4.2 billion barrels of indicated reserves. Inferred reserves as estimated by the USGS were approximately 23 billion barrels. The undiscovered economic resources ranged between 50 billion and 127 billion barrels.

Not all of the in-place oil is there for the taking. Geologists believe that about 32 per cent of the total can be recovered in the United States in 1978. The remaining identified subeconomic resources range from 120 billion to 140 billion barrels and the undiscovered subeconomic resources range from 44 billion to 111 billion barrels. These values are based on an assumption that future prices and improved technology will make an additional 28 per cent of the resources recoverable. Thus about 60 per cent of the total in-place oil may eventually be recoverable.

As new wells are discovered, the estimated numbers will shift from undiscovered to identified. As the degree of certainty increases that an identified resource has oil, the estimated values will shift from the inferred reserves to the indicated and measured reserves. And with increasing prices and improved technology, some subeconomic categories will be reclassified as economic.

Techniques for evaluating and assessing our petroleum resources change as the availability of data increases. In the early stages of

Oil-drilling rig off the coast of Louisiana is one of hundreds
placed as a result of new techniques for finding oil beneath the sea.

exploration, as in frontier or undrilled areas, there is little data. Estimates of what a basin may hold rely heavily upon subjective methods —estimates of sedimentary volumes combined with special statistical studies. Increased exploration, geophysical surveys, drilling, and geochemical studies produce more information, and objective data becomes dominant in the appraisal. Geologists can then examine each specific rock layer or geologic unit in detail. They may even go on to make detailed estimates of the prospects of an individual field or pool.

The USGS will continue to refine its resource-appraisal system for oil and gas. It is also planning to develop appraisal programs for uranium, coal, and geothermal resources. We now have much geologic and geophysical data that must be analyzed and incorporated into the appraisal system. And each day, new data are being generated from exploration and drilling activities. In updating, refining, and adding critical information to the appraisal system, the USGS shares and coordinates information with other groups that are private as well as governmental.

Some geologists have predicted that world oil supplies will peak no later than 1990. This creates an urgent need for reliable data on worldwide energy alternatives. However, energy planners are hampered by the lack of reliable data on world energy resources. They need better information for nations who must trade, compete, and cooperate with one another in the years ahead.

The USGS is developing a program that focuses on worldwide energy resources, including oil and gas, oil shale, coal, uranium, thorium, lithium (a vital source of radioactive tritium used in the fusion process), and geothermal energy. Its basic objectives are to measure these resources for developing: (1) a national plan relative to energy use in the balance of trade; (2) model studies to enhance domestic resource assessment and exploration; and (3) a data base for aiding foreign countries in their own appraisals. Fortunately, the USGS already has much of the information needed for a world energy-resource assessment program. For more than 30 years, we have been collecting geologic and energy and mineral resource data in a number of other countries around the world.

Apart from the long-range needs for a world assessment, many immediate problems can be resolved by acquiring data on energy resources. Among these are the United Nations Law of the Sea negotiations, international boundary settlements, and nuclear nonproliferation. For example, learning about the availability of petroleum resources within their boundaries should make third world nations less likely to insist on obtaining their energy from the atom.

All federal agencies that work with the USGS recognize the need for a world energy-resource assessment program and agree that one should be developed. It is imperative not only for the United States to develop an energy policy, but also for all nations to plan how they will use the finite resources of the earth.

Index

This index covers the contents of the 1977, 1978, and 1979 editions of *Science Year,* The World Book Science Annual.

Each index entry is followed by the edition year in *italics* and the page numbers:

Lymphocytes, *79*-294, *78*-297, *77*-273

This means that information about lymphocytes begins on the pages indicated for each of the editions.

An index entry that is the title of an article appearing in *Science Year* is printed in boldface italic letters: ***Archaeology.*** An entry that is not an article title, but a subject discussed in an article of some other title, is printed: **Plutonium.**

The various "See" and "See also" cross references in the index are to other entries within the index. Clue words or phrases are used when the entry needs further definition or when two or more references to the same subject appear in *Science Year.* These make it easy to locate the material on the page.

Neuroscience, *79*-311, *78*-314, *77*-312; biofeedback, *Special Report, 78*-76.

See also **Brain.**

The indication *"il."* means that the reference is to an illustration only, as:

Electronic plant probe, *il., 79*-345

Index

A

Aalto, Alvar, 77-394
Abdomen: surgery, 78-307
Aborigines, 78-231
Absorption lines, 78-246, 77-246
Accretion disk: star birth, *Special Report,* 79-66
Achievement, educational, 78-333
Acid phosphatase, 79-297
Acoustic microscope, 79-330
Acrylonitrile: environment, 79-280
Adaptation: ecology, 79-269
Acupuncture: electronics, 77-273
Additives, food: drugs, 78-266; public health, *Close-Up,* 77-336
Adenine arabinoside, 79-267
Adenosine triphosphate, 78-228
Adenovirus 2: genetics, 79-281
Adrenalin: allergies, 77-159
Adrian, Lord Edgar Douglas: deaths, 79-394
Aedui, 78-232
Aeronautics: *Gossamer Condor, Special Report,* 79-85
Aerosols: environment, 78-281; meteorology, 77-305; technology, 79-346
Aerospace: awards and prizes, 79-391, 78-391, 77-391
Afar: *Special Report,* 79-43
Africa: anthropology, 78-229
Agassiz Medal, 77-388
Agriculture, 79- 226, 78-226, 77-226; arid lands, *Special Report,* 79-157; *Books of Science,* 77-250; Old World archaeology, 78-232. See also *Botany; Chemical Technology; Climate; Food; Nutrition; Pesticide.*
Aigai: archaeology, 79-233
Ainu: anthropology, 78-230
Air Mass Transformation Experiment, 78-311
Air pollution: agriculture, 77-226; energy, 77-274; environment, 78-279, *Close-Up,* 78-282; meteorology, 77-305; wind engineering, *Special Report,* 78-200. See also *Automobile; Climate; Environment; Pollution.*
Airbags, 79-347, 77-347
Airlines: meteorology, 77-306
Airship: *Special Report,* 77-190
Akuplas: electronics, 77-274
ALA-synthetase: liver, *Special Report,* 79-175
Alaska: wolves, *Special Report,* 78-113
Albedo: asteroids, *Special Report,* 79-147
Alberta Fireball, *il.,* 77-216
Alcator: plasma physics, 77-329
Alcohol: energy, 78-278; liver, *Special Report,* 79-177; nutrition, 78-318
Alder aphids: zoology, 79-349

Alfalfa, *78-226*
Algae: botany, 79-254; *ils., 77-253*
Alikhanian, Artemii I.: deaths, 79-394
Allende meteorite, 79-285, 77-286
Allergies: biochemistry, 79-249; *Special Report,* 77-153
Allied Chemical Corp., 78-279
Alpha decay: nuclei, *Special Report,* 78-118
Alpha waves: biofeedback, *Special Report,* 78-81
Alpine Snow and Avalanche Project: avalanche, *Special Report,* 77-110
Aluminum: geochemistry, 77-286
Alvin: Galapagos Rift Valley, *Special Report,* 79-14; oceanography, 78-319
Amaranth: environment, 77-280; useful plants, *Special Report,* 77-68
Amino-acid dating: mummies, *Special Report,* 77-93
Amino acids: allergies, *Special Report,* 77-161; genetics, 78-283; nutrition, 79-315; origins of life, *Special Report,* 77-124
Ammonia: chemistry, 77-260
Amoco Cadiz: environment, 79-280
Amor asteroids: asteroids, *Special Report,* 79-146
Amygdala: endogenous opiates, *Special Report,* 78-130
Analgesics: chemistry, 78-260
Anderson, Philip W.: awards, 79-387
Andromeda Nebula: cosmology, *Special Report,* 77-102
Anemia: internal medicine, 78-303
Angina pectoris: nutrition, 78-318
Angiogenesis: internal medicine, 78-303
Animal behavior: light, *Special Report,* 79-113; psychology, 79-333; wolves, *Special Report,* 78-103; zoology, 79-248
Anisotropy: cosmology, 79-245
Ankle, artificial, 77-302
Anopheles mosquito: malaria, *Special Report,* 79-71
Ant: zoology, 79-349, 78-349, 77-349
Antarctica, *il.,* 78-320; oceanography, 79-316
Anteater: zoology, 78-352
Anthropology, 79-230, 78-229, 77-230; *Books of Science,* 79-250, 78-252; early man in Afar, *Special Report,* 79-43; mummies, *Special Report,* 77-81. See also *Archaeology.*
Anti-antibodies, 77-293
Antibiotics: biochemistry, 78-251, 77-247; drugs, 78-267, 77-265; public health, 78-337; science fair, 78-371
Antibodies: allergies, *Special Report,* 77-154; genetics, 78-284; immunology, 79-295, 78-297, 77-293
Antigens: immunology, 79-294, 78-299, 77-293

Antihistamines: allergies, *Special Report,* 77-158
Anti-idiotype antibodies, 77-293
Antiquarks: elementary particles, 79-321, 77-323
Antitumor drug therapy, 77-297
Anxiety: biofeedback, *Special Report,* 78-84; psychology, 77-334
Apes: anthropology, 79-230
Aphid, *il.,* 78-269; zoology, 79-349
Aplastic anemia, 78-303
Apollo asteroids: asteroids, *Special Report,* 79-146
Apollo-Soyuz Test Project: space exploration, 77-343; space shuttle, *Special Report,* 79-40; stellar astronomy, 77-242
Aqualon: chemical technology, 77-257
Aquapulse gun: oil exploration, *Special Report,* 77-18
Aquasol: technology, 79-346
Ara-A: drugs, 79-267
Archaebacteria: microbiology, 79-310
Archaeology, 79-233, 78-232, 77-232; *Books of Science,* 78-252, 77-250; Ebla, *Special Report,* 78-183; New World, 79-235, 78-234, 77-234, *Close-Up,* 78-236, 77-236, Old World, 79-233, 78-232 77-232. See Also *Anthropology; Geoscience.*
Archaeopteryx: dinosaurs, *Special Report,* 77-65
Archimède: Galapagos Rift Valley, *Special Report,* 79-16
Architecture: wind engineering, *Special Report,* 78-196
Arctic Ice Dynamics Joint Experiment (AIDJEX): oceanography, 77-319
Arctowski Medal: awards and prizes, 79-391
Arethusa: asteroids, *Special Report,* 79-148
Argo Merchant: environment, 78-283
Arid land: *Special Report,* 79-157
Arms Control and Disarmament Agency, U.S.: energy, 78-276
Artery: microsurgery, *Special Report,* 77-49, *il.,* 77-44
Artificial gene: *Close-Up,* 78-249. See also *Recombinant DNA.*
Artificial joints, 77-302
Artificial organs: diabetes, *Special Report,* 78-57; liver, *Special Report,* 79-180
Artificial sweetener: drugs, 78-266
Artificial-vision device: electronics, 77-272
Artificial-voice machine: technology, 79-345
Ascites: surgery, 78-307
Asilomar Conference: DNA, *Special Report,* 78-35; *Essay,* 78-398
Assertiveness: psychology, 77-334
Asteroids: *Special Report,* 79-143
Asthenosphere, 77-289

Index

Index

Index

Index

Index

Mileage: chemical technology, 79-255

Milk: agriculture, 78-228; nutrition, 78-317

Milky Way: cosmology, 79-245, *Special Report,* 77-102; stellar astronomy, 78-241

Mimicry: zoology, 79-248

Mind. See **Brain;** *Psychology.*

Mineralogy: *Books of Science,* 77-251

Minkowsky, Rudolph L., 77-395

Misar: electronics, 79-272

Mitochondria, *ils.,* 77-249

Mixed function oxidase system: liver, *Special Report,* 79-173

Miyashiro, Akiho: awards, 78-388

Mobile phone: communications, 79-265

Molecular sieve: chemistry, 79-262

Molecule: atomic and molecular physics, 78-323; chemistry, 78-261, 77-258

Monazite, *il.,* 78-123

Monod, Jacques, 77-395

Monopole mode: nuclear physics, 79-325

Moon. See headings beginning **Lunar. . . .**

Moran, James M., Jr., 79-391

Moray eel, *il.,* 79-353

Morrison Formation: dinosaurs, 77-53

Mosasaurs: paleontology, 79-292

Mosquitoes: botany, 77-254; chemical technology, 78-259; malaria, *Special Report,* 79-71

Mott, Sir Nevill F.: awards, 79-387

Mount Pastukhov, 77-241

Mountains: avalanche, *Special Report,* 77-109

Müller, Erwin W., 78-395

Muller, Richard A.: awards, 79-388

Multiple sclerosis: internal medicine, 77-296

Mummies: anthropology, 78-231, 77-232; *Special Report,* 77-81

Munk, Walter Heinrich, 77-388

Muons, 78-324, 77-325

Murchison, *il.,* 79-151

Muschenheim, Carl, 78-395

Muscle: biofeedback, *Special Report,* 78-78

Musgrave, F. Story, *il.,* 77-345

Music: technology, 79-345

MWC 349: stellar astronomy, 79-241

N

N-nitroso compounds, 77-336

N-type semiconductor: solar cells, *Special Report,* 79-103; solid-state physics, 79-329

Nab ataeans: agriculture, *Special Report,* 79-158; archaeology, 79-234

Nabid, *il.,* 78-269

Narcotics: endogenous opiates, *Special Report,* 78-128

National Academy of Sciences (NAS): DNA, *Special Report,* 78-35; science policy, 79-341; useful plants, *Special Report,* 77-68

National Aeronautics and Space Administration (NASA): science policy, 79-337; space exploration, 78-343, 77-344, *Special Report,* 79-37

National Cancer Institute (NCI): science policy, 79-341

National Fire Prevention and Control Administration (NFPCA), 79-198

National Fire Prevention Association, 79-198

National Institutes of Health: Center for Disease Control, *Special Report,* 78-222; DNA, *Special Report,* 78-36; *Essay,* 78-398; science policy, 79-337, 77-342

National Medal of Science, 79-391, 78-392, 77-392

National Oceanic and Atmospheric Administration (NOAA), 77-305

National Research Council: environment, 78-281

National Science Foundation: science policy, 79-337, 77-341

Natural gas: geology, 78-291; oil exploration, *Special Report,* 77-14

Natural history: *Books of Science,* 78-254, 77-251

Natural killer (NK) cell: immunology, 78-297

Ndutu, Lake: anthropology, 78-229

Nebcin: drugs, 77-266

Neptune: astronomy, 79-239

Nerve growth factor, 78-357

Nervous system: biofeedback, *Special Report,* 78-76; endogenous opiates, *Special Report,* 78-128. See also **Brain;** *Neuroscience.*

Neuroscience, 79-311, 78-314, 77-312, biofeedback, *Special Report,* 78-76. See also **Brain; Nervous system.**

Neurotoxin: zoology, *Close-Up,* 78-351

Neutral Indians: archaeology, 79-236

Neutrinos: elementary particles, 79-322, 78-325, 77-325

Neutron: energy, 79-274; nuclei, *Special Report,* 78-118; physics, 79-325, 78-327, 77-330

Neutron generator: physics, 78-302

Nevada arc: geology, 79-286

New Zealand, *il.,* 78-74

NGC 6624: high-energy astronomy, 77-243

Nickel: chemistry, 77-258; geochemistry 78-287; nutrition, 79-315

Nicotine: psychology, 78-333

1978 CA: asteroids, *Special Report,* 79-146

Niobium: solid state physics, 77-332

Nitrates: public health, *Close-Up,* 77-336

Nitrites: public health, *Close-Up,* 77-336

Nitrogen: agriculture, 77-226; useful plants, *Special Report,* 77-75

Nitrogen fixation: agriculture, 78-229; botany, 78-256; chemistry, 77-260

Nitrosamines: public health, *Close-Up,* 77-336

No-plow farming: agriculture, 77-229

NOAA. See **National Oceanic and Atmospheric Administration.**

Nobel prizes: chemistry, 79-387, 78-387, 77-387; medicine, 79-389, 78-389, 77-390; physics, 79-387, 78-387, 77-387

Nonnucleated algae, *ils.,* 77-253

Norpace: drugs, 79-267

North Pacific Experiment: oceanography, 77-319

North Sea, *il.,* 78-280

Novas: stellar astronomy, 77-242

Noyes, Eliot F., 79-395

Nuclear fission, 78-119

Nuclear magnetic resonance (NMR): chemistry, 79-259

Nuclear physics. See *Physics (nuclear).*

Nuclear power: energy, 78-275; science policy, 78-341. See also **Accelerator, particle;** *Physics.*

Nuclear power plants: energy, 79-274, environment, 78-281, 77-281; science policy, 79-341

Nuclear waste: oceanography, 77-320

Nuclei, *il.,* 78-256; *Special Report,* 78-117

Nucleic acid: origins of life, *Special Report,* 77-124

Nucleotide: biochemistry, 78-248; genetics, 78-283

Nuées ardentes: Center for Short-Lived Phenomena, *Special Report,* 77-79

Nut-cracker man: early man in Afar, *Special Report,* 79-45

Nutrient Film Technique: agriculture, 78-226

Nutrition, 79-313, 78-316, 77-314; neuroscience, 79-313. See also **Diet; Food.**

Nylon: chemical technology, 77-257

Nysa: asteroids, *Special Report,* 79-148

O

O star: star birth, *Special Report,* 79-58

OB associations: star birth, *Special Report,* 79-61

Index

Index

Shiva: plasma physics, *79*-328
Shrimp: chemical technology, *77*-258
Shroud of Turin: Old World archaeology, *79*-235
Siegel, Carl L.: awards, *79*-392
Sight: electronics, *78*-273
Signal-receptor inhibition: allergies, *Special Report, 77*-161
Silicon: solar cells, *Special Report, 79*-103
Single-atom detection, *78*-322
Sivapithecus: anthropology, *79*-230
16-S ribonucleic acid: microbiology, *79*-309
Skin cancer: environment, *78*-281; internal medicine, *78*-301
Skin-grafting: surgery, *78*-305
Skylab: Center for Short-Lived Phenomena, *Special Report, 77*-223; space exploration, *79*-343; space shuttle, *Special Report, 79*-38
Slab avalanche, *77*-109
Smallpox: *Close-Up, 78*-338
Smalltalk: personal computers, *Special Report, 79*-188
Smell, sense of: zoology, *77*-351
Smog: chemistry, *79*-261; *Close-Up, 78*-282
Smoke: fires, *Special Report, 79*-206
Smoke detector, *78*-345
Smoking: psychology, *78*-333; public health, *79*-335, *78*-339, *77*-337
Snail darter: environment, *79*-281, *78*-283
Snakes, *78*-351, *77*-351
Snell, George D., *79*-392
Snow: avalanche, *Special Report, 77*-109
Social behavior, *77*-334
Social Darwinists: science policy, *Close-Up, 79*-338
Sociobiology: science policy, *Close-Up, 79*-338
Soil, lunar. See Lunar soil.
Solar cells: electronics, *78*-274; physics, *79*-329; *Special Report, 79*-101
Solar collector: solar cells, *Special Report, 79*-101
Solar energy: cellulose, *Special Report, 77*-166; chemistry, *77*-261; energy, *79*-276, *78*-278, *77*-276; heating, *78*-347; science policy, *79*-340, *77*-341
Solar greenhouses: agriculture, *79*-228
Solar satellite: energy, *79*-276
Solar system: asteroids, *Special Report, 79*-143; geochemistry, *77*-284
Solid-State Physics, 79-329, *78*-331, *77*-330
Soliton: astronomy, *77*-239
Solvation cage: lasers, *Special Report, 79*-217
Somatostatin: biochemistry, *79*-247; diabetes, *Special Report, 78*-54
Sombrero Galaxy, *78*-243

Sommerfeld, Richard A., *77*-110
Song sparrow: zoology, *79*-350
Soufrière, La, *il., 78*-290; volcano, *Special Report, 78*-63
Sound synthesizer: technology, *79*-345
Sound waves, *77*-331
South America: archaeology, *79*-237, *77*-237
South Tropical Disturbance: astronomy, *77*-239
Southern Oceans Study, International, *77*-318
Soybean: agriculture, *77*-226
Soyuz: Apollo-Soyuz, *77*-344; Russian manned missions, *78*-343, *77*-345
Space Exploration, 79-342, *78*-343, *77*-343; *Books of Science, 78*-254; Center for Short-Lived Phenomena, *Special Report, 77*-222; planetary astronomy, *78*-239; space shuttle, *Special Report, 79*-28; Viking series, *Special Report, 78*-13. See also *Astronomy* (planetary); *Science Policy.*
Space shuttle: energy, *79*-276; space exploration, *79*-342, *78*-344, *77*-344; *Special Report, 79*-28
Space station, *il., 79*-36. See also *Space Exploration.*
Spacelab, *79*-37, 343, *78*-344
Sparrows: zoology, *79*-350
Spectinomycin, *78*-337
Speech synthesizer, *il., 79*-272
Spence, Sir Basil, *78*-395
Sperm oil, *77*-72
Spiders: zoology, *77*-352
Spinars: stellar astronomy, *77*-242
Spinel, *il., 78*-288
Split genes: genetics, *79*-281
Spontaneous generation: origins of life, *Special Report, 77*-125
Sporn, Philip, *79*-395
Sporozoites: malaria, *Special Report, 79*-73
Sprague, George F.: awards, *79*-392
Sprinkler system: fire, *Special Report, 79*-202
Standard light-rail vehicles (SLRV): transportation, *79*-348
Stanford Positron-Electron Accelerating Ring (SPEAR), *78*-332
Stegosaurus, il., 77-60
Stellar Astronomy: 79-241, *78*-241, *77*-241; cosmology, *79*-245; *Special Report, 79*-57
Stereophonograph: electronics, *79*-272
Sterilization: vasectomy reversal, *77*-301
Sterkfontein: anthropology, *78*-229
Steroids: allergies, *77*-159
Sterols: nutrition, *79*-314
Steward, James T.: awards, *79*-391
Stillman, Irwin M., *77*-395
Stomach: surgery, *79*-303
Stomata: botany, *79*-252

Stone Award, *79*-389
Storms: meteorology, *77*-306
Strange quark, *78*-324, *77*-324
Stratosphere: meteorology, *77*-305
Strawberry: agriculture, *79*-226
Streetcar: transportation, *79*-348
Streptomyces: microbiology, *79*-310
Stress: biofeedback, *Special Report, 78*-80; *Special Report, 77*-27
Strip farming: agriculture in arid lands, *Special Report, 79*-159
Structural chemistry: See *Chemistry.*
Structural mechanics, *78*-196
Strutinsky, V. M.: awards, *79*-387
Stubble-mulch farming: agriculture in arid lands, *Special Report, 79*-160
Studier, F. William: awards, *79*-387
Substance P: neuroscience, *79*-311
Suede: chemical industry, *79*-257
Sugar: agriculture, *77*-227; dentistry, *77*-295; diabetes, *Special Report, 78*-49
Sugar cane: energy, *78*-278
Sulfur: astronomy, *77*-238; chemistry, *77*-255
Sulfur dioxide: environment, *79*-277
Sulfuric acid: Venus, *77*-181
Sullivan, James L., *79*-398
Sun: and plants, *Special Report, 78*-169; cosmology, *Special Report, 77*-99; meteorology, *78*-309; space exploration, *77*-344; stellar astronomy, *77*-242. See also headings beginning Solar . . . .
Sun Day: science policy, *79*-430
Sunspots: meteorology, *78*-310; stellar astronomy, *79*-241
Super-proton synchrotron, *78*-326
Superconductors: electronics, *79*-271
Superfluidity: solid-state physics, *79*-330
Superheavy element: nuclei, *Special Report, 78*-120
Supernova remnant: geochemistry, *79*-286; stellar astronomy, *79*-241, *78*-241
Suppressor T cell: immunology, *78*-299
Surgery. See *Medicine* (surgery); Microsurgery.
Surtsey, *77*-212
SV40: genetics, *77*-282
Swine influenza virus, *78*-219, *77*-335
Sycamores, *il., 77*-167
Synapse: neurology, *78*-314
Synchrotron radiation, *78*-331
Synthesizer: technology, *79*-345
Synthetic natural gas (SNG): chemical technology, *79*-257
Systemic lupus erythematosus (SLE), *78*-299

T

T cells: immunology, *78*-297, *77*-294; *Close-Up, 78*-298

Index

Acknowledgments

The publishers of *Science Year* gratefully acknowledge the courtesy of the following artists, photographers, publishers, institutions, agencies, and corporations for the illustrations in this volume. Credits should be read from left to right, top to bottom, on their respective pages. All entries marked with an asterisk (*) denote illustrations created exclusively for *Science Year*. All maps, charts, and diagrams were prepared by the *Science Year* staff unless otherwise noted.

Cover
Cleveland Museum of Natural History

Advisory Board
7   Stanford University; Roland Patry*; Dennis Galloway*; John Swanberg*; Kitt Peak National Observatory; State University of New York at Stony Brook; Duke University Medical Center

Special Reports
10   Handelan-Pedersen, Inc.*; Steve Hale*; Nancy Meyers, UCLA; Judy MacCready; Anne Norcia*
13   © National Geographic Society
15   James Teason*
17   © National Geographic Society
18-19   Angus Towed Camera, Woods Hole Oceanographic Institution
20-21   James Teason*
22   John B. Corliss, Oregon State University; Galapagos Hydrothermal Expedition
23   Robert D. Ballard, Woods Hole Oceanographic Institution; John B. Corliss, Oregon State University; Jack R. Dymond, Oregon State University
24-25   John M. Edmond, M.I.T.; Steve Hale*
26   Robert D. Ballard, Woods Hole Oceanographic Institution; Sharon Hamer*
28-29   Manuel E. Alvarez, Rockwell International
31   James Teason*
32-33   Manuel E. Alvarez, Rockwell International; NASA; NASA
36-37   Ted Brown, Rockwell International
38   NASA
39   Martin Marietta Aerospace; NASA
40   Manuel E. Alvarez, Rockwell International
42   David Brill, © National Geographic Society
46   Jerry Cooke, *Life* © 1949 Time Inc.; J. Higgins from John T. Robinson
47   © Bob Campbell; Cleveland Museum of Natural History
48   Donald Johanson, Cleveland Museum of Natural History
49-51   David Brill, © National Geographic Society
52   Cleveland Museum of Natural History
53   David Cunningham*
54   David Brill, © National Geographic Society
56   © California Institute of Technology and Carnegie Institution of Washington, from Hale Observatories
59-62   Ernest Norcia*
63   T. R. Gull, R. A. R. Parker and R. P. Kirchner, NASA
64-67   Ernest Norcia*
70   © Robert Frerck; Robert Gwadz, M.D., National Institute of Allergy and Infectious Diseases, NIH; Steve Hale*
73   Björn Klingwall
74   Bobbye Cochran*
75   Bobbye Cochran*; Robert Lewert, M.D., University of Chicago
76-78   Steve Hale*
79   National Institute of Allergy and Infectious Diseases, NIH
81   Steve Hale*
82   David Brill; Björn Klingwall; Naud, AAA photo
84   Judy MacCready
86   Bettmann Archive
87   Keystone
88   Mickey Pfleger, Sygma; U.S. Fish and Wildlife Service
89   Paul B. MacCready (Steve Hale*); Peter Lissaman
90   Jack Lambie; Karen Lambie; Don Monroe
91   Albert Moldvay; James Joseph

92   Don Monroe
94   Tom Morgan*
96   Albert Moldvay
98   © 1978 Kevin L. Martin
100-103   Handelan-Pedersen Inc.*
104   Handelan-Pedersen Inc.*; Motorola Inc.; Handelan-Pedersen Inc.*
105   Dow Corning Corporation; Motorola Inc.; Dow Corning Corporation
107   NASA; Solarex Corporation
108   Solarex Corporation; Handelan-Pedersen Inc.*
110   © David Cupp, Woodfin Camp, Inc.; Team Inc.
112   Jane Burton, Bruce Coleman Inc.
115   Robert Carr, Tom Stack & Assoc.; J. Lee Kavanau, UCLA; J. Lee Kavanau, UCLA; Ron Garrison, San Diego Zoo
116   Alan Blank, Bruce Coleman Inc.; Jane Burton, Bruce Coleman Inc.; Nancy Meyers, UCLA
117   Jane Burton, Bruce Coleman Inc.
120   Ron Austing, Bruce Coleman Inc.; Al Nelson, Tom Stack & Assoc.; Thase Daniel, Bruce Coleman Inc.
122   Larry L. Fausett, UCLA; Nancy Meyers, UCLA; Thomas R. Loughlin, National Marine Fisheries Service, NOAA
123   Nancy Meyers, UCLA
126   Daniel E. Vanjason, Black Star; Keith Gunnar, Bruce Coleman Inc.; Copyright National Geographic Society-Palomar Observatory Sky Survey (California Institute of Technology); Joseph Keyerleber, Uniphoto
128   J. Kim Vandiver; Copyright Reserved
129   Group T-3, Theoretical Division, Los Alamos Scientific Laboratory
131   Produced by Education Development Center for the National Committee for Fluid Mechanics Films with support from the National Science Foundation. *Low Reynolds Number Flows* © 1966 Education Development Center, Inc.; Office National d'Études et de Recherches Aérospatiales, France; Harold Simon, Tom Stack & Assoc.; Steve Hale*
132   J. Kim Vandiver
134   National Aeronautical Establishment, National Research Council of Canada
135   Robert H. Glaze, Artstreet
136   NASA; Richard S. Williams, Jr., U.S. Geological Survey (NASA Landsat Image); Michael Karweit, Chesapeake Bay Institute, Johns Hopkins University in cooperation with National Center for Atmospheric Research Computing Facility
137   Anne Norcia*
138-139   Steve Hale*
142-149   Kinuko Craft*
151   Cornell University
152-153   Kinuko Craft*
154   NASA
156   Grant Heilman
159   UNESCO
160   Soil Conservation Service, U.S. Department of Agriculture
161   Grant Heilman
162   U.S. Department of Agriculture
163   Texas Agricultural Experiment Station
164   U.S. Department of Agriculture; Runk/Schoenberger from Grant Heilman
166-167   Norman J. Rosenberg, University of Nebraska at Lincoln
168   Gail Rubin, Bruce Coleman Inc.
170   Bobbye Cochran*
172   The British Museum, London
73-174   Bobbye Cochran*
176   Bobbye Cochran*; C. S. Lieber, L. M. DeCarli, H. Gang, G. Walker and E. Rubin: Hepatice Effects of Long Term Ethanol Consumption in Primates from *Medical Primatology*, (Karger, Basel 1972); Hidejiro Yokoo, M.D.; C. S. Lieber, L. M. DeCarli, H. Gang, G. Walker

Typography
Display — Univers
Total Typography, Inc., Chicago
Text — Baskerville Linofilm
Total Typography, Inc., Chicago
Text — Baskerville Linotron
Black Dot Computer Typesetting
Corporation, Chicago

Offset Positives
Collins, Miller, & Hutchings, Chicago
Schawkgraphics, Inc., Chicago
Capper, Inc., Knoxville, Tenn.
Liberty Photo Engraving Company, Chicago

Printing
Kingsport Press, Inc., Kingsport, Tenn.

Binding
Kingsport Press, Inc., Kingsport, Tenn.

Paper
Text
Childcraft Text, Web Offset (basis 60 pound)
Mead, Escanaba, Mich.

Cover Material
Oyster White Lexotone
Holliston Mills, Inc., Kingsport, Tenn.
White Offset Blubak
Holliston Mills, Inc., Kingsport, Tenn.